2020

The ARRL HANDBOOK FOR RADIO COMMUNICATIONS

NINETY-SEVENTH EDITION

Volume 1: Introduction and Fundamental Theory — Ch. 1-4

Volume 2: Practical Design and Principles Part 1 — Ch. 5-11

Volume 3: Practical Design and Principles Part 2 — Ch. 12-18

▶ **Volume 4:** Antenna Systems and Radio Propagation — Ch. 19-21

Volume 5: Equipment Construction and Station Accessories — Ch. 22-24

Volume 6: Test Equipment, Troubleshooting, RFI, and Index — Ch. 25-28

Editor
H. Ward Silver, N0AX

Contributing Editors
Steven R. Ford, WB8IMY
Mark J. Wilson, K1RO

Editorial Assistant
Maty Weinberg, KB1EIB

Technical Consultants
Bob Allison, WB1GCM
Edward F. Hare, Jr., W1RFI
Zachary H.J. Lau, W1VT

Cover Design
Sue Fagan, KB1OKW
Bob Inderbitzen, NQ1R

Production
Michelle Bloom, WB1ENT
Jodi Morin, KA1JPA
David F. Pingree, N1NAS

Additional Contributors to the 2020 Edition
John Brooks, N9ZL
Jim Brown, K9YC
Glen Brown, W6GJB
Ralph Crumrine, N0KC

Don Daso, K4ZA
Joel Hallas, W1ZR
Bill Koch, W2RMA
Rick Lindquist, WW1ME
Glenn Loake, G0GBI
Helmut Berka, DL2MAJ
Oliver Micic, DG7XO
Carl Luetzelschwab, K9LA
Phil Salas, AD5X
Rob Sherwood, NC0B
Cory Sickles, WA3UVV
George Steber, WB9LVI
Jim Tonne, W4ENE
Paul Wade, W1GHZ

Published by:
ARRL The national association for AMATEUR RADIO®
225 Main Street, Newington, CT 06111-1400 USA
www.arrl.org

Copyright © 2019 by
The American Radio Relay League, Inc.

Copyright secured under the Pan-American Convention

International Copyright secured

All rights reserved. No part of this work may be reproduced in any form except by written permission of the publisher. All rights of translation are reserved.

Printed in the USA

Quedan reservados todos los derechos

ISBN: 978-1-62595-107-6 Softcover
ISBN: 978-1-62595-113-7 Six-Volume Set

Kindle eBook Editions
   ISBN: 978-1-62595-091-8 — Volume 1
   ISBN: 978-1-62595-092-5 — Volume 2
   ISBN: 978-1-62595-093-2 — Volume 3
   ISBN: 978-1-62595-094-9 — Volume 4
   ISBN: 978-1-62595-095-6 — Volume 5
   ISBN: 978-1-62595-096-3 — Volume 6

Ninety-Seventh Edition

About the cover:
The collection of components comprises the HF Packer miniHFPA2 amplifier kit. Although the kit is not featured in this 2020 edition of the ARRL Handbook, its components represent the spirit of project design and craftsmanship that has been part of Amateur Radio from the beginning.

Contents

A more detailed Table of Contents is included at the beginning of each chapter.

VOLUME 1

INTRODUCTION AND FUNDAMENTAL THEORY

1 **What is Amateur (Ham) Radio?**
 1.1 Do-It-Yourself Wireless
 1.2 Joining the Ham Radio Community
 1.3 Your Ham Radio Station
 1.4 Getting on the Air
 1.5 Your Ham Radio "Lifestyle"
 1.6 Public Service
 1.7 Ham Radio in the Classroom
 1.8 Resources
 1.9 Glossary

2 **Electrical Fundamentals**
 2.1 Introduction to Electricity
 2.2 Resistance and Conductance
 2.3 Basic Circuit Principles
 2.4 Power and Energy
 2.5 Circuit Control Components
 2.6 Capacitance and Capacitors
 2.7 Inductance and Inductors
 2.8 Semiconductor Devices
 2.9 References and Bibliography

3 **Radio Fundamentals**
 3.1 AC Waveforms
 3.2 Measuring AC Voltage, Current and Power
 3.3 Effective Radiated Power
 3.4 AC in Capacitors and Inductors
 3.5 Working with Reactance
 3.6 Impedance
 3.7 Quality Factor (Q) of Components
 3.8 Resonant Circuits
 3.9 Analog Signal Processing
 3.10 Electromagnetic Waves
 3.11 References and Bibliography

4 **Circuits and Components**
 4.1 Practical Resistors
 4.2 Practical Capacitors
 4.3 Practical Inductors
 4.4 Transformers
 4.5 Practical Semiconductors
 4.6 Amplifiers
 4.7 Operational Amplifiers
 4.8 Miscellaneous Analog ICs
 4.9 Analog-Digital Interfacing
 4.10 Analog Device and Circuits Glossary
 4.11 Heat Management
 4.12 References and Bibliography

VOLUME 2

PRACTICAL DESIGN AND PRINCIPLES — PART 1

5 RF Techniques
5.1 Introduction
5.2 Lumped-Element versus Distributed Characteristics
5.3 Effects of Parasitic (Stray) Characteristics
5.4 Semiconductor Circuits at RF
5.5 Ferrite Materials
5.6 Impedance Matching Networks
5.7 RF Transformers
5.8 Noise
5.9 Two-Port Networks
5.10 RF Design Techniques Glossary
5.11 References and Bibliography

6 Computer-Aided Circuit Design
6.1 Circuit Simulation Overview
6.2 Simulation Basics
6.3 Limitations of Simulation at RF
6.4 Electromagnetic Analysis of RF Circuits
6.5 References and Bibliography

7 Power Sources
7.1 Power Processing
7.2 AC-AC Power Conversion
7.3 Power Transformers
7.4 AC-DC Power Conversion
7.5 Voltage Multipliers
7.6 Current Multipliers
7.7 Rectifier Types
7.8 Power Filtering
7.9 Power Supply Regulation
7.10 "Crowbar" Protective Circuits
7.11 DC-DC Switchmode Power Conversion
7.12 High-Voltage Techniques
7.13 Batteries
7.14 Glossary of Power Source Terms
7.15 References and Bibliography
7.16 Power Supply Projects

8 DSP and SDR Fundamentals
8.1 Introduction to DSP
8.2 Introduction to SDR
8.3 Analog-Digital Conversion
8.4 Data Converters for SDR and DSP
8.5 Digital Signal Processors
8.6 Digital (Discrete-time) Signals
8.7 The Fourier Transform
8.8 Glossary of DSP and SDR Terms
8.9 References and Bibliography

9 Oscillators and Synthesizers
9.1 How Oscillators Work
9.2 LC Variable Frequency Oscillator (VFO) Circuits
9.3 Building an Oscillator
9.4 Crystal Oscillators
9.5 Oscillators at UHF and Above
9.6 Frequency Synthesizers
9.7 Phase Noise
9.8 Glossary of Oscillator and Synthesizer Terms
9.9 References and Bibliography

10 Analog and Digital Filtering
10.1 Introduction
10.2 Filter Basics
10.3 Passive LC Filters
10.4 Active Audio Filters
10.5 Digital Filters
10.6 Quartz Crystal Filters
10.7 SAW Filters
10.8 Transmission Line VHF/UHF/Microwave Filters
10.9 Helical Resonators
10.11 Filter Projects
10.12 Glossary of Filter Terms
10.13 References and Bibliography

11 Modulation
11.1 Introduction
11.2 Amplitude Modulation (AM)
11.3 Angle Modulation
11.4 FSK and PSK
11.5 Quadrature Modulation
11.6 Analytic Signals and Modulation
11.7 Image Modulation
11.8 Spread Spectrum Modulation
11.9 Pulse Modulation
11.10 Modulation Bandwidth and Impairments
11.11 Glossary of Modulation Terms
11.12 References and Further Reading

VOLUME 3

PRACTICAL DESIGN AND PRINCIPLES — PART 2

12 Receiving
12.1 Characterizing Receivers
12.2 Heterodyne Receivers
12.3 SDR Receivers
12.4 Mixing and Mixers
12.5 Demodulation and Detection
12.6 Automatic Gain Control (AGC)
12.7 Noise Management
12.8 References and Bibliography

13 Transmitting
13.1 Characterizing Transmitters
13.2 Transmitter Architecture
13.3 Modulators
13.4 Transmitting CW
13.5 Transmitting AM and SSB
13.6 Transmitting Angle Modulation
13.7 Effects of Transmitted Noise
13.8 Microphones and Speech Processing
13.9 Voice Operation
13.10 Transmitter Power Stages
13.11 References and Bibliography

14 Transceiver Design Topics
14.1 Signal Chains in SDR Transceivers
14.2 User Interfaces
14.3 Configuration and Control Interfaces
14.4 SDR Design Tools

15 Digital Protocols and Modes
15.1 Digital "Modes"
15.2 Unstructured Digital Modes
15.3 Fuzzy Modes
15.4 Structured Digital Modes
15.5 Networking Modes
15.6 Digital Mode Table
15.7 Glossary of Digital Protocol and Mode Terms
15.8 References and Bibliography

16 Amateur Radio Data Platforms
16.1 Platform Overview
16.2 Sensors
16.3 Navigation Data and Telemetry
16.4 Payloads
16.5 High Altitude Balloon Platforms
16.6 Unmanned Aerial Vehicles (UAVs)
16.7 Rockets
16.8 Robotics
16.9 Fixed Stations
16.10 References and Bibliography

17 RF Power Amplifiers
17.1 High Power, Who Needs It?
17.2 Types of Power Amplifiers
17.3 Vacuum Tube Basics
17.4 Tank Circuits
17.5 Transmitting Tube Ratings
17.6 Sources of Operating Voltages
17.7 Tube Amplifier Cooling
17.8 Vacuum Tube Amplifier Stabilization
17.9 MOSFET Design for RF Amplifiers
17.10 Solid-State RF Amplifiers
17.11 Solid State Amplifier Projects
17.12 Tube Amplifier Projects
17.13 References and Bibliography

18 Repeaters
18.1 A Brief History
18.2 Repeater Overview
18.3 FM Voice Repeaters
18.4 D-STAR Repeater Systems
18.5 System Fusion Repeater Systems
18.6 Digital Mobile Radio (DMR)
18.7 Other Digital Voice Repeater Technologies
18.8 Glossary of FM and Repeater Terminology
18.9 References and Bibliography

VOLUME 4

ANTENNA SYSTEMS AND RADIO PROPAGATION

19 Propagation of Radio Signals
19.1 Fundamentals of Radio Waves
19.2 Sky-Wave Propagation and the Sun
19.3 MUF Predictions
19.4 Propagation in the Troposphere
19.5 VHF/UHF Mobile Propagation
19.6 Propagation for Space Communications
19.7 Noise and Propagation
19.8 Propagation Below the AM Broadcast Band
19.9 Glossary of Radio Propagation Terms
19.10 References and Bibliography

20 Transmission Lines
20.1 Transmission Line Basics
20.2 Choosing a Transmission Line
20.3 The Transmission Line as Impedance Transformer
20.4 Matching Impedances in the Antenna System
20.5 Baluns and Transmission-Line Transformers
20.6 PC Transmission Lines
20.7 Waveguides
20.8 Glossary of Transmission Line Terms
20.9 References and Bibliography

21 Antennas
21.1 Antenna Basics
21.2 Dipoles and the Half-Wave Antenna
21.3 Vertical (Ground-Plane) Antennas
21.4 T and Inverted-L Antennas
21.5 Slopers and Vertical Dipoles
21.6 Yagi Antennas
21.7 Quad and Loop Antennas
21.8 HF Mobile Antennas
21.9 VHF/UHF Mobile Antennas
21.10 VHF/UHF Antennas
21.11 VHF/UHF Beams
21.12 Radio Direction Finding Antennas
21.13 Rotators
21.13 Glossary
21.14 References and Bibliography

VOLUME 5

EQUIPMENT CONSTRUCTION AND STATION ACCESSORIES

22 Component Data and References
22.1 Component Data
22.2 Resistors
22.3 Capacitors
22.4 Inductors
22.5 Transformers
22.6 Semiconductors
22.7 Tubes, Wire, Materials, Attenuators, Miscellaneous
22.8 Computer Connectors
22.9 RF Connectors and Transmission Lines
22.10 Reference Tables

23 Construction Techniques
23.1 Electronic Shop Safety
23.2 Tools and Their Use
23.3 Soldering Tools and Techniques
23.4 Surface Mount Technology (SMT)
23.5 Constructing Electronic Circuits
23.6 CAD for PCB Design
23.7 Microwave Construction
23.8 Mechanical Fabrication

24 Assembling a Station
24.1 Fixed Stations
24.2 Mobile Installations
24.3 Portable Installations
24.4 Remote Stations

VOLUME 6

TEST EQUIPMENT, TROUBLESHOOTING, RFI, AND INDEX

25 Test Equipment and Measurements
25.1 Introduction
25.2 DC Measurements
25.3 AC Measurements
25.4 RF Measurements
25.5 Receiver Measurements
25.6 Transmitter Measurements
25.7 Antenna System Measurements
25.8 Miscellaneous Measurements
25.9 Construction Projects
25.10 References and Further Reading
25.11 Glossary of Test Equipment and Measurement Terms

26 Troubleshooting and Maintenance
26.1 Test Equipment
26.2 Components
26.3 Getting Started
26.4 Inside the Equipment
26.5 Testing at the Circuit Level
26.6 After the Repairs
26.7 Professional Repairs
26.8 Typical Symptoms and Faults
26.9 Radio Troubleshooting Hints
26.10 Antenna Systems
26.11 Repair and Restoration of Vintage Equipment
26.12 References and Bibliography

27 RF Interference
27.1 Managing Radio Frequency Interference
27.2 FCC Rules and Regulations
27.3 Elements of RFI
27.4 Identifying the Type of RFI Source
27.5 Locating Sources of RFI
27.6 Power-Line Noise
27.7 Elements of RFI Control
27.8 Troubleshooting RFI
27.9 Automotive RFI
27.10 RFI Projects
27.11 Glossary of RFI Terms
27.12 References and Bibliography

28 Safety
28.1 Electrical Safety
28.2 Antenna and Tower Safety
28.3 RF Safety

Advertiser's Index
Index
Project Index
Author's Index

DOWNLOADABLE CONTENT AND TOOLS
Space Communications
Digital Communications
Image Communications
Digital Basics
Station Accessories and Projects
2020 HF Transceiver Survey
Radio Mathematics

Contents

19.1 Fundamentals of Radio Waves
    19.1.1 Velocity
    19.1.2 Free Space Attenuation and Absorption
    19.1.3 Refraction
    19.1.4 Scattering
    19.1.5 Reflection
    19.1.6 Knife-Edge Diffraction
    19.1.7 Ground Wave

19.2 Sky-Wave Propagation and the Sun
    19.2.1 Structure of the Earth's Atmosphere
    19.2.2 The Ionosphere
    19.2.3 Ionospheric Refraction
    19.2.4 Maximum and Lowest Usable Frequencies
    19.2.5 NVIS Propagation
    19.2.6 Ionospheric Fading
    19.2.7 Polarization at HF
    19.2.8 The 11-Year Solar Cycle
    19.2.9 The Sun's 27-Day Rotation
    19.2.10 Disturbances to Propagation
    19.2.11 D-Layer Propagation
    19.2.12 E-Layer Propagation
    19.2.13 F-Layer Propagation
    19.2.14 Emerging Theories of HF and VHF Propagation
    19.2.15 WSJT

19.3 MUF Predictions
    19.3.1 MUF Forecasts
    19.3.2 Statistical Nature of Propagation Predictions
    19.3.3 Direct Observation
    19.3.4 WWV and WWVH
    19.3.5 Beacons
    19.3.6 Other Methods for Real-Time Assessment of the Ionosphere
    19.3.7 Space Weather Information
    19.3.8 Online Predictions

19.4 Propagation in the Troposphere
    19.4.1 Line of Sight
    19.4.2 Tropospheric Scatter
    19.4.3 Refraction and Ducting in the Troposphere
    19.4.4 Tropospheric Fading

19.5 VHF/UHF Mobile Propagation
    19.5.1 Rayleigh Fading
    19.5.2 Multipath Propagation
    19.5.3 Effect on the Receiver

19.6 Propagation for Space Communications
    19.6.1 Faraday Rotation
    19.6.2 Scintillation
    19.6.3 Earth-Moon-Earth
    19.6.4 Satellites

19.7 Noise and Propagation
    19.7.1 Man-Made Noise
    19.7.2 Lightning
    19.7.3 Precipitation Static and Corona Discharge
    19.7.4 Cosmic Sources

19.8 Propagation Below the AM Broadcast Band

19.9 Glossary of Radio Propagation Terms

19.10 References and Bibliography

Chapter 19 — Downloadable Supplemental Content

Supplemental Files

- "The Penticton Solar Flux Receiver" by John White, VA7JW and Ken Tapping
- "Hands-On Radio: Recording Signals" by Ward Silver, NØAX
- "The Reverse Beacon Network" by Pete Smith, N4ZR and Ward Silver, NØAX
- "The Solar Eclipse QSO Party" by Ward Silver, NØAX
- "F-Region Propagation and the Equatorial Ionosphere Anomaly" by Jim Kennedy, K6MIO/KH7
- "Upper Level Lows and 6-Meter Sporadic E" by Joe Dzekevich, K1YOW
- "The New Sunspot Numbers" by Carl Luetzelschwab, K9LA
- "Gray Line Propagation, or Florida to Cocos (Keeling) on 80m" by Ed Callaway, N4II

Projects

- "Build a Homebrew Radio Telescope" by Mark Spencer, WA8SME

Chapter 19

Propagation of Radio Signals

Radio waves, like light waves — and all other forms of electromagnetic radiation — normally travel in straight lines. Obviously this does not happen all the time, because long-distance communication depends on radio waves traveling beyond the horizon. How radio waves propagate in other than straight-line paths is a complicated subject, but one that need not be a mystery. This chapter, originally by Emil Pocock, W3EP, with updates by Carl Luetzelschwab, K9LA, provides basic understanding of the principles of electromagnetic radiation, the structure of the Earth's atmosphere and solar-terrestrial interactions necessary for a working knowledge of radio propagation. The section on VHF/UHF mobile propagation was contributed by Alan Bloom, N1AL. More detailed discussions and the underlying mathematics of radio propagation physics can be found in the references listed at the end of this chapter.

19.1 Fundamentals of Radio Waves

Radio belongs to a family of electromagnetic radiation that includes infrared (radiation heat), visible light, ultraviolet, X-rays and the even shorter-wavelength gamma and cosmic rays. Radio has the longest wavelength and thus the lowest frequency of this group. See **Table 19.1**.

Electromagnetic waves are composed of an inter-related electric and magnetic field. The electric and magnetic components are oriented at right angles to each other and are also perpendicular to the direction of travel. The polarization of a radio wave is usually designated the same as the orientation of its electric field. This relationship can be visualized in **Figure 19.1**. Unlike sound waves or ocean waves, electromagnetic waves need no propagating medium, such as air or water. This property enables electromagnetic waves to travel through the vacuum of space.

19.1.1 Velocity

Radio waves, like all forms of electromagnetic radiation, travel nearly 300,000 km (186,400 miles) per second in a vacuum. Radio waves travel more slowly through any other medium. The decrease in speed through the atmosphere is so slight that it is usually ignored, but sometimes even this small difference is significant. The speed of a radio wave in a piece of wire, by contrast, is about 95% that in free space, and the speed can be even slower in other media.

The speed of a radio wave is always the product of wavelength and frequency, whatever the medium. That relationship can be stated simply as:

$$c = f \lambda$$

where
  c = speed in meters/second
  f = frequency in Hz
  λ = wavelength in meters

The wavelength (λ) of any radio frequency can be determined from this simple formula by rearranging the above equation to $\lambda = c/f$. For example, in free space the wavelength of a 30 MHz radio signal is thus 10 meters. A simplified equation in metric units is λ in meters = 300 divided by the frequency in MHz. Alternately in English units, λ in feet = 984 divided by

Table 19.1
The Electromagnetic Spectrum

Radiation	Frequency	Wavelength
Radio	10 kHz – 300 GHz	30 km – 1 mm
Infrared	300 GHz – 428.6 THz	1 mm – 700 nm
Visible light	428.6 THz – 750 THz	700 nm – 400 nm
Ultraviolet	750 THz – 3 × 10^3 THz	400 nm – 100 nm
Extreme Ultraviolet	3 × 10^3 THz – 3 × 10^4 THz	100 nm – 10 nm
"Soft" X-ray	3 × 10^4 THz – 3 × 10^5 THz	10 nm – 1 nm
"Hard" X-ray	3 × 10^5 THz – 3 × 10^6 THz	1 nm – 0.1 nm

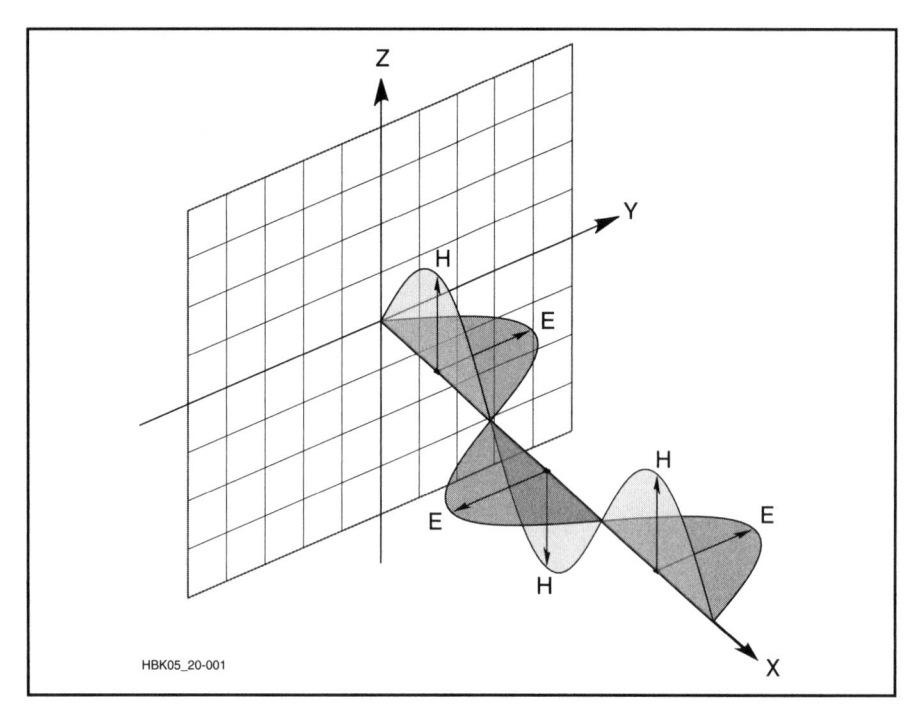

Figure 19.1 — Electric and magnetic field components of the electromagnetic wave. The polarization of a radio wave is the same direction as the plane of its electric field.

the frequency in MHz.

Wavelength decreases in other media because the propagating speed is slower. In a piece of wire, the wavelength of a 30 MHz signal shortens to about 9.5 meters. This factor must be taken into consideration in antenna designs, in transmission line designs, and in other applications.

19.1.2 Free Space Attenuation and Absorption

The intensity of a radio wave decreases as it travels. There are two mechanisms by which the intensity decreases: free space attenuation and absorption.

Free-space attenuation results from the spherical spreading of radio energy from its source. See **Figure 19.2**. Attenuation grows rapidly with distance because signal strength decreases with the square of the distance from the source. (The signal's field strength in V/m decreases linearly with distance and its power density in W/m² decreases with the square of distance.) If the distance between transmitter and receiver is increased from 1 km to 10 km (0.6 to 6 miles), the signal power will be reduced by a factor of 100. Attenuation increases with frequency as well. Free space attenuation (path loss) can be expressed as

$$L_{fs} = 32.45 + 20 \log d + 20 \log f$$

where

L_{fs} = free space path loss in dB
d = distance in km
f = frequency in MHz

Free-space attenuation is a major factor governing signal strength, but radio signals undergo a variety of other losses as well. Energy is lost to absorption when radio waves travel through media other than a vacuum. Radio waves propagate through the atmosphere or solid material (like a wire) by exciting electrons, which then reradiate energy at the same frequency. This process is not perfectly efficient, so some radio energy is transformed into heat and retained by the medium. The amount of radio energy lost in this way depends on the characteristics of the medium and on the frequency. Attenuation in the atmosphere is minor from 10 MHz to 3 GHz, but at higher frequencies, absorption due to water vapor and oxygen can be high.

Radio energy is also lost during refraction, diffraction and reflection — the very phenomena that allow long-distance propagation. Indeed, any form of useful propagation is accompanied by attenuation. This may vary from the slight losses encountered by refraction from sporadic E clouds near the maximum usable frequency, to the more considerable losses involved with tropospheric forward *scatter* (not enough ionization for refraction or reflection, but enough to send weak electromagnetic waves off into varied directions) or D layer absorption in the lower HF bands. These topics will be covered later. In many circumstances, total losses can become so great that radio signals become too weak for communication (they are below the sensitivity of a receiver or receiving system).

19.1.3 Refraction Below the Ionosphere

Electromagnetic waves travel in straight lines until they are deflected by something. Radio waves are *refracted*, or bent, slightly when traveling from one medium to another. Radio waves behave no differently from other familiar forms of electromagnetic radiation in this regard. The apparent bending of a pencil partially immersed in a glass of water demonstrates this principle quite dramatically.

Refraction is caused by a change in the velocity of a wave when it crosses the boundary between one propagating medium and another. If this transition is made at an angle, one portion of the wavefront slows down (or speeds up) before the other, thus bending the wave slightly. This is shown schematically in **Figure 19.3**.

The amount of bending increases with the ratio of the *refractive indices* of the two media. Refractive index is simply the velocity of a

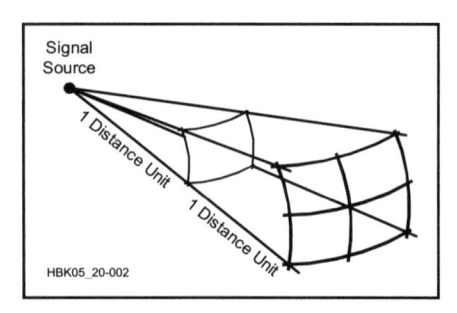

Figure 19.2 — Radio energy disperses as the square of the distance from its source. For the change of one distance unit shown the signal's power per unit of area is only one quarter as strong. Each spherical section has the same surface area.

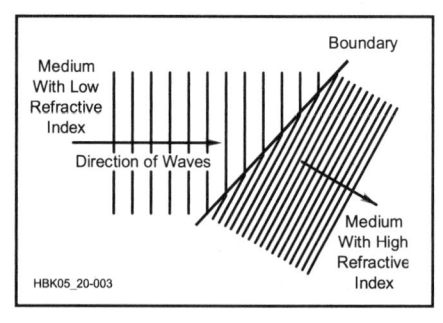

Figure 19.3 — Radio waves are refracted as they pass at an angle between dissimilar media. The lines represent the crests of a moving wave front and the distance between them is the wavelength. The direction of the wave changes because one end of the wave slows down before the other as it crosses the boundary between the two media. The wavelength is simultaneously shortened, but the wave frequency (number of crests that pass a certain point in a given unit of time) remains constant.

radio wave in free space divided by its velocity in the medium. The refractive properties of air may be calculated from temperature, moisture and atmospheric pressure. The index of refraction of air, at a very wide range of frequencies, may be calculated from:

$$N = \frac{77.6\,p}{T} + \frac{3.73 \times 10^5\,e}{T^2}$$

where
- N = index of refraction, N units (number of millionths by which the index of refraction exceeds 1.0)
- p = atmospheric pressure, millibars (mb)
- e = partial pressure of water vapor, millibars
- T = temperature, K

Note that the index of refraction below the ionosphere is greater than 1, causing more bending.

The refraction of radio signals is a function of the change in the index of refraction with altitude. N varies between 290 and 400 at the Earth's surface and normally diminishes with altitude at the rate of 40 N units per kilometer within the first few kilometers.

Radio waves are commonly refracted when they travel through different layers of the atmosphere, whether the highly charged ionospheric layers roughly 100 km (60 miles) and higher, or the weather-sensitive area near the Earth's surface. When the ratio of the refractive indices of two media is great enough, radio waves can be reflected, just like light waves striking a mirror. The Earth is a rather lossy reflector, but a metal surface works well if it is several wavelengths in diameter.

19.1.4 Scattering

The direction of radio waves can also be altered through *scattering*. The effect seen by a beam of light attempting to penetrate fog is a good example of light-wave scattering. Even on a clear night, a highly directional searchlight is visible due to a small amount of atmospheric scattering perpendicular to the beam. Radio waves are similarly scattered when they encounter randomly arranged objects of wavelength size or smaller, such as masses of electrons or water droplets. When the density of scattering objects becomes great enough, they behave more like a propagating medium with a characteristic refractive index.

If the scattering objects are arranged in some alignment or order, scattering takes place only at certain angles. A rainbow provides a good analogy for *field-aligned scattering* of light waves. The arc of a rainbow can be seen only at a precise angle away from the Sun, while the colors result from the variance in scattering across the light-wave frequency range. Ionospheric electrons can be field-aligned by magnetic forces in auroras and under other unusual circumstances. Scattering in such cases is best perpendicular to the Earth's magnetic field lines.

19.1.5 Reflection

At amateur frequencies above 30 MHz, reflections from a variety of large objects, such as water towers, buildings, airplanes, mountains and the like, can provide a useful means of extending over-the-horizon paths several hundred km. Two stations need only beam toward a common reflector, whether stationary or moving.

Maximum range is limited by the radio line-of-sight distance of both stations to the reflector and by reflector size and shape. The reflectors must be many wavelengths in size and ideally have flat surfaces. Large airplanes make fair reflectors and may provide the best opportunity for long-distance contacts. The calculated limit for airplane reflections is 900 km (560 miles), assuming the largest jets fly no higher than 12,000 meters (40,000 ft), but actual airplane reflection contacts are likely to be considerably shorter.

19.1.6 Knife-Edge Diffraction

Radio waves can also pass behind solid objects with sharp upper edges, such as a mountain range, by *knife-edge diffraction*. This is a common natural phenomenon that affects light, sound, radio and other coherent waves, but it is difficult to comprehend. **Figure 19.4** depicts radio signals approaching an idealized knife-edge. The portion of the radio waves that strike the base of the knife-edge is entirely blocked, while that portion passing several wavelengths above the edge travel on relatively unaffected. It might seem at first glance that a knife-edge as large as a mountain, for example, would completely prevent radio signals from appearing on the other side but that is not quite true. Something quite unexpected happens to radio signals that pass just over a knife-edge.

Normally, radio signals along a wave front interfere with each other continuously as they propagate through unobstructed space, but the overall result is a uniformly expanding wave. When a portion of the wave front is blocked by a knife-edge, the resulting interference pattern is no longer uniform. This can be understood by visualizing the radio signals right at the knife-edge as if they constituted a new and separate transmitting point, but in-phase with the source wave at that point. The signals adjacent to the knife-edge still interact with signals passing above the edge, but they cannot interact with signals that have been obstructed below the edge. The resulting *interference pattern* no longer creates a uniformly expanding wave front, but rather appears as a pattern of alternating strong and weak bands of waves that spread in a nearly 180° arc behind the knife-edge.

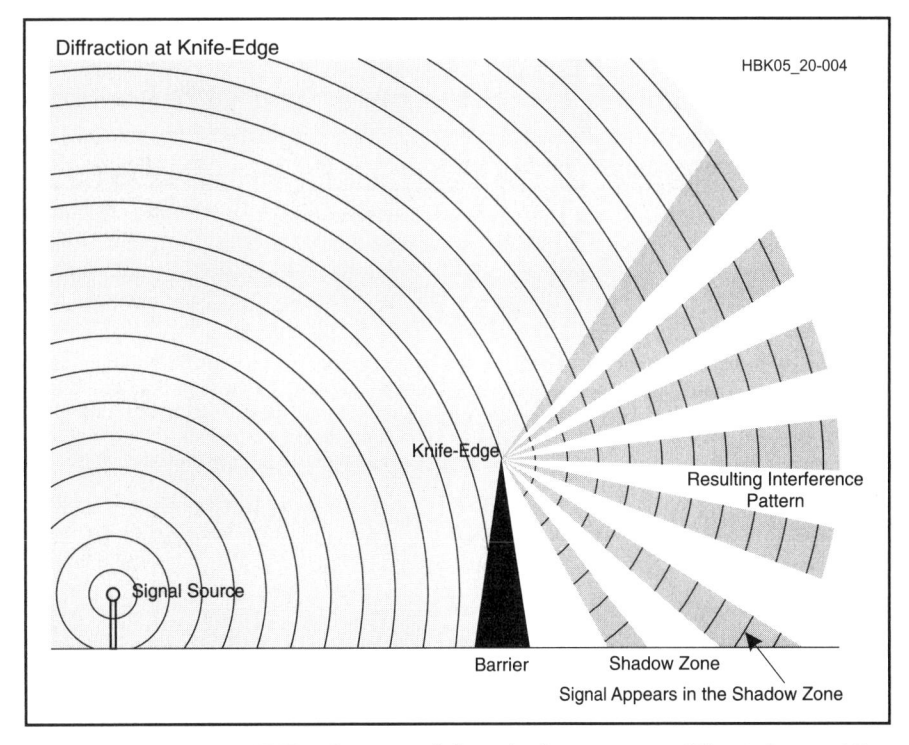

Figure 19.4 — VHF and UHF radio waves, light and other waves are diffracted around the sharp edge of a solid object that is large in terms of wavelengths. Diffraction results from interference between waves right at the knife-edge and those that are passing above it. Some signals appear behind the knife-edge as a consequence of the interference pattern. Hills or mountains can serve as natural knife-edges at radio frequencies.

Propagation Summary, by Band

LOW FREQUENCY (LF) BANDS AND MEDIUM FREQUENCY (MF) BANDS

135.7-137.8 kHz (2200 meters) and 472-479 kHz (630 meters)

See section 19.8 for a discussion of propagation on these bands.

1.8-2.0 MHz (160 meters)

160 meters suffers from daytime D layer absorption. Daytime communication is limited to ground-wave coverage and a single E hop out to about 1500 km for well equipped stations (running the full legal limit, quarter-wave verticals with a good ground system, and a low noise receiving environment). At night, the D layer quickly disappears and worldwide 160 meter communication becomes possible via F_2 layer skip and ducting. Atmospheric and man-made noise limits propagation. Tropical and mid latitude thunderstorms cause high levels of static in summer, making winter evenings the best time to work DX at 1.8 MHz. A proper choice of receiving antenna (Beverage, 4-square, small loop) can often significantly reduce the amount of received noise to improve the signal-to-noise ratio.

HIGH FREQUENCY (HF) BANDS (3-30 MHz)

A wide variety of propagation modes are useful on the HF bands. The lowest two bands in this range share many daytime characteristics with 160 meters. The transition between bands primarily useful at night or during the day appears around 10 MHz. Most long-distance contacts are made via F_2 layer skip. Above 21 MHz, more exotic propagation, including TE, sporadic E, aurora and meteor scatter, begins to be practical.

3.5-4.0 MHz (80 meters for the lower end, 75 meters for the higher end)

The lowest HF band is similar to 160 meters in many respects. Daytime absorption is significant, but not quite as extreme as at 1.8 MHz. At night, signals are often propagated halfway around the world. As at 1.8 MHz, atmospheric noise is a nuisance, making winter the most attractive season for the 80/75 meter DXer.

5.3-5.4 MHz (60 meters)

The distance covered during daytime propagation will fall in between that achievable on the 80 meter and 40 meter bands. At night, worldwide propagation is possible in spite of the relatively low power limit. Signal strengths will typically be higher than on 80 meters but not as high as on 40 meters.

7.0-7.3 MHz (40 meters)

The popular 40 meter band has a clearly defined skip zone during the day due to insufficient ionization to refract high angles. D layer absorption is not as severe as on the lower bands, so short-distance skip via the E and F layers is possible. During the day, a typical station can cover a radius of approximately 800 km (500 miles). At night, reliable worldwide communication via F_2 is common on the 40 meter band.

Atmospheric noise is much less troublesome than on 160 and 80 meters, and 40 meter DX signals are often of sufficient strength to override even high-level summer static. For these reasons, 40 meters is the lowest-frequency amateur band considered reliable for DX communication in all seasons. Even during the lowest point in the solar cycle, 40 meters may be open for worldwide DX throughout the night.

10.1-10.15 MHz (30 meters)

The 30 meter band is unique because it shares characteristics of both daytime and nighttime bands. D layer absorption is not a significant factor. Communication up to 3000 km (1900 miles) is typical during the daytime, and this extends halfway around the world via all-darkness paths. The band is generally open via F_2 on a 24-hour basis, but during a solar minimum, the MUF on some DX paths may drop below 10 MHz at night. Under these conditions, 30 meters adopts the characteristics of the daytime bands at 14 MHz and higher. The 30 meter band shows the least variation in conditions over the 11-year solar cycle, thus making it generally useful for long-distance communication anytime.

14.0-14.35 MHz (20 meters)

The 20 meter band is traditionally regarded as the amateurs' primary long-haul DX favorite. Regardless of the 11-year solar cycle, 20 meters can be depended on for at least a few hours of worldwide F_2 propagation during the day. During solar-maximum periods, 20 meters will often stay open to distant locations throughout the night. Skip distance is usually appreciable and is always present to some degree. Daytime E layer propagation may be detected along very short paths. Atmospheric noise is not a serious consideration, even in the summer. Because of its popularity, 20 meters tends to be very congested during the daylight hours.

18.068-18.168 MHz (17 meters)

The 17 meter band is similar to the 20 meter band in many respects, but the effects of fluctuating solar activity on F_2 propagation are more pronounced. During the years of high solar activity, 17 meters is reliable for daytime and early-evening long-range communication, often lasting well after sunset. During moderate years, the band may open only during sunlight hours and close shortly after sunset. At solar minimum, 17 meters will open to middle and equatorial latitudes, but only for short periods during midday on north-south paths.

21.0-21.45 MHz (15 meters)

The 15 meter band has long been considered a prime DX band during solar cycle maxima, but it is sensitive to changing solar activity. During peak years, 15 meters is reliable for daytime F_2 layer DXing and will often stay open well into the night. During periods of moderate solar activity, 15 meters is basically a daytime-only band, closing shortly after sunset. During solar minimum periods, 15 meters may not open at all except for infrequent north-south transequatorial circuits. Sporadic E is observed occasionally in early summer and mid-winter, although this is not common and the effects are not as pronounced as on the higher frequencies.

24.89-24.99 MHz (12 meters)

This band offers propagation that combines the best of the 10 and 15 meter bands. Although 12 meters is primarily a daytime band during low and moderate sunspot years, it may stay open well after sunset during the solar maximum. During years of moderate solar activity, 12 meters opens to the low and middle latitudes during the daytime hours, but it seldom remains open after sunset. Periods of low solar activity seldom cause this band to go completely dead, except at higher latitudes. Occasional daytime openings, especially in the lower latitudes, are likely over north-south paths. The main sporadic E season on 24 MHz lasts from late spring through summer and short openings may be observed in mid-winter.

28.0-29.7 MHz (10 meters)

The 10 meter band is well known for extreme variations in characteristics and a variety of propagation modes. During solar maxima, long-distance F_2 propagation is so efficient that very low power can produce strong signals halfway around the globe. DX is abundant with modest equipment. Under these conditions, the band is usually open from sunrise to a few hours past sunset. During periods of moderate solar activity, 10 meters usually opens only to low and transequatorial latitudes around noon. During the solar minimum, there may be no F_2 propagation at any time during the day or night.

Sporadic E is fairly common on 10 m, especially May through August, although it may appear at any time. Short skip, as sporadic E is sometimes called on the HF bands, has little relation to the solar cycle and occurs regardless of F layer conditions. It provides single-hop communication from 300 to 2300 km (190 to 1400 miles) and multiple-hop opportunities of 4500 km (2800 miles) and farther.

Ten meters is a transitional band in that it also shares some of the propagation modes more characteristic of VHF. Meteor scatter, aurora, auroral E and transequatorial propagation provide the means of making contacts out to 2300 km (1400 miles) and farther, but these modes often go unnoticed at 28 MHz. Techniques similar to those used at VHF can be very effective on 10 meters, as signals are usually stronger and more persistent. These exotic modes can be more fully exploited, especially during the solar minimum when F_2 DXing has waned.

VERY HIGH FREQUENCY (VHF) BANDS (30-300 MHz)

A wide variety of propagation modes are useful in the VHF range. F layer skip appears on 50 MHz during solar cycle peaks. Sporadic E and several other E layer phenomena are most effective in the VHF range. Still other forms of VHF ionospheric propagation, such as field-aligned irregularities (FAI) and transequatorial propagation (TE), are rarely observed at VHF. Tropospheric propagation, which is not a factor at HF, becomes increasingly important above 50 MHz.

50-54 MHz (6 meters)

The lowest amateur VHF band shares many of the characteristics of both lower and higher frequencies. In the absence of any favorable ionospheric propagation conditions, well-equipped 50 MHz stations work regularly over a radius of 300 km (190 miles) via tropospheric scatter, depending on terrain, power, receiver capabilities and antenna. Weak-signal troposcatter allows the best stations to make 500 km (310 mile) contacts nearly any time. Weather effects may extend the normal range by a few hundred km, especially during the summer months, but true tropospheric ducting is rare.

During the peak of the 11-year sunspot cycle (especially during the winter months), worldwide 50 MHz DX is possible via the F_2 layer during daylight hours. F_2 backscatter provides an additional propagation mode for contacts as far as 4000 km (2500 miles) when the MUF is just below 50 MHz. TE paths as long as 8000 km (5000 miles) across the magnetic equator are common around the spring and fall equinoxes of peak solar cycle years.

Sporadic E is probably the most common and certainly the most popular form of propagation on the 6 meter band. Single-hop E-skip openings may last many hours for contacts from 600 to 2300 km (370 to 1400 miles), primarily during the spring and early summer. Multiple-hop E_s provides transcontinental contacts several times a year, and contacts between the US and South America, Europe and Japan via multiple-hop E-skip occur nearly every summer.

Other types of E layer ionospheric propagation make 6 meters an exciting band. Maximum distances of about 2300 km (1400 miles) are typical for all types of E layer modes. Propagation via FAI often provides additional hours of contacts immediately following sporadic E events. Auroral propagation often makes its appearance in late afternoon when the geomagnetic field is disturbed. Closely related auroral E propagation may extend the 6 meter range to 4000 km (2500 miles) and sometimes farther across the northern states and Canada, usually after midnight. Meteor scatter provides brief contacts during the early morning hours, especially during one of the dozen or so prominent annual meteor showers.

144-148 MHz (2 meters)

Ionospheric effects are significantly reduced at 144 MHz, but they are far from absent. F layer propagation is unknown except for TE, which is responsible for the current 144 MHz terrestrial DX record of nearly 8000 km (5000 miles). Sporadic E occurs as high as 144 MHz less than a tenth as often as at 50 MHz, but the usual maximum single-hop distance is the same, about 2300 km (1400 miles). Multiple-hop sporadic E contacts greater than 3000 km (1900 miles) have occurred from time to time across the continental US, as well as across Southern Europe.

Auroral propagation is quite similar to that found at 50 MHz, except that signals are weaker and more Doppler-distorted. Auroral E contacts are rare. Meteor-scatter contacts are limited primarily to the periods of the great annual meteor showers and require much patience and operating skill. Contacts have been made via FAI on 144 MHz, but its potential has not been fully explored.

Tropospheric effects improve with increasing frequency, and 144 MHz is the lowest VHF band at which terrestrial weather plays an important propagation role. Weather-induced enhancements may extend the normal 300 to 600 km (190 to 370 mile) range of well-equipped stations to 800 km (500 miles) and more, especially during the summer and early fall. Tropospheric ducting extends this range to 2000 km (1200 miles) and farther over the continent and at least to 4000 km (2500 miles) over some well-known all-water paths, such as that between California and Hawaii.

222-225 MHz (135 cm)

The 135 cm band shares many characteristics with the 2 meter band. The normal working range of 222 MHz stations is nearly as far as comparably equipped 144 MHz stations. The 135 cm band is slightly more sensitive to tropospheric effects, but ionospheric modes are more difficult to use. Auroral and meteor-scatter signals are somewhat weaker than at 144 MHz, and sporadic E contacts on 222 MHz are extremely rare. FAI and TE may also be well within the possibilities of 222 MHz, but reports of these modes on the 135 cm band are uncommon. Increased activity on 222 MHz will eventually reveal the extent of the propagation modes on the highest of the amateur VHF bands.

ULTRA-HIGH FREQUENCY (UHF) BANDS (300-3000 MHz) AND HIGHER

Tropospheric propagation dominates the bands at UHF and higher, although some forms of E layer propagation are still useful at 432 MHz. Above 10 GHz, atmospheric attenuation increasingly becomes the limiting factor over long-distance paths. Reflections from airplanes, mountains and other stationary objects may be useful adjuncts to propagation at 432 MHz and higher.

420-450 MHz (70 cm)

The lowest amateur UHF band marks the highest frequency on which ionospheric propagation is commonly observed. Auroral signals are weaker and more Doppler distorted; the range is usually less than at 144 or 222 MHz. Meteor scatter is much more difficult than on the lower bands, because bursts are significantly weaker and of much shorter duration. Although sporadic E and FAI are unknown as high as 432 MHz and probably impossible, TE may be possible.

Well-equipped 432 MHz stations can expect to work over a radius of at least 300 km (190 miles) in the absence of any propagation enhancement. Tropospheric refraction is more pronounced at 432 MHz and provides the most frequent and useful means of extended-range contacts. Tropospheric ducting supports contacts of 1500 km (930 miles) and farther over land.

The current 432 MHz terrestrial DX record of more than 4000 km (2500 miles) was accomplished by ducting over water.

902-928 MHz (33 cm) and Higher

Ionospheric modes of propagation are nearly unknown in the bands above 902 MHz. Auroral scatter may be just within amateur capabilities at 902 MHz, but signal levels will be well below those at 432 MHz. Doppler shift and distortion will be considerable, and the signal bandwidth may be quite wide. No other ionospheric propagation modes are likely, although high-powered research radars have received echoes from auroras and meteors as high as 3 GHz.

Almost all extended-distance work in the UHF and microwave bands is accomplished with the aid of tropospheric enhancement. The frequencies above 902 MHz are very sensitive to changes in the weather. Tropospheric ducting occurs more frequently than in the VHF bands and the potential range is similar. At 1296 MHz, 2000 km (1200 mile) continental paths and 4000 km (2500 mile) paths between California and Hawaii have been spanned many times. Contacts of 1000 km (620 miles) have been made on all bands through 10 GHz in the US and over 1600 km (1000 miles) across the Mediterranean Sea. Well-equipped 903 and 1296 MHz stations can work reliably up to 300 km (190 miles), but normal working ranges generally shorten with increasing frequency.

Other tropospheric effects become evident in the GHz bands. Evaporation inversions, which form over very warm bodies of water, are usable at 3.3 GHz and higher. It is also possible to complete paths by scattering from rain, snow and hail in the lower GHz bands. Above 10 GHz, attenuation caused by atmospheric water vapor and oxygen become the most significant limiting factors in long-distance communication.

The crest of a range of hills or mountains 50 to 100 wavelengths long can produce knife-edge diffraction at UHF and microwave frequencies. Hillcrests that are clearly defined and free of trees, buildings and other clutter make the best knife-edges, but even rounded hills may serve as a diffracting edge. Alternating bands of strong and weak signals, corresponding to the interference pattern, will appear on the surface of the Earth behind the mountain, known as the *shadow zone*. The phenomenon is generally reciprocal, so that two-way communication can be established under optimal conditions. Knife-edge diffraction can make it possible to complete paths of 100 km or more that might otherwise be entirely obstructed by mountains or seemingly impossible terrain.

19.1.7 Ground Wave

A *ground wave* is the result of a special form of diffraction that primarily affects longer-wavelength vertically polarized radio waves. It is most apparent in the 80 and 160 meter amateur bands, where practical ground-wave distances may extend beyond 200 km (120 miles). It is also the primary mechanism used by AM broadcast stations in the medium-wave bands. The term ground wave is often mistakenly applied to any short-distance communication, but the actual mechanism is unique to the longer-wave bands.

Radio waves are bent slightly as they pass over a sharp edge, but the effect extends to edges that are considerably rounded. At medium and long wavelengths, the curvature of the Earth looks like a rounded edge. Bending results when the lower part of the wave front loses energy due to currents induced in the ground. This slows down the lower part of the wave, causing the entire wave to tilt forward slightly. This tilting follows the curvature of the Earth, thus allowing low- and medium-wave radio signals to propagate over distances well beyond line of sight.

Ground wave is most useful during the day at 1.8 and 3.5 MHz, when D layer absorption makes skywave propagation more difficult. Vertically polarized antennas with excellent ground systems provide the best results. Ground-wave losses are reduced considerably over saltwater and are worst over dry and rocky land.

19.2 Sky-Wave Propagation and the Sun

The Earth's atmosphere is composed primarily of nitrogen (78%), oxygen (21%) and argon (1%), with smaller amounts of a dozen other gases. Water vapor can account for as much as 5% of the atmosphere under certain conditions. This ratio of gases is maintained until an altitude of about 80 km (50 miles), when the mix begins to change. At the highest levels, helium and hydrogen predominate.

Solar radiation acts directly or indirectly on all levels of the atmosphere. Adjacent to the surface of the Earth, solar warming controls all aspects of the weather, powering wind, rain and other familiar phenomena. *Solar ultraviolet (UV) radiation* creates small concentrations of ozone (O_3) molecules between 10 and 50 km (6 and 30 miles). Most UV radiation is absorbed by this process and never reaches the Earth.

At even higher altitudes, EUV (Extreme UV) and X-ray radiation partially ionize atmospheric gases. Electrons freed from gas atoms eventually recombine with positive ions to recreate neutral gas atoms, but this takes some time. In the low-pressure environment at the highest altitudes, atoms are spaced far apart and the gases may remain ionized for many hours. At lower altitudes, recombination happens rather quickly, and only constant radiation can keep any appreciable portion of the gas ionized.

19.2.1 Structure of the Earth's Atmosphere

The atmosphere, which reaches to more than 600 km (370 miles) altitude, is usually divided into a number of regions based on a transitioning characteristic of the atmosphere — like temperature. For propagation purposes, the important regions are shown in **Figure 19.5**. The weather-producing *troposphere* lies between the surface and an average altitude of 10 km (6 miles). Between 10 and 50 km (6 and 30 miles) are the *stratosphere* and the embedded *ozonosphere*, where ultraviolet-absorbing ozone reaches its highest concentrations. About 99% of atmospheric gases are contained within these two lowest regions.

Above 50 km to about 600 km (370 miles) is the *ionosphere*, notable for its effects on radio propagation. At these altitudes, atomic oxygen, molecular oxygen, molecular nitrogen, and nitric oxide predominate under very low pressure and are the important species to consider for propagation. High-energy solar EUV and X-ray radiation ionize these constituents, creating a broad region where ions are created in relative abundance. The ionosphere is subdivided into distinctive D, E and F regions.

The *magnetosphere* begins around 600 km (370 miles) and extends as far as 160,000 km (100,000 miles) into space. The predominant component of atmospheric gases gradually shifts from atomic oxygen, to helium and finally to hydrogen at the highest levels. The lighter gases may reach escape velocity or be swept off the atmosphere by the *solar wind* (electrically charged particles emitted by the Sun and traveling through space). At about 3200 and 16,000 km (2000 and 9900 miles, respectively), the Earth's magnetic field traps energetic electrons and protons in two bands, known as the *Van Allen belts*. These have only a minor effect on terrestrial radio propagation.

19.2.2 The Ionosphere

The ionosphere plays a basic role in long-distance communications in all the amateur bands from 1.8 MHz to 30 MHz. The effects of the ionosphere are less apparent at the very high frequencies (30-300 MHz), but they persist at least through 432 MHz. As early as 1902, Oliver Heaviside and Arthur E. Kennelly independently suggested the existence of a layer in the upper atmosphere that could account for the long-distance radio transmissions made the previous year by Guglielmo Marconi and others. Edward Appleton confirmed the existence of the Kennelly-Heaviside layer in publications beginning in 1925 and used the letter E on his diagrams to designate the strength of the electric field of the waves that were apparently reflected from the layer he measured.

In late 1927 Appleton reported the existence of an additional layer in the "ionosphere." (Robert Watson-Watt coined the term "ionosphere", but it wasn't commonly used until 1932.) The additional higher-altitude layer was named "F" and subsequently another was termed "D." For a time during the 1930s, a "C" layer was proposed, and later discarded. Appleton was reluctant to alter this arbitrary nomenclature for fear of discovering yet other lower layers, so it has stuck to the present day. The basic physics of ionospheric propagation was largely worked out by the 1930s, yet both amateur and professional experimenters made further discoveries during the 1930s, 1940s and 1950s. Sporadic E, aurora, trans-equatorial, meteor scatter and several types of field-aligned scattering were among additional ionospheric phenomena that required explanation.

Although the term "layer" is used in this chapter, this could lead to the erroneous assumption that the ionosphere consists of distinct thin sheets separated by emptiness in between. This is not so, and as we'll see later in the chapter the ionosphere is a continuous electronic density versus altitude, with definite peaks and inflections points that define the D, E, F_1 and F_2 regions. Studies have shown that the height of the various layers may also vary by latitude. Research into ionospheric physics is ongoing in an attempt to better understand the variability of the ionosphere.

Figure 19.5 — Regions of the lower atmosphere and the ionosphere.

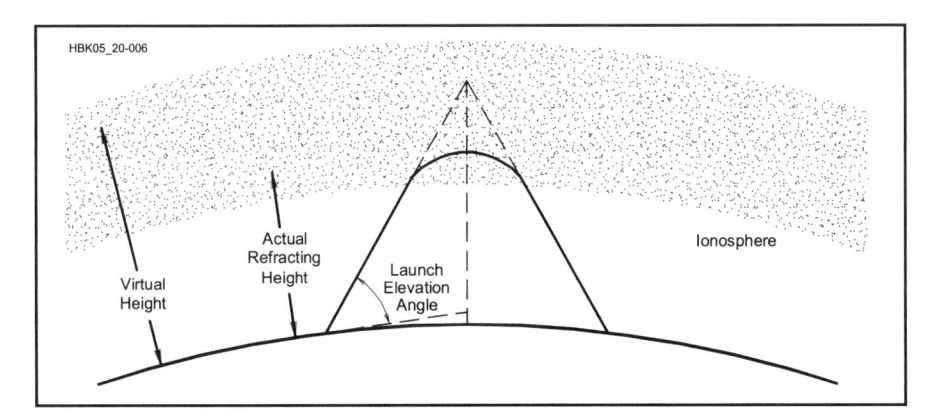

Figure 19.6 — Gradual refraction in the ionosphere allows radio signals to be propagated long distances. It is often convenient to imagine the process as a reflection with an imaginary reflection point at some virtual height above the actual refracting region. The other figures in this chapter show ray paths as equivalent reflections, but you should keep in mind that the actual process is a gradual refraction.

19.2.3 Ionospheric Refraction

The refractive index of an ionospheric layer decreases from a value of 1.00 as the density of free-moving electrons increases (this is opposite from the refractive index in the troposphere since the ionosphere is a dispersive medium). In the densest regions of the F layer, that density can reach a trillion electrons per cubic meter (10^{12} e/m^3). Even at this high level, radio waves are refracted gradually over a considerable vertical distance, usually amounting to tens of km. Radio waves become useful for terrestrial propagation only when they are refracted enough to bring them back to Earth. See **Figure 19.6**.

Although refraction is the primary mechanism of ionospheric propagation, it is usually more convenient to think of the process as a reflection. The *virtual height* of an ionospheric layer is the equivalent altitude of a reflection that would produce the same effect as the actual refraction. The virtual height of any ionospheric layer can be determined using

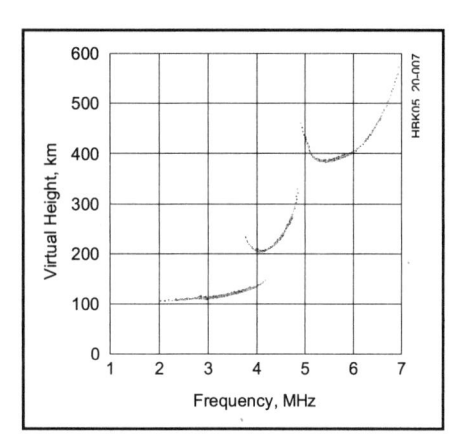

Figure 19.7 — Simplified vertical incidence ionogram showing echoes returned from the E, F_1 and F_2 layers. The critical frequencies of each layer (4.1, 4.8 and 6.8 MHz) can be read directly from the ionogram scale.

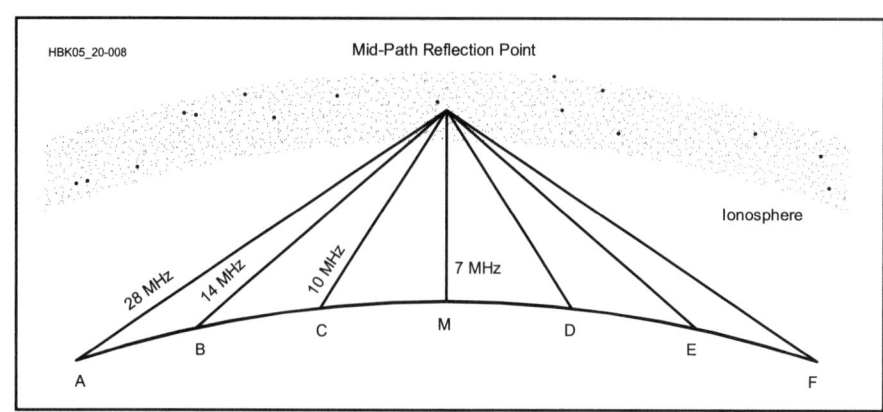

Figure 19.8 — The relationships between critical frequency, maximum usable frequency (MUF) and skip zone can be visualized in this simplified, hypothetical case. The critical frequency is 7 MHz, allowing frequencies below this to be used for short-distance ionospheric communication by stations in the vicinity of point M. These stations cannot communicate by the ionosphere at 14 MHz. Stations at points B and E (and beyond) can communicate because signals at this frequency are refracted back to Earth because they encounter the ionosphere at an oblique angle of incidence. At greater distances, higher frequencies can be used because the MUF is higher at the larger angles of incidence (low launch angles). In this figure, the MUF for the path between points A and F, with a small launch angle, is shown to be 28 MHz. Each pair of stations can communicate at frequencies at or below the MUF of the path between them, but not below the LUF — see text.

an ionospheric sounder, or *ionosonde*, a sort of vertically oriented radar. The ionosonde sends pulses that sweep over a wide frequency range, generally from 2 MHz to 20 MHz or higher, straight up into the ionosphere. The frequencies of any echoes are recorded against time and then plotted as distance on an *ionogram*. **Figure 19.7** depicts a simple ionogram. Real-time ionograms can be found online at the Digital Ionogram Database, sponsored by the University of Massachusetts Lowell (**http://umlcar.uml.edu/DIDBase/**). For an extensive discussion of ionogram interpretation, download *UAG-23A: URSI Handbook of Ionogram Interpretation and Reduction* from the Australian IPS (Ionospheric Prediction Service) website at **www.ips.gov.au/IPSHosted/INAG/uag_23a/uag_23a.html**.

The highest frequency that returns echoes from the E and F regions at vertical incidence is known as the *vertical incidence* or *critical frequency*. (There is a D region critical frequency, but its value is well below 1 MHz and thus has minimal impact on our Amateur Radio bands.) The critical frequency is a function of ion density. The higher the ionization at a particular altitude, the higher becomes the critical frequency. Strictly speaking, the critical frequency is the term applicable to the peak electron density of a region. Physicists call any electron density in any part of the ionosphere a *plasma frequency*, because technically gases in the ionosphere are in a plasma, or partially ionized state. F layer critical frequencies commonly range from about 1 MHz to as high as 15 MHz.

19.2.4 Maximum and Lowest Usable Frequencies

When the frequency of a vertically incident signal is raised above the critical frequency of an ionospheric layer, that portion of the ionosphere is unable to refract the signal back to Earth. However, a signal above the critical frequency may be returned to Earth if it enters the layer at an *oblique angle*, rather than at vertical incidence. This is fortunate because it permits two widely separated stations to communicate on significantly higher frequencies than the critical frequency. See **Figure 19.8**.

The highest frequency supported by the ionosphere between two stations is the *maximum usable frequency* (MUF) for that path. If the separation between the stations is increased, a still higher frequency can be supported at lower launch angles. The MUF for this longer path is higher than the MUF for the shorter path because more refraction can occur for electromagnetic waves that encounter the ionosphere at more oblique angles. When the distance is increased to the maximum one-hop distance, the launch angle of the signals between the two stations is zero (that is, the ray path is tangential to the Earth at the two stations) and the MUF for this path is the highest that can be supported by that layer of the ionosphere at that location. This maximum distance is about 4000 km (2500 miles) for the F_2 layer and about 2000 km (1250 miles) for the E layer. See **Figure 19.9**.

The MUF is a function of path, time of day, season, location, solar UV and X-ray radiation levels and ionospheric disturbances. For vertically incident waves, the MUF is the same as the critical frequency. For path lengths at the limit of one-hop propagation, the MUF can be

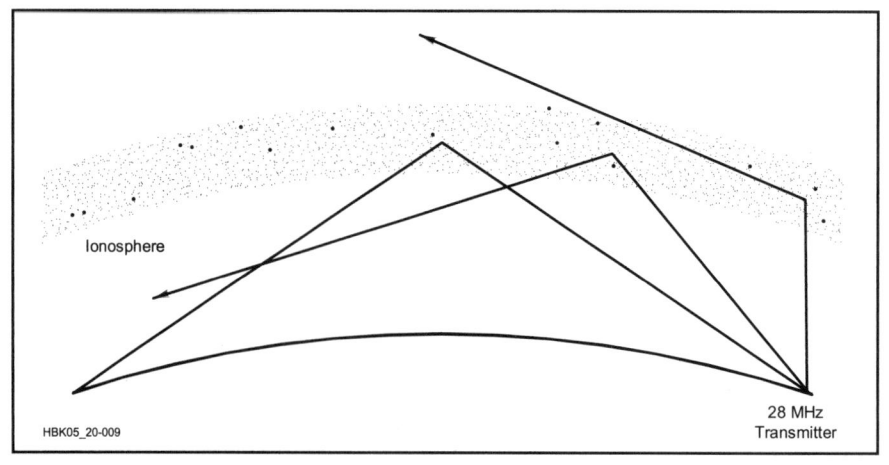

Figure 19.9 — Signals at the MUF propagated at a low angle to the horizon provide the longest possible one-hop distances. In this example, 28 MHz signals entering the ionosphere at higher angles are not refracted enough to bring them back to Earth.

several times the critical frequency. The ratio between the MUF and the critical frequency is known as the *M-factor*.

The M-factor can be estimated using simple geometry in a spherical model of the Earth-ionosphere system. The angle of incidence on the ionosphere of an electromagnetic wave launched from the ground depends on the launch angle and the height of the ionospheric region. Due to the spherical geometry of the Earth-ionosphere system, the angle of incidence on the ionosphere does not approach zero as the launch angle approaches zero — it is limited to approximately 19° and 11° for the F_2 and E regions, respectively, which then limits the M-factor to approximately 3 and 5 for these two regions (from the equation MUF = 1 / the sine of the angle of incidence on the ionosphere). See **Table 19.2** for typical M-factors of the various regions.

The term *skip zone* is closely related to MUF. When two stations are unable to communicate with each other on a particular frequency because the ionosphere is unable to refract the signal enough from one to the other through the required angle — that is, the operating frequency is above the MUF — the stations are said to be in the skip zone for that frequency. Stations within the skip zone may be able to work each other on a lower frequency, or by ground wave or other mechanisms if they are close enough. There is no skip zone at frequencies below the MUF.

The MUF at any time on a particular path is just that — the *maximum* usable frequency. Frequencies below the MUF will also propagate along the path, but ionospheric absorption and noise at the receiving location (due to man-made noise and/or noise from local or distant thunderstorms) may make the received signal-to-noise ratio too low to be usable. In this case, the frequency is said to be below the *lowest usable frequency* (LUF). This occurs most frequently below 10 MHz, where atmospheric and man-made noises are most troublesome.

The LUF can be lowered somewhat by the use of high power and directive antennas, or through the use of communication modes that permit reduced receiver bandwidth or are less demanding of SNR — CW or PSK31 instead of SSB, for example. This is not true of the MUF, which is limited by the physics of ionospheric refraction, no matter how high your transmitter power or how narrow your receiver bandwidth. The LUF can be higher than the MUF. This is a common occurrence on 160 meters during the day due to too much absorption; another scenario would be too much noise on the higher bands due to thunderstorm activity or man-made noise. When the LUF is higher than the MUF, there is no frequency that supports communication on the particular path at that time.

19.2.5 NVIS Propagation

In the previous section, the statement was made that *stations within the skip zone may be able to work each other at a lower frequency, or by ground wave if they are close enough*. This statement summarizes the purpose of Near Vertical Incidence Skywave (*NVIS*) propagation — to bridge the gap between where ground wave is too weak and where the skip zone ends. By going to lower frequencies, communications can be maintained over these relatively short distances.

Propagation over short distances means high elevation angles — this is not DXing in which lower angles in general are most effective. For example, a path from San Francisco to Sacramento is 75 miles, and requires an average elevation angle of 78 degrees. To radiate maximum energy at these higher angles, relatively low height antennas need to be used.

In the December 2005 issue of *QST*, Dean Straw N6BV used the *VOACAP* propagation prediction program to analyze a variety of NVIS paths centered on San Francisco. His analysis showed area coverage maps (signal strength contours versus distance from the transmitter) and elevation patterns of antennas at various height. His analysis allowed him to formulate a very nice summary: *As a rule-of-thumb, for ham band NVIS, I would recommend that 40 meters be used during the day; 80 meters during the night.* Additionally, during a winter night near solar minimum, changing to 160 meters may be necessary. Tom Kamp, DF5JL, also studied NVIS on the 60 meter band in Germany. See the References section entry for his article in *CQ DL*.

19.2.6 Ionospheric Fading

HF signal strengths typically rise and fall over periods of a few seconds to several minutes, and rarely hold at a constant level for very long. Fading is generally caused by the interaction of several radio waves from the same source arriving along different propagation paths. Waves that arrive in-phase combine to produce a stronger signal, while those out-of-phase cause destructive interference and lower net signal strength. Short-term variations in ionospheric conditions may change individual path lengths or signal strengths enough to cause fading. Even signals that arrive primarily over a single path may vary as the propagating medium changes. Fading may be most notable at sunrise and sunset, especially near the MUF, when the ionosphere undergoes dramatic transformations. Other ionospheric traumas, such as auroras and geomagnetic storms, also produce severe forms of HF fading.

19.2.7 Polarization at HF

Although the ionosphere varies on a short-term basis and results in somewhat random polarization, there is more order to polarization than realized. The ionosphere is immersed in the Earth's magnetic field, and the result of an electromagnetic wave propagating through an ionized medium (called a plasma, which is what our ionosphere is) immersed in a magnetic field is the propagation of two characteristic waves: the ordinary wave (O-wave) and the extraordinary wave (X-wave). Ordinary and extraordinary are terms borrowed from the science of optics. These two waves are generally elliptically polarized (the tip of the polarization vector traces out an ellipse), and are orthogonal to each other.

Upon entering the ionosphere, and depending on the location and the heading, a linearly polarized wave (from our horizontal or vertical antenna) will either couple all of its energy into the O-wave, all of its energy into the X-wave, or divide its energy into the O-wave and X-wave. Our horizontal antenna will couple best into one characteristic wave, and our vertical antenna will couple best into the other characteristic wave. The same coupling issue is present when the characteristic waves exit the ionosphere. The bottom line is that on the HF bands of 80 meters and higher, both characteristic waves generally propagate with similar absorption, and thus the use of a vertical or horizontal antenna is not too critical with respect to polarization. One of the characteristic waves will couple into whichever antenna is being used.

On 160 meters, though, the X-wave is heavily absorbed, leaving the O-wave. In general, vertical polarization is best for those of us in North America and at high northern latitudes. However, 160 meter operators have observed that under some conditions,

Table 19.2
Maximum Usable Frequency Factors (M-factors) for 2000 km E Hops and 3000 km F Hops

Layer	Maximum Critical Frequency (MHz)	M-factor	Useful Operating Frequencies (MHz)
F_2	15.0	3.3-4.0	1-60
F_1*	5.5	4.0	10-20
E*	4.0	4.8	5-20
Es	30.0	5.3	20-160

*Daylight only

horizontally polarized antennas outperform vertically polarized antennas.

19.2.8 The 11-Year Solar Cycle

The density of ionospheric layers depends on the amount of solar radiation reaching the Earth, but solar radiation is not constant. Variations result from daily and seasonal motions of the Earth, the Sun's own 27-day rotation and the 11-year cycle of solar activity. One visual indicator of both the Sun's rotation and the solar cycle is the periodic appearance of dark spots on the Sun, which have been observed continuously since the mid-18th century. On average, the number of *sunspots* reaches a maximum every 10.7 years, but the period has varied between 7 and 17 years. Cycle 19 peaked in 1958, with a smoothed sunspot number of 201, the highest recorded to date. **Figure 19.10** shows the smoothed sunspot numbers (these values are the new Version 2.0 sunspot data) for the past six cycles.

Sunspots are cooler areas on the Sun's surface associated with high magnetic activity. Active regions adjacent to sunspot groups, called *plages*, are capable of producing great flares and sustained bursts of radiation in the radio through X-ray spectrum. During the peak of the 11-year solar cycle, average solar radiation increases along with the number of flares and sunspots. The ionosphere becomes more intensely ionized as a consequence, resulting in higher critical frequencies, particularly sin the F_2 layer. The possibilities for long-distance communications are considerably improved during solar maxima, especially in the higher-frequency bands.

One key to forecasting F layer critical frequencies, and thus long-distance propagation, is the intensity of ionizing UV and X-ray radiation. Until the advent of satellites, UV and X-ray radiation could not be measured directly, because they were almost entirely absorbed in the upper atmosphere during the process of ionization. The sunspot number provided the most convenient approximation of general solar activity. The sunspot number is not a simple count of the number of visual spots, but rather the result of a complicated formula that takes into consideration size, number and grouping. The smoothed sunspot number (equivalent to a running average of monthly mean sunspot numbers from 6 months before to 6 months after the desired month) varies from near zero during the solar cycle minimum to over 200 during an extremely active solar cycle.

Another method of gauging solar activity is the *solar flux*, which is a measure of the intensity of 2800 MHz (10.7 cm) radio noise coming from the Sun (10^{-22} W m^{-2} Hz^{-1}). The smoothed 2800 MHz radio flux is an indication of the intensity of ionizing UV and X-ray radiation and provides a convenient alternative to sunspot numbers. Solar flux values commonly vary on a scale of 60-300 and can be related to sunspot numbers, as shown in **Figure 19.11** (note that this is only valid for converting between smoothed values). The Dominion Radio Astrophysical Observatory, Penticton, British Columbia, measures the 2800 MHz solar flux three times a day (centered on local noon). (A supplemental article, "The Penticton Solar Flux Receiver" from February 2013 *QST* is with the downloadable supplemental content.) Radio station WWV broadcasts the latest solar-flux index at 18 minutes after each hour; WWVH does the same at 45 minutes after the hour. Solar flux and other useful data is also available online at **www.swpc.noaa.gov**.

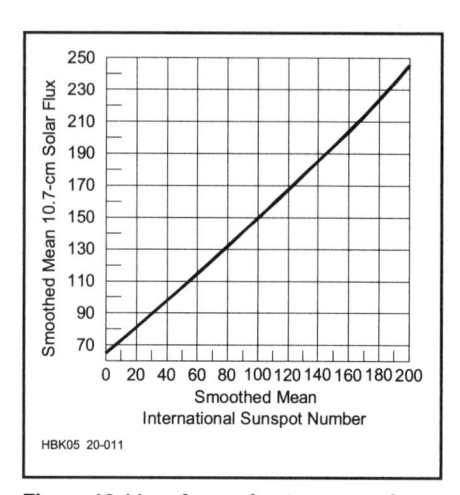

Figure 19.11 — Approximate conversion between solar flux and sunspot number. Note that this is for smoothed values of Solar Flux and Sunspot Numbers.

The Penticton solar flux is employed in a wide variety of other applications. Daily, weekly, monthly and even smoothed solar flux readings are commonly used in propagation predictions (but be aware that our HF propagation predictions are based on the correlation between smoothed solar flux or smoothed sunspot number and monthly median ionospheric parameters — more on this later in the chapter).

High flux values generally result in higher MUFs, but the actual procedures for predicting the MUF at any given hour and path is quite complicated. Solar flux is not the sole determinant, as the angle of the Sun to the Earth, season, time of day, exact location of the radio path and other factors must all be taken into account. MUF forecasting a few days or months ahead involves additional variables and even more uncertainties.

TRENDS IN SOLAR CYCLES

If one looks at all 23 recorded solar cycles, three characteristics stand out. First, we see a cyclic nature to the maximum smoothed sunspot numbers. Second, we've been through three high cycle periods of 50 years or so (consisting of several solar cycles) and two low cycle periods of 50 years or so (again, consisting of several solar cycles), and we appear to be headed into a third low cycle period. Third, we've lived through the highest period of high cycle activity (but this is currently being challenged by solar scientists through an in-depth review of old sunspot records), which has allowed excellent worldwide propagation on the higher frequency bands and provided great enjoyment for radio amateurs.

If we look at solar cycles prior to recorded history through various proxies for solar

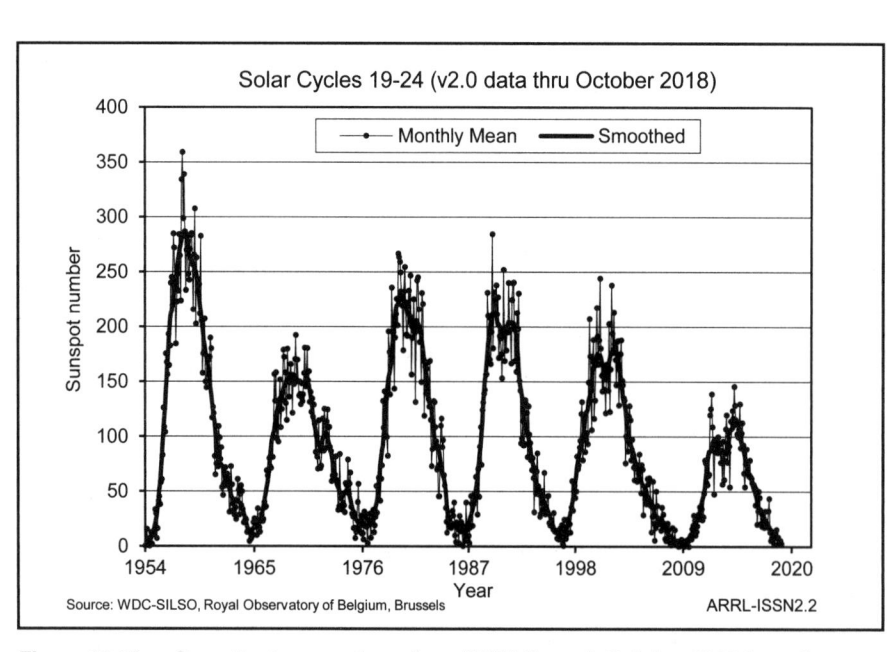

Figure 19.10 — Smoothed sunspot numbers (SSN) through October 2018 for solar cycles 19 to 24.

Status of Solar Cycle 24

(This information was prepared in November 2018 by Carl Leutzelschwab, K9LA)

Figure 19.A1 updates the monthly mean 10.7 cm solar flux through October 2018 (gray curve) and the smoothed 10.7 cm solar flux through April 2018 (black curve). Cycle 24 continues its descent to solar minimum between Cycles 24 and 25, which is still expected to occur in late 2019 or early 2020. This is supported by planetary A index (Ap) data that indicates we have a way to go to "official" solar minimum.

Based on historical data of previous solar minimum periods and recent data, it appears that the solar minimum we're in right now is going to be another long one — just like the solar minimum between Cycles 23 and 24. That solar minimum lasted almost five years as defined by when the smoothed sunspot number was below 20, compared to only two years for the previous five solar minimum periods going back to the solar minimum between Cycles 18 and 19.

With Cycle 24 being the smallest solar cycle in our lifetimes and predictions of a small Cycle 25 (see the "Status of Solar Cycle 24" on page 19.11 in the 2019 *ARRL Handbook*), there's always the talk of another Maunder Minimum (approximately 1645 to 1715) when there was a dearth of sunspots. This talk appears to be unwarranted as the decrease in the magnetic field strength of sunspots has leveled off at around 2100 Gauss, which is above the 1500 Gauss limit below which we do not see sunspots. See **leif.org/research/Livingston%20and%20Penn.png** for this data.

Additionally, as of November 17, 2018, three new sunspots from Cycle 25 have been observed. **Figure 19.A2** shows magnetograms for these three new sunspots. Solar scientists can tell if a sunspot is from the new solar cycle by where it emerges on the solar disk (sunspots from the new cycle emerge at the higher solar latitudes) and from the polarity of the sunspot's magnetic field (the polarity is opposite of low-latitude old sunspots in the same hemisphere).

Thus it looks like Cycle 25 is alive, and we should see more Cycle 25 spots and fewer Cycle 24 sunspots as time progresses. Although Cycle 25 may be a small one, we'll still have good propagation on 10 meters and 6 meters via the F2 region around solar maximum (likely to occur in the 2023 to 2024 timeframe) in the fall and winter months — just like we did around the peak of Cycle 24.

Don't forget sporadic E in the summer months and get on FT8 to take advantage of its ability to decode signals down lower in the noise. In fact, FT8 will likely make this solar minimum period the most active in history.

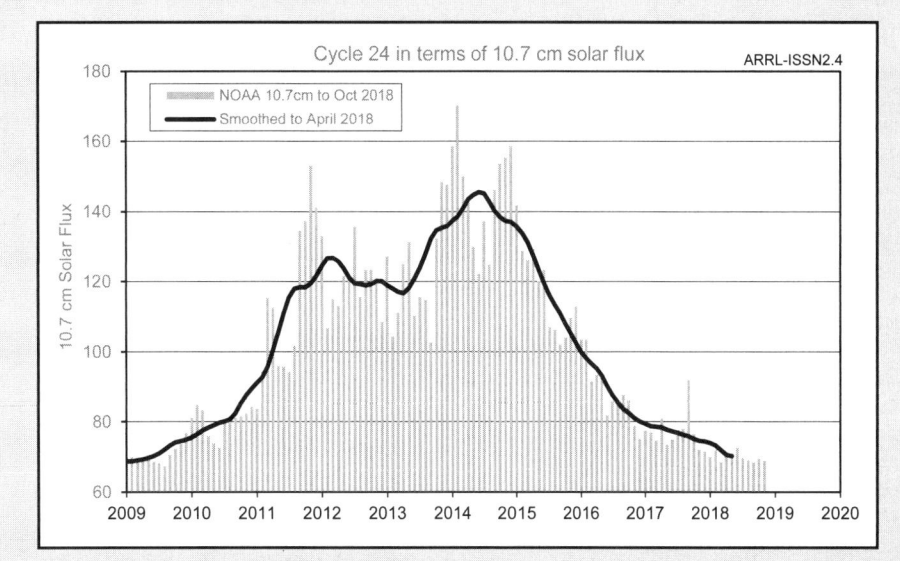

Figure 19.A1 — Monthly mean and smoothed 10.7 cm solar flux data through October 2018 and April 2018, respectively.

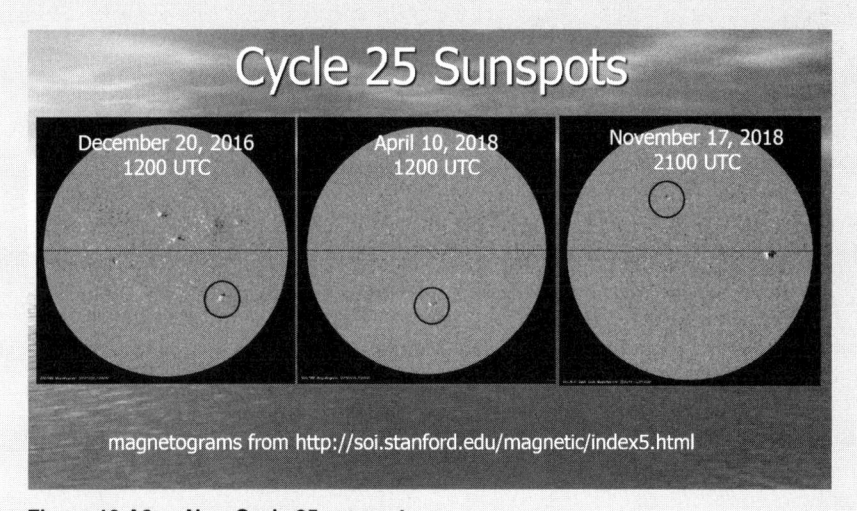

Figure 19.A2 — New Cycle 25 sunspots.

---

activity (for example, carbon-14 in trees and beryllium-10 in ice cores), we'll see extended periods of very low solar activity referred to as Grand Minima (for example, the Maunder Minimum between 1640 and 1710 AD). It's likely that we'll again enter one of these extended periods, but trying to predict when this will happen is, at best, a wild guess.

With respect to solar minimum periods between solar cycles, historical data shows a great variation. The average length of solar minimum, for example defined as the number of months in which the smoothed sunspot number is below 20, is around 37 months. Using this definition, the shortest minimum was 17 months (between Cycles 1 and 2) and the longest minimum was 96 months (between Cycles 5 and 6). The minimum period between Cycle 23 and Cycle 24 turned out to be 56 months. Interestingly, up until the minimum between Cycle 23 and Cycle 24, in our lifetimes we have experienced minimum periods of approximately 24 months — much shorter than the average. This leads us to believe this recent solar minimum period was unusual. But historical data, with its great amount of variation, says otherwise.

19.2.9 The Sun's 27-Day Rotation

Sunspot observations also reveal that the Sun rotates on its own axis. The Sun is composed of extremely hot gases and does not turn uniformly (it is essentially a fluid). At the equator, the period is just over 25 days, but it approaches 35 days at the poles. Sunspots that affect the Earth's ionosphere, which appear almost entirely within 35° of the Sun's equator, take about 26 days for one rotation. After taking into account the Earth's movement around the Sun, the apparent period of solar rotation is about 27 days.

Active regions must face the Earth in the proper orientation to have an impact on the ionosphere. They may face the Earth only once before rotating out of view, but they often persist for several solar rotations. The net effect is that solar activity often appears in 27-day cycles corresponding to the Sun's rotation, even though the active regions themselves may last for several solar rotations.

The downloadable supplemental content includes articles about observing solar phenomena, including a *QST* article by Mark Spencer, WA8SME on building your own radio telescope. Numerous online sources such as **solar-center.stanford.edu/observe** explain how to view the Sun for yourself. When observing the Sun, be sure to follow safe viewing practices as described in the online *Sky and Telescope* article "Safe Solar Viewing" by Jeff Medkeff (**www.skyandtelescope.com/observing/objects/sun/3309106.html**).

19.2.10 Disturbances to Propagation

Like a campfire that occasionally spits out a flaming ember, our Sun sometimes erupts spasmodically — but on a much grander scale than a summer campfire here on Earth. After all, any event that violently releases as much as 10 billion tons of solar material traveling up to four and a half million miles per hour or releases large amounts of electromagnetic radiation at extremely short wavelengths has to be considered pretty impressive!

Following the lead of the Space Weather Prediction Center, there are three types of disturbances to propagation: geomagnetic storms (designated G), solar radiation storms (designated S) and radio blackouts (designated R). For more details and the scaling associated with these designators, visit **www.swpc.noaa.gov/noaa-scales-explanation**.

GEOMAGNETIC STORMS

Geomagnetic storms are generally caused by *coronal mass ejections* and high speed wind streams from *coronal holes*. A *coronal mass ejection* (CME) originates in the Sun's outer atmosphere — its corona. With several sophisticated satellites launched in the mid 1990s, we have gained powerful new tools to monitor the intricacies of solar activity. Using the latest satellite technology (and also some re-engineered earthbound instruments), scientists have observed many CMEs, greatly expanding our knowledge about them. Previously, the only direct observations we had of coronal activity were during solar eclipses — and eclipses don't occur very often. CMEs are observed with an instrument called a *coronagraph*, which has an occulting disk to block out the main portion of the Sun. In essence a coronagraph creates an artificial eclipse.

A *coronal hole* is a region on the Sun where the magnetic field is open to the interplanetary magnetic field (IMF) and ionized particles can escape into the solar wind. Normally the solar wind blows at approximately 400 km per second. During CMEs and coronal holes, solar wind speeds can increase to 2000 km per second.

Coronal holes and coronal mass ejections that are Earth-directed (these are also called full halo CMEs, as the explosion surrounds the occulting disk of a coronagraph) concurrent with the IMF oriented in a southerly direction result in the most disturbance to propagation. It usually takes up to a couple days for a CME or the effects of a coronal hole to reach and impact the Earth's ionosphere, so this generally gives us ample warning of the impending disturbance.

SOLAR RADIATION STORMS AND RADIO BLACKOUTS

Solar radiation storms and radio blackouts are caused by large *solar flares*. When a large solar flare erupts from the Sun's surface, it can launch out into space a wide spectrum of electromagnetic energy. Since electromagnetic energy travels at the speed of light, the first indication of a solar flare reaches the Earth in about eight minutes. A large flare shows up as an increase in visible brightness near a sunspot group, accompanied by increases in UV and X-ray radiation and high levels of noise in the VHF radio bands. It is the X-ray radiation that results in radio blackouts on the daytime side of the Earth due to increased D region absorption, and this is called a *sudden ionospheric disturbance* (SID). The lower frequencies are affected for the longest period. In extreme cases, nearly all background noise will be gone as well. SIDs may last up to an hour, after which ionospheric conditions return to normal.

A large solar flare can also release matter into space, mainly in the form of very energetic protons. These cause solar radiation storms, whereby increased absorption in the polar cap (that area inside the auroral oval) degrades over-the-pole paths. This is called a *polar cap absorption* (PCA) event. A PCA event may last for days, dramatically affecting transpolar HF propagation. An interesting fact with respect to PCAs is that they do not necessarily affect the northern and southern polar regions similarly. Thus if the short path between two points is degraded over one pole, the long path may still be available over the other pole.

At one time, scientists believed that solar flares and CMEs were causally related, but now they recognize that many CMEs occur without an accompanying flare. And while many flares do result in an ejection of some solar material, many do not. It now seems clear that flares don't cause CMEs and vice versa.

Since geomagnetic storms have the most impact to propagation, it is instructive to understand their occurrence statistics. The number of geomagnetic storms varies considerably from year to year, but peak geomagnetic activity follows the peak of solar activity. See **Figure 19.12**. Also, geomagnetic activity affects the ionosphere mostly in the equinox months (March and September).

MONITORING GEOMAGNETIC ACTIVITY

Geomagnetic activity is monitored by devices known as *magnetometers*. These may be as simple as a magnetic compass rigged to record its movements. Small variations in the geomagnetic field are scaled to two measures known as the K and A indices. The *K index*

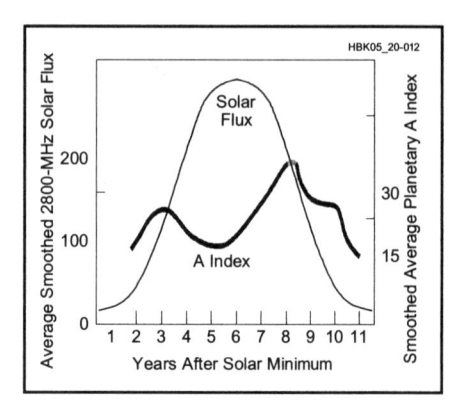

Figure 19.12 — Geomagnetic activity (measured as the A index) also follows an 11-year cycle. Average values over the past few cycles show that geomagnetic activity peaks before and after the peak of solar flux.

Table 19.3
Geomagnetic Storms

Typical Kp	Description	Days per Solar Cycle
9	Extreme	4
8	Severe	60
7	Strong	130
6	Moderate	360
5	Minor	900

provides an indication of magnetic activity on a finite logarithmic scale of 0-9, and it is updated every three hours. Very quiet conditions are reported as 0 or 1, while geomagnetic storm levels begin at 4. See **Table 19.3** for the latest NOAA descriptions of geomagnetic storms.

A worldwide network of magnetometers constantly monitors the Earth's magnetic field, because the Earth's magnetic field varies with location. K indices that indicate average planetary conditions are indicated as K_p. Daily geomagnetic conditions are also summarized by the open-ended linear A index, which corresponds roughly to the cumulative K index values (it's the daily average of the eight K indices after converting the K indices to a linear scale). The A index commonly varies between 0 and 30 during quiet to active conditions, and up to 100 or higher during geomagnetic storms.

At 18 minutes past the hour, radio station WWV broadcasts the solar flux measured at 2000 UTC, the prior day's planetary A Index and the latest mid latitude K Index. In addition, they broadcast a descriptive account of the condition of the geomagnetic field and a forecast for the next three hours. For more details about WWV broadcasts, visit **www.nist.gov/pml/div688/grp40/wwv_format.cfm**. You should keep in mind that the A Index is a description of what happened yesterday. Strictly speaking, the K Index is valid only for mid latitudes. However, the trend of the K Index is very important for propagation analysis and forecasting. A rising K foretells worsening HF propagation conditions, particularly for transpolar paths. At the same time, a rising K alerts VHF operators to the possibility of enhanced auroral activity, particularly when the K Index rises above 3. Another source of useful information about solar disturbances is **www.spaceweather.com**.

19.2.11 D Layer Propagation

The *D layer* is the lowest region of the ionosphere, situated between 55 and 90 km (30 and 60 miles). See **Figure 19.13**. It is ionized primarily by the strong emission of solar hydrogen at 121.5 nanometers and short-wavelength X-rays (so-called hard X-rays), both of which penetrate through the upper atmosphere to ionize nitric oxide (radiation at 121.5 nm) and all other constituents (hard X-rays). The D layer exists only during daylight, because constant radiation is needed to replenish ions that quickly recombine into neutral molecules. The D layer abruptly disappears at night so far as amateur MF and HF signals are concerned. D layer ionization varies a small amount over the solar cycle. It is unsuitable as a refracting medium for MF and HF radio signals, but it is very important for VLF signals.

During daylight hours, radio energy as high as 5 MHz is effectively absorbed by the D layer, severely limiting the range of daytime 1.8- and 3.5 MHz signals. Signals at 7 MHz and 10 MHz pass through the D layer and on to the E and F layers only at relatively high angles. Low-angle waves, which must travel a much longer distance through the D layer, are subject to greater absorption. As the frequency increases above 10 MHz, radio waves pass through the D layer with increasing ease (less absorption).

D layer ionization falls 100-fold as soon as the Sun sets and the source of ionizing radiation is removed. Low-band HF signals are then free to pass through to the E layer (also greatly diminished at night) and on to the F layer, where the MUF is almost always high enough to propagate 1.8 and 3.5 MHz signals half way around the world. Long-distance propagation at 7 and 10 MHz generally improves at night as well, because absorption is less and low-angle waves are able to reach the F layer.

19.2.12 E Layer Propagation

The *E layer* lies between 90 and 150 km (60 and 90 miles) altitude, but a narrower region centered at 95 to 120 km (60 to 70 miles) is more important for radio propagation. In the E layer nitric oxide and molecular oxygen are ionized by short-wavelength UV and long-wavelength X-ray radiation (so-called soft X-rays). The normal E layer exists primarily during daylight hours, because like the D layer, it requires a constant source of ionizing radiation. Recombination is not as fast as in the denser D layer and absorption is much less. The E layer has a daytime critical frequency that varies between 3 and 4 MHz with the solar cycle. At night, the normal E layer decays to a minimum critical frequency of 0.3 – 0.5 MHz, which is still enough to refract low elevation angle 1.8 MHz signals.

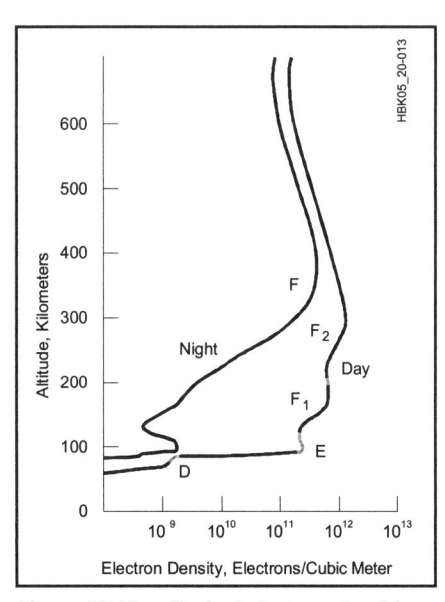

Figure 19.13 — Typical electron densities for the various ionospheric regions.

DAYTIME E LAYER

The E layer plays a small role in propagating HF signals but can be a major factor limiting propagation during daytime hours. Its usual critical frequency of 3 to 4 MHz, with an M-factor of about 5, suggests that single-hop E layer skip might be useful between 5 and 20 MHz at distances up to 2300 km (1400 miles). In practice this is not the case, because the potential for E layer skip is severely limited by D layer absorption. Signals radiated at low angles at 7 and 10 MHz, which might be useful for the longest-distance contacts, are largely absorbed by the D layer. Only high-angle signals pass through the D layer at these frequencies, but high-angle E layer skip is typically limited to 1200 km (750 miles) or so. Signals at 14 MHz penetrate the D layer at lower angles at the cost of some absorption, but the casual operator may not be able to distinguish between signals propagated by the E layer or higher-angle F layer propagation.

An astonishing variety of other propagation modes find their home in the E layer, and this perhaps more than makes up for its ordinary limitations. Each of these other modes — sporadic E, field-aligned irregularities, aurora, auroral E and meteor scatter — are related forms of E layer propagation with unique characteristics. They are primarily useful only on the highest HF and lower VHF bands.

SPORADIC E

Short skip, long familiar on the 10 meter band during the summer months, affects the VHF bands as high as 222 MHz. *Sporadic E* (E_s), as this phenomenon is properly called, commonly propagates 28, 50 and 144 MHz radio signals between 500 and 2300 km (300 and 1400 miles). Signals are apt to be exceedingly strong, allowing even modest stations to make E_s contacts. At 21 MHz, the skip distance may only be a few hundred km. During the most intense E_s events, skip may shorten to less than 200 km (120 miles) on the 10 meter band and disappear entirely on 15 meters. Multiple-hop E_s has supported contacts up to 10,000 km (6200 miles) on 28 and 50 MHz and more than 3000 km (1900 miles) on 144 MHz. The first confirmed 220 MHz E_s contact was made in June 1987, but such contacts are likely to remain very rare.

Sporadic E at mid latitudes (roughly 15° to 45°) may occur at any time, but it is most common in the Northern Hemisphere during May, June and July, with a less-intense season at the end of December and early January. Its appearance is independent of the solar cycle. Sporadic E propagation is most likely to occur from 9 AM to noon local time and again early in the evening between 5 PM and 8 PM. Mid latitude E_s events may last only a few minutes or can persist for many hours. In contrast, sporadic E is an almost constant feature of the

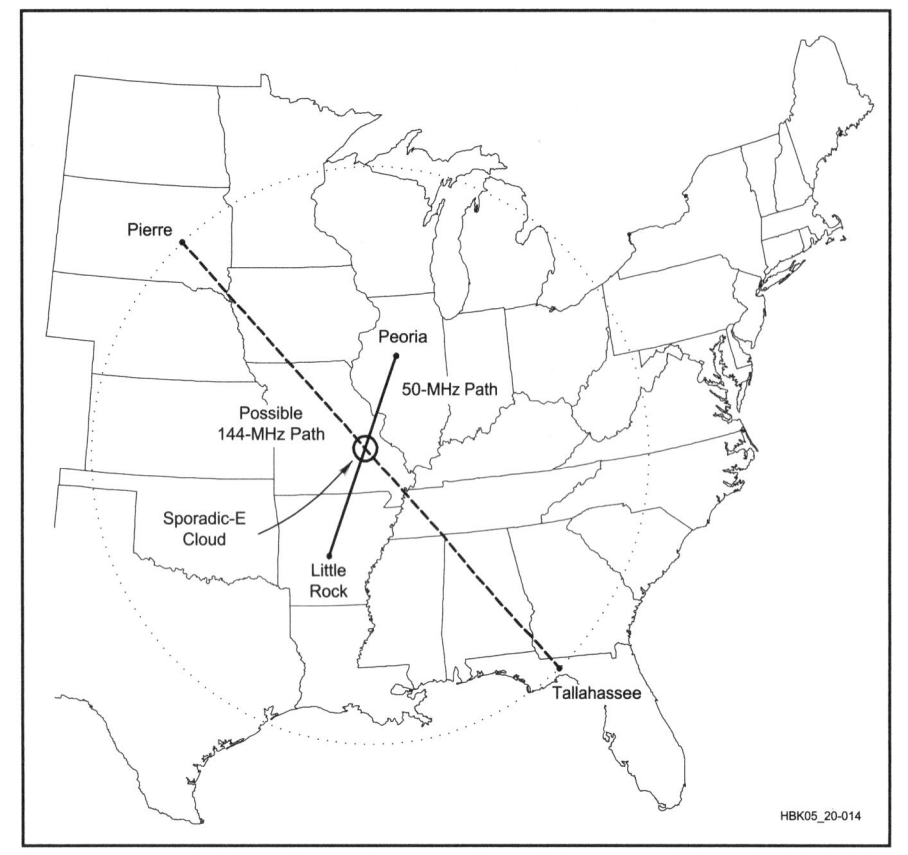

Figure 19.14 — 50 MHz sporadic E contacts of 700 km (435 miles) or shorter (such as between Peoria and Little Rock) indicate that the MUF on longer paths is above 144 MHz. Using the same sporadic E region reflecting point, 144 MHz contacts of 2200 km (1400 miles), such as between Pierre and Tallahassee, should be possible.

polar regions at night and the equatorial belt during the day.

Efforts to predict mid latitude E_s have not been successful, probably because its causes are complex and not well understood. Studies have demonstrated that thin and unusually dense patches of ionization in the E layer, between 100 and 110 km (60 and 70 miles) altitude and 10 to 100 km (6 to 60 miles) in extent, are responsible for most E_s reflections. Sporadic E clouds may form suddenly, move quickly from their birthplace, and dissipate within a few hours. Professional studies have recently focused on the role of heavy metal ions, probably of meteoric origin, and wind shears as two key factors in creating the dense patchy regions of E layer ionization.

Sporadic E clouds exhibit an MUF that can rise from 28 MHz through the 50 MHz band and higher in just a few minutes. When the skip distance on 28 MHz is as short as 400 or 500 km (250 or 310 miles), it is an indication that the MUF has reached 50 MHz for longer paths at low launch angles. Contacts at the maximum one-hop sporadic E distance, about 2300 km (1400 miles), should then be possible at 50 MHz. *E-skip* (yet another term for sporadic E) contacts as short as 700 km (435 miles) on 50 MHz, in turn, may indicate that 144 MHz contacts in the 2300 km (1400 mile) range can be completed. See **Figure 19.14**. Sporadic E openings occur about a tenth as often at 144 MHz as they do at 50 MHz and for much shorter periods.

Sporadic E can also have a detrimental effect on HF propagation by masking the F_2 layer from below. HF signals may be prevented from reaching the higher levels of the ionosphere and the possibilities of long F_2 skip. Reflections from the tops of sporadic E clouds can also have a masking effect, but they may also lengthen the F_2 propagation path with a top-side intermediate hop that never reaches the Earth.

E LAYER FIELD-ALIGNED IRREGULARITIES

Amateurs have experimented with a little-known scattering mode known as *field-aligned irregularities* (FAI) at 50 and 144 MHz since 1978. FAI commonly appears directly after sporadic E events and may persist for several hours. Oblique-angle scattering becomes possible when electrons are compressed together due to the action of high-velocity ionospheric acoustic (sound) waves. The resulting irregularities in the distribution of free electrons are aligned parallel to the Earth's magnetic field, in something like moving vertical rods. A similar process of electron field-alignment takes place during radio aurora, making the two phenomena quite similar.

Most reports suggest that 8 PM to midnight may be the most productive time for FAI. Stations attempting FAI contacts point their antennas toward a common scattering region that corresponds to an active or recent E_s reflection point. The best direction must be probed experimentally, for the result is rarely along the great-circle path. Stations in south Florida, for example, have completed 144 MHz FAI contacts with north Texas when participating stations were beamed toward a common scattering region over northern Alabama.

FAI-propagated signals are weak and fluttery, reminiscent of aurora signals. Doppler shifts of as much as 3 kHz have been observed in some tests. Stations running as little as 100 W and a single Yagi should be able to complete FAI contacts during the most favorable times, but higher power and larger antennas may yield better results. Contacts have been made on 50 and 144 MHz, and 222 MHz FAI seems probable as well. Expected maximum distances should be similar to other forms of E layer propagation, or about 2300 km (1400 miles).

AURORA

Radar signals as high as 3000 MHz have been scattered by the *aurora borealis* or northern lights (*aurora australis* in the Southern Hemisphere), but amateur aurora contacts are common only from 28 through 432 MHz. By pointing directional antennas generally north toward the center of aurora activity, oblique paths between stations up to 2300 km (1400 miles) apart can be completed. See **Figure 19.15**. High power and large antennas are not necessary. Stations with small Yagis and as little as 10 W output have used auroras on frequencies as high as 432 MHz, but contacts at 902 MHz and higher are exceedingly rare. Auroral propagation works just as well in the Southern Hemisphere, in which case antennas must be pointed south.

The appearance of auroras is closely linked to solar activity. During massive geomagnetic storms, low energy particles that were trapped in the magnetosphere flow into the atmosphere near the polar regions, where they ionize the gases of the E layer and higher. This unusual ionization produces spectacular visual auroral displays, which often spread southward into the mid latitudes. Higher energy electrons get down to lower altitudes to cause auroral ionization (via collisions with neutral particles) in the E layer, and this scatters radio signals in the VHF and UHF ranges.

In addition to scattering radio signals, auroras have other effects on worldwide radio propagation. Communication below 20 MHz is disrupted in high latitudes, primarily by

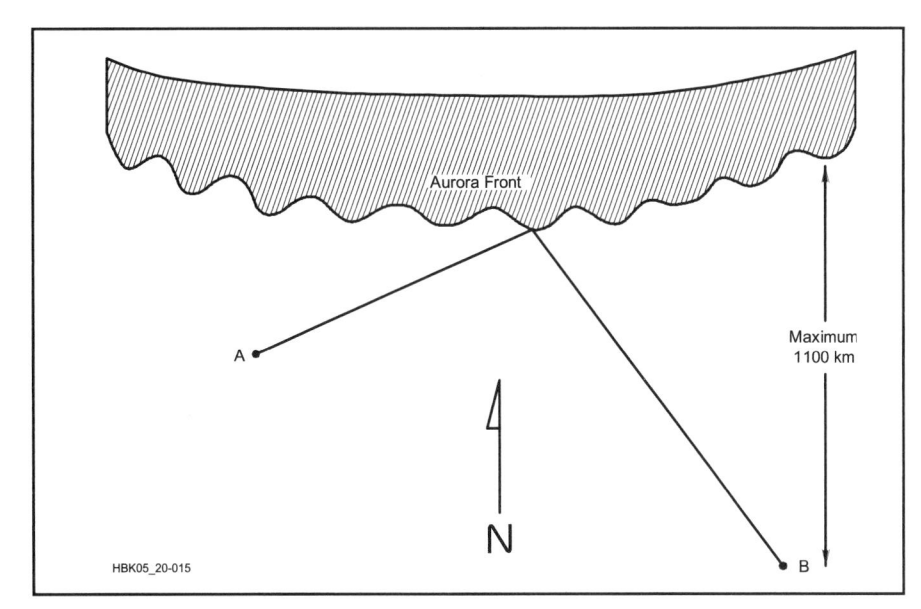

Figure 19.15 — Point antennas generally north to make oblique long-distance contacts on 28 through 432 MHz via aurora scattering. Optimal antenna headings may shift considerably to the east or west depending on the location of the aurora. This necessitates moving your antenna azimuth direction for best propagation, and continuing to do so as the aurora progresses.

absorption, and is especially noticeable over polar and near-polar paths. Signals on the AM broadcast band through the 40 meter band late in the afternoon may become weak and watery. The 20 meter band may close down altogether. Satellite operators have also noticed that 144 MHz downlink signals are often weak and distorted when satellites pass near the polar regions. At the same time, the MUF in equatorial regions may temporarily rise dramatically, including an enhancement of transequatorial paths at frequencies as high as 50 MHz.

Auroras occur most often around the spring and fall equinoxes (March-April and September-October), but auroras may appear in any month. Aurora activity generally peaks about two years before and after solar cycle maximum (the "before" generally due to CMEs and the "after" generally due to high-speed wind streams from coronal holes). Radio aurora activity is usually heard first in late afternoon and may reappear later in the evening. Auroras may be anticipated by following the A and K indices reports on WWV. A K index of five or greater and an A index of at least 30 are indications that a geomagnetic storm is in progress and an aurora likely. The probability, intensity and southerly extent of auroras increase as the two index numbers rise. Stations north of 42° latitude in North America experience many auroral openings each year, while those in the Gulf Coast states may hear auroral signals no more than once a year, if that often.

Aurora-scattered signals are easy to identify. On 28- and 50 MHz SSB, signals sound very distorted and somewhat wider than normal; at 144 MHz and above, the distortion may be so severe that only CW is useful. Auroral CW signals have a distinctive note variously described as a buzz, hiss or mushy sound. This characteristic auroral signal is due to Doppler broadening, caused by the movement of electrons within the aurora. An additional Doppler shift of 1 kHz or more may be evident at 144 MHz and several kilohertz at 432 MHz. This second Doppler shift is the result of massive electrical currents that sweep electrons toward the Sun side of the Earth during magnetic storms. Doppler shift and distortion increase with higher frequencies, while signal strength dramatically decreases.

It is not necessary to see an aurora to make auroral contacts. Useful auroras may be 500-1000 km (310-620 miles) away and below the visual horizon. Antennas should be pointed generally north and then probed east and west to peak signals, because auroral ionization is field aligned. This means that for any pair of stations, there is an optimal direction for aurora scatter. Offsets from north are usually greatest when the aurora is closest and often provide the longest contacts. There may be some advantage to antennas that can be elevated, especially when auroras are high in the sky.

AURORAL E

Radio auroras may evolve into a propagation mode known as *auroral E* at 21, 28, 50 and rarely 144 MHz. Auroral E is essentially sporadic E in the auroral zone. Doppler distortion disappears and signals take on the characteristics of sporadic E. The most effective antenna headings shift dramatically away from oblique aurora paths to direct great-circle bearings. The usual maximum distance is 2300 km (1400 miles), typical for E layer modes, but 28 and 50 MHz auroral E contacts of 5000 km (3100 miles) are sometimes made across Canada and the northern US, apparently using two hops. Contacts at 50 MHz between Alaska and the east coasts of Canada and the northern US have been completed this way. Transatlantic 50 MHz auroral E paths are also likely.

Typically, 28 and 50 MHz auroral E appears across the northern third of the US and southern Canada when aurora activity is diminishing. This usually happens after midnight on the eastern end of the path. Auroral E signals sometimes have a slightly hollow sound to them and build slowly in strength over an hour or two, but otherwise they are indistinguishable from sporadic E. Auroral E paths are almost always east-west oriented, perhaps because there are few stations at very northern latitudes to take advantage of this propagation. A common auroral E path on 28 MHz and 21 MHz is from North America in the late afternoon hours in the autumn months to the Scandinavian countries. This path is open when normal F layer propagation is not possible — even to more southern locations in Europe.

Auroral E may also appear while especially intense auroras are still in progress, as happened during the great aurora of March 1989. On that occasion, 50 MHz propagation shifted from Doppler-distorted aurora paths to clear-sounding auroral E over a period of a few minutes. Many 6 meter operators as far south as Florida and Southern California made single- and double-hop auroral E contacts across the country. At about the same time, the MUF reached 144 MHz for stations west of the Great Lakes to the Northeast, the first time auroral E had been reported so high in frequency.

METEOR SCATTER

Contacts between 800 and 2300 km (500 and 1400 miles) can be made at 28 through 432 MHz via reflections from the ionized trails left by meteors as they travel through the atmosphere. The kinetic energy of meteors no larger than grains of rice are sufficient to ionize a column of air 20 km (12 miles) long in the E layer. The particle itself evaporates and never reaches the ground, but the ionized column may persist for a few seconds to a minute or more before it dissipates. This is enough time to make very brief contacts by reflections from the ionized trails. Millions of meteors enter the Earth's atmosphere every day, but few have the required size, speed and orientation to the Earth to make them useful for meteor-scatter propagation.

Radio signals in the 30 to 100 MHz range are reflected best by meteor trails, making the 50 MHz band prime for meteor-scatter work. The early morning hours around dawn are

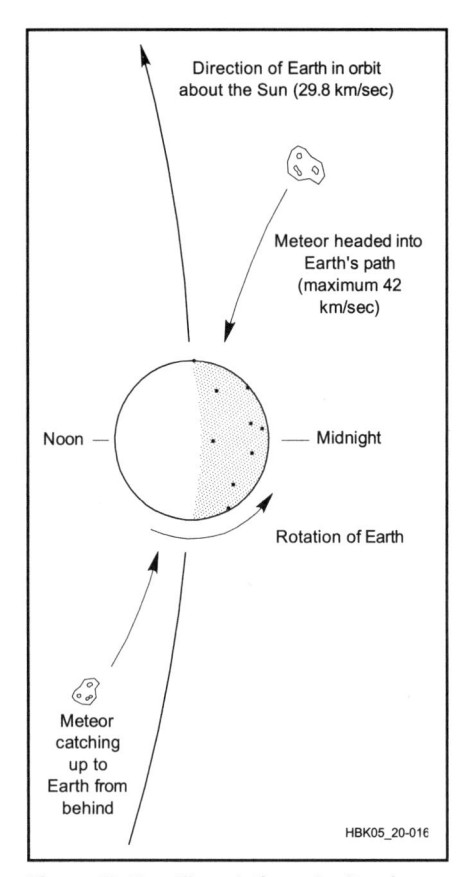

Figure 19.16 — The relative velocity of meteors that meet the Earth head-on is increased by the rotational velocity of the Earth in orbit. Fast meteors strike the morning side of the Earth because their velocity adds to the Earth's rotational velocity, while the relative velocity of meteors that "catch up from behind" is reduced.

usually the most productive, because the morning side of the Earth faces in the direction of the planet's orbit around the Sun. The relative velocity of meteors that head toward the Earth's morning side are thus increased by up to 30 km/sec, which is the average rotational speed of the Earth in orbit. See **Figure 19.16**. The maximum velocity of meteors in orbit around the Sun is 42 km/sec. Thus when the relative velocity of the Earth is considered, most meteors must enter the Earth's atmosphere somewhere between 12 and 72 km/sec.

Meteor contacts ranging from a second or two to more than a minute can be made nearly any morning at 28 or 50 MHz. Meteor-scatter contacts at 144 MHz and higher are more difficult because reflected signal strength and duration drop sharply with increasing frequency. A meteor trail that provides 30 seconds of communication at 50 MHz will last only a few seconds at 144 MHz, and less than a second at 432 MHz.

Meteor scatter opportunities are somewhat better during July and August for North America because the average number of meteors entering the Earth's atmosphere peaks during those months. The best times are during one of the great annual *meteor showers*, when the number of useful meteors may increase ten-fold over the normal rate of five to ten per hour. See **Table 19.4**. A meteor shower occurs when the Earth passes through a relatively dense stream of particles, thought to be the remnants of a comet in orbit around the Sun. The most-productive showers are relatively consistent from year to year, although several can occasionally produce great storms.

Because meteors provide only fleeting moments of communication even during one of the great meteor showers, special operating techniques are often used to increase the chances of completing a contact. Prearranged schedules between two stations establish times, frequencies and precise operating standards. Usually, each station transmits on alternate 15-second periods until enough information is pieced together a bit at a time to confirm contact. High-speed Morse code of several hundred words per minute, generated and slowed down by special computer programs, can make effective use of very short meteor bursts. Non-scheduled random meteor contacts are common on 50 MHz and 144 MHz, but short transmissions and alert operating habits are required.

It is helpful to run several hundred watts to a single Yagi, but meteor-scatter can be used by modest stations under optimal conditions. During the best showers, a few watts and a small directional antenna are sufficient at 28 or 50 MHz. At 144 MHz, at least 100 W output and a long Yagi are needed for consistent results. Proportionately higher power is required for 222 and 432 MHz even under the best conditions.

A technique allowing even smaller VHF/UHF stations to take advantage of meteor scatter and other modes (ionospheric scatter and even moonbounce) is available in software called *WSJT*. This software uses the sound card in a PC and a variety of modulation and coding techniques to allow reception of signals up to 10 dB below your noise level. For more information, visit **www.physics.princeton.edu/pulsar/K1JT/**.

19.2.13 F Layer Propagation

The region of the *F layers*, from 150 km (90 miles) to over 400 km (250 miles) altitude, is by far the most important for long-distance HF communications. F-region oxygen atoms are ionized primarily by ultraviolet radiation. During the day, ionization reaches maxima in two distinct layers. The F_1 layer forms between 150 and 250 km (90 and 160 miles), is most prevalent in the summer months, and disappears at night. The F_2 layer extends above 250 km (160 miles), with a peak of ionization around 300 km (190 miles). At night, F-region ionization collapses into one broad layer at 300-400 km (190-250 miles) altitude. Ions recombine very slowly at these altitudes, because atmospheric density is relatively low. Maximum ionization levels change significantly with time of day, season and year of the solar cycle.

F_1 LAYER

The daytime F_1 layer is not very important to HF communication. In reality it is an inflection point in the electron density profile, not a peak. It exists only during daylight hours and is largely absent in winter. Radio signals below 10 MHz are not likely to reach the F_1 layer, because they are either absorbed by the D layer or refracted by the E layer. Signals higher than 20 MHz that pass through both of the lower ionospheric regions are likely to pass through the F_1 layer as well, because the F_1 MUF rarely rises above 20 MHz. Absorption diminishes the strength of any signals that continue through to the F_2 layer during the day. Some useful F_1 layer refraction may take place between 10 and 20 MHz during summer days, yielding paths as long as 3000 km (1900 miles), but these would be practically indistinguishable from F_2 skip.

F_2 AND NIGHTTIME F LAYERS

The F_2 layer forms between 250 and 400 km (160 and 250 miles) during the daytime and persists throughout the night as a single consolidated F region 50 km (30 miles) higher in altitude. Typical ion densities are the highest of any ionospheric layer, with the possible exception of some unusual E layer phenomena. In contrast to the other ionospheric layers, F_2 ionization varies considerably with time of day, season and position in the solar cycle, but it is never altogether absent. These two characteristics make the F_2 layer the most important for long-distance HF communications.

The F_2 layer MUF is nearly a direct function of ultraviolet (UV) solar radiation, which in turn closely follows the solar cycle. During the lowest years of the cycle, the daytime MUF may climb above 14 MHz for only a few hours a day. In contrast, the MUF may rise beyond 50 MHz during peak years and stay

Table 19.4
Major Annual Meteor Showers

Name	Peak Dates	Approximate Rate (meteors/hour)
Quadrantids	Jan 3	50
Arietids	Jun 7-8	60
Perseids	Aug 11-13	80
Orionids	Oct 20-22	20
Geminids	Dec 12-13	60

Figure 19.17 — Multihop paths can take many different configurations, including a mixture of E and F layer hops. (A) Two F layer hops. Five or more consecutive F layer hops are possible. (B) An E layer hookup to the F layer. (C) A top-side E layer reflection can shorten the distance of two F layer hops. (D) Refraction in the E layer above the MUF is insufficient to return the signal to Earth, but it can go on to be refracted in the F layer. (E) The Pedersen Ray, which originates from a signal launched at a relatively high angle above the horizon into the E or F region, may result in a single-hop path, 5000 km (3100 miles) or more. This is considerably further than the normal 4000 km (2500 mile) maximum F-region single-hop distance, where the signal is launched at a very low takeoff angle. The Pedersen Ray can easily be disrupted by any sort of ionospheric gradient or irregularity. Not shown in this figure is a chordal hop — since chordal hops are most prevalent in the equatorial ionosphere, refer to Figure 19.21 and Figure 19.22.

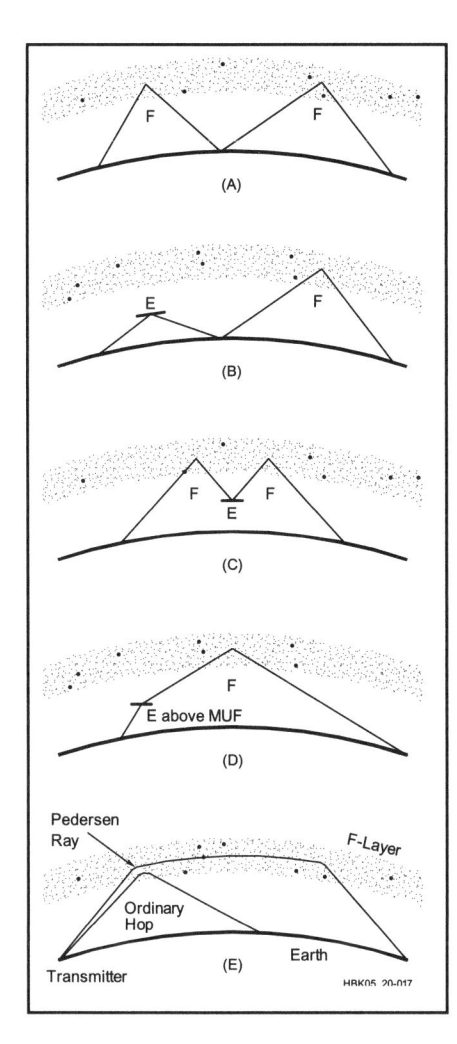

above 14 MHz throughout the night. The virtual height of the F_2 region averages 330 km (210 miles), but varies between 200 and 400 km (120 and 250 miles). Maximum one-hop distance is about 4000 km (2500 miles). Near-vertical incidence skywave propagation just below the critical frequency provides reliable coverage out to 200-300 km (120-190 miles) with no skip zone. It is most often observed on 7 MHz during the day.

The extremely high-angle *Pedersen ray* can create effective single-hop paths of 5000 to 12,000 km under certain conditions, but most operators will not be able to distinguish Pedersen Ray paths from normal F layer propagation. A Pederson ray is a path that follows the contour of the Earth near the height of the maximum F_2 region electron density, and requires a fairly stable ionosphere. Pedersen ray paths are most evident over high-latitude east-west paths at frequencies near the MUF. They appear most often about noon local time at mid-path when the geomagnetic field is very quiet. Pedersen ray propagation may be responsible for 50 MHz paths between the US Northeast and Western Europe, for example, when ordinary MUF analysis could not explain the 5000 km contacts. See part E in **Figure 19.17**.

At any given location on Earth, in general both F_2 layer ionization and MUF at that point build rapidly at sunrise, usually reaching a maximum after local noon, and then decrease to a minimum at night prior to the next sunrise. Depending on the season, the MUF is generally highest within 20° of the equator and lower toward the poles. For this reason, transequatorial paths may be open at a particular frequency when all other paths are closed

In contrast to all the other ionospheric layers, daytime ionization in the winter F_2 layer averages four times the level of the summer at the same period in the solar cycle, doubling the MUF. This so-called *winter anomaly* is caused by a seasonal increase in the ratio of atoms to molecules at F_2 layer heights (atoms are instrumental in the production of electrons, whereas molecules are instrumental in the loss of electrons). Winter daytime F_2 conditions are much superior to those in summer, because the MUF is much higher.

MULTIHOP F LAYER PROPAGATION

Most HF communication beyond 4000 km (2500 miles) takes place via multiple ionospheric hops. Radio signals are reflected from the Earth back toward space for additional ionospheric refractions. A series of ionospheric refractions and terrestrial reflections commonly create paths half-way around the Earth. Each hop involves additional attenuation and absorption, so the longest-distance signals tend to be the weakest. Even so, it is possible for signals to be propagated completely around the world and arrive back at their originating point. Multiple reflections within the F layer may at times bypass ground reflections altogether, creating what are known as *chordal hops*, with lower total attenuation. It takes a radio signal about 0.14 seconds to make an around-the-world trip.

Multihop paths can take on many different configurations, as shown in the examples of Figure 19.17. E layer (especially sporadic E) and F layer hops may be mixed. In practice, multi-hop signals arrive via many different paths, which often increases the problems of fading. Analyzing multi-hop paths is complicated by the effects of D and E layer absorption, possible reflections from the tops of sporadic E layers, disruptions in the auroral zone and other phenomena.

In general, when a band is opening and closing as the MUF changes, extremely low elevation angles are dictated (less than 5°). During the main part of the opening, the elevation angle is higher — generally in the range of 5° to 20°. This is why stations with extremely high antennas (which have higher gain at lower takeoff angles) perform better at band openings and closings.

F LAYER LONG PATH

Most HF communication takes place along the shortest great-circle path between two stations. Short-path propagation is always less than 20,000 km (12,000 miles) — halfway around the Earth. Nevertheless, it may be possible at times to make the same contact in exactly the opposite direction via the *long path*. The long-path distance will be 40,000 km (25,000 miles) minus the short-path length. Signal strength via the long path is usually considerably less than the more direct short-path. When both paths are open simultaneously, there may be a distinctive sort of echo on received signals. The time interval of the echo represents the difference between the short-path and long-path distances.

Sometimes there is a great advantage to using the long path when it is open, because signals can be stronger and fading less troublesome, or because fewer interfering signals lie along the path between the stations. There are times when the short path may be closed or disrupted by E layer *blanketing* (when the E-region ionization is high enough to keep waves from penetrating, regardless of elevation angle), D layer absorption or F layer gaps, especially when operating just below the MUF. Long paths that predominantly cross the night side of the Earth, for example, are sometimes useful because they generally avoid blanketing and absorption problems. Daylight-side long paths may take advantage of higher F layer MUFs that occur over the sunlit portions of the Earth.

F LAYER GRAY-LINE

Gray-line paths can be considered a special form of long-path propagation that takes into account the unusual ionospheric configuration

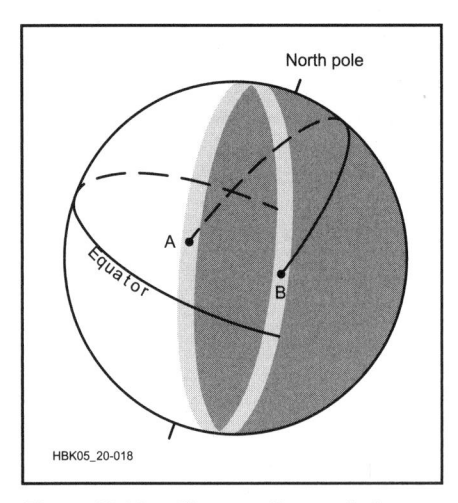

Figure 19.18 — The gray line encircles the Earth, but the tilt at the equator to the poles varies over 46° with the seasons. Long-distance contacts on 1.8 MHz and 3.5 MHz at more than halfway around the Earth can be enabled by the gray line, putting both ends of the path near darkness and allowing RF to cut across the dark ionosphere with minimal absorption. The strength of the signals indicates that multiple Earth-ionosphere hops are not the likely mode of propagation, since losses in many such hops would be prohibitive. Ducting in the electron density valley above the E region peak in the dark ionosphere is the likely mechanism.

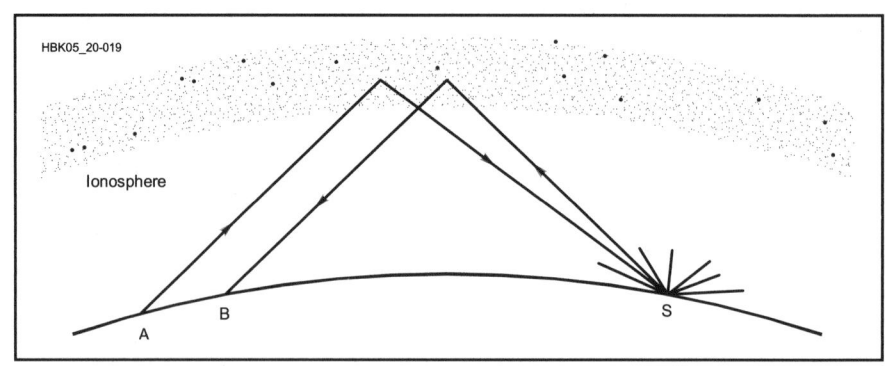

Figure 19.19 — Schematic of a simple backscatter path. Stations A and B are too close to make contact via normal F layer ionospheric refraction. Signals scattered back from a distant point on the Earth's surface (S), often the ocean, may be accessible to both and create a backscatter circuit.

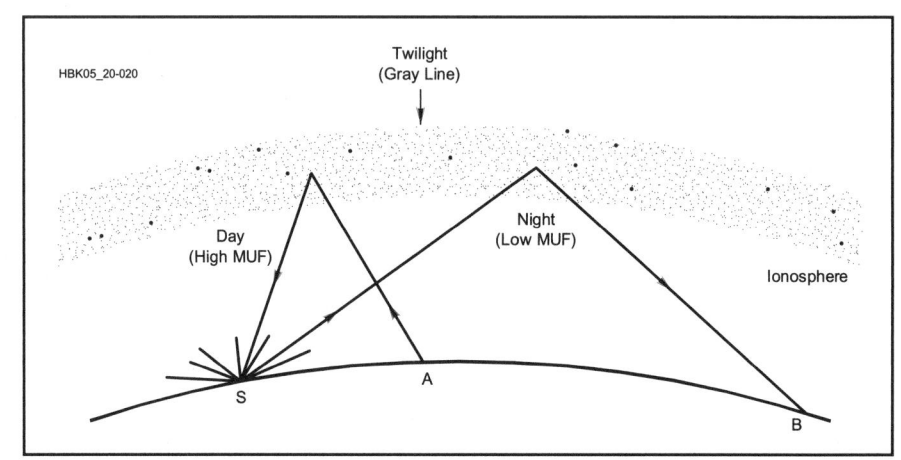

Figure 19.20 — Backscatter path across the gray line. Stations A and B are too close to make contact via normal ionospheric refraction, but may hear each other's signals scattered from point S. Station A makes use of a high-angle refraction on the day side of the gray line, where the MUF is high. Station B makes use of a night-time refraction, with a lower MUF and lower angle of propagation. Note that station A points away from B to complete the circuit.

along the twilight region between night and day. The gray line, as the twilight region is sometimes called, extends completely around the world. It is not precisely a line, for the distinction between daylight and darkness is a gradual transition due to atmospheric scattering. On one side, the gray line heralds sunrise and the beginning of a new day; on the opposite side, it marks sunset and the end of the day.

The ionosphere undergoes a significant transformation between night and day. As day begins, the highly absorbent D and E layers are recreated, while the F layer MUF rises from its pre-dawn minimum. At the end of the day, the D and E layers quickly disappear, while the F layer MUF continues its slow decline from late afternoon. For a brief period just along the gray-line transition, the D and E layers are not well formed, yet the F_2 MUF usually remains higher than 5 MHz. This would normally provide a special opportunity for stations at 1.8 and 3.5 MHz but for:

• ionospheric absorption is still high on these bands in this twilight region from an understanding of the physics of absorption, and

• the electron density gradient across the gray line (also known as the terminator) skews RF away from the day ionosphere into the night ionosphere (shown by ray tracing studies taking into account the Earth's magnetic field and the electron-neutral collision frequency.

What this means is that contrary to decades of popular belief, propagation along the terminator on the low bands is not efficient and it is not possible for RF on these bands to even follow the terminator. This is supported by the fact that there has never been a report of enhanced propagation on these bands along a short path that is aligned with the gray line.

Normally, long-distance communication on these two amateur bands takes place only via all-darkness paths because of daytime D layer absorption. The gray-line propagation path extends completely around the world. See **Figure 19.18**. Thus what's important about gray line is that it puts both ends of the path very near darkness. What really appears to be happening is that the RF is taking a short cut across the dark ionosphere. This requires a skew point to join the two great circle paths in the dark ionosphere out of each end of the path, and the auroral zone is the likely area for the skew. For an investigation of this phenomena, read the article *Gray Line Propagation, or Florida to Cocos (Keeling) on 80m* with the downloadable supplemental content.

To take advantage of these paths, you need to understand the mechanics of gray line. The gray line generally runs north-south, but it varies by 23° either side of true north as measured at the equator over the course of the year. This variation is caused by the tilt in the Earth's axis. The gray line is exactly north-south through the poles at the equinoxes (March 21 and September 21) and is at its 23° extremes on June 21 and December 20. Over a one-year period, the gray line crosses a 46° sector of the Earth north and south of the equator, providing optimum paths to slightly different parts of the world each day. Many commonly available computer programs plot the gray line on a flat map or globe.

A web-based application to calculate

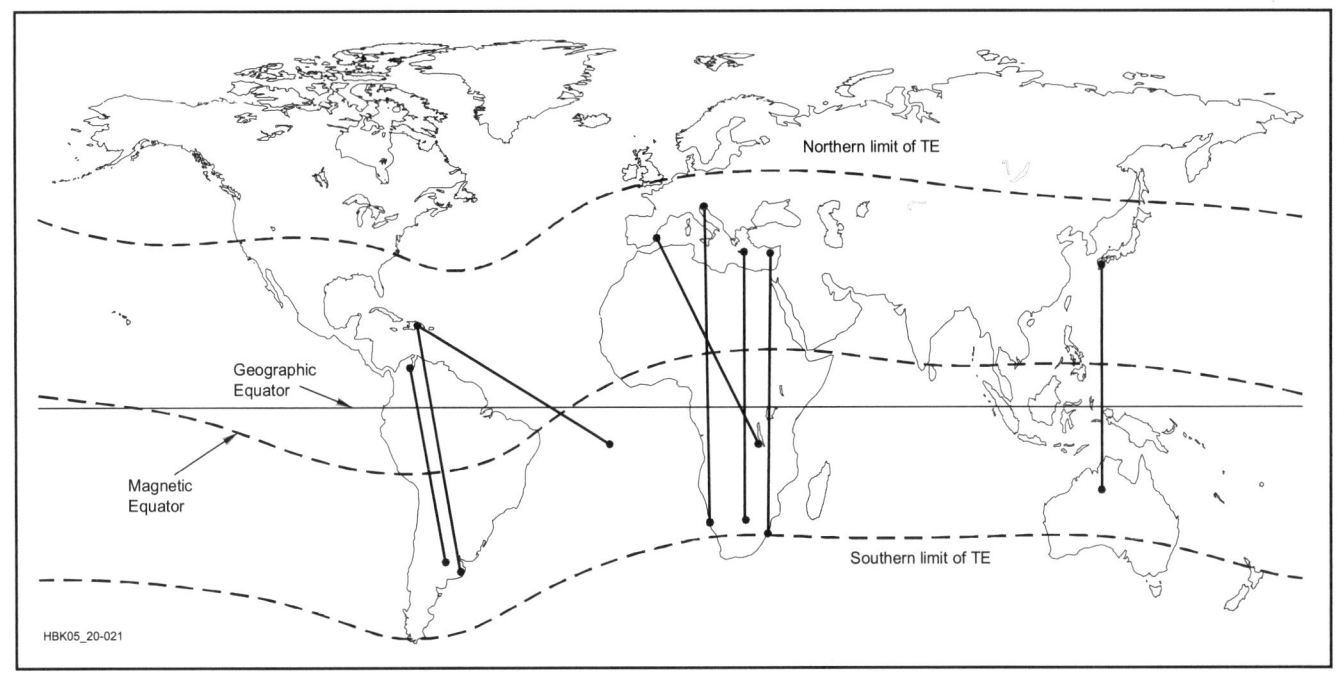

Figure 19.21 — Transequatorial propagation takes place between stations equidistant across the geomagnetic equator. Distances up to 8000 km (5000 miles) are possible on 28 through 432 MHz. Note the geomagnetic equator is considerably south of the geographic equator in the Western Hemisphere.

worldwide sunrise and sunset times is available at **aa.usno.navy.mil/data/docs/RS_OneDay.html**. An alternative method of determining sunrise and sunset times, along with seeing great circle paths on the same plot, is W6EL's *W6ELProp* software, available free at **www.qsl.net/w6elprop**. For an online gray line map, visit **dx.qsl.net/propagation/greyline.html**.

F LAYER BACKSCATTER AND SIDESCATTER

Special forms of F layer scattering can create unusual paths within the skip zone. *Backscatter* and *sidescatter* signals are usually observed just below the MUF for the direct path and allow communications not normally possible by other means. Stations using backscatter point their antennas toward a common scattering region at the one-hop distance, rather than toward each other. Backscattered signals are generally weak and have a characteristic hollow sound. Useful communication distances range from 100 km (60 miles) to the normal one-hop distance of 4000 km (2500 miles).

Backscatter and sidescatter are closely related and the terminology does not precisely distinguish between the two. Backscatter usually refers to single-hop signals that have been scattered by the Earth or the ocean at some distant point back toward the transmitting station. Two stations spaced a few hundred km apart can often communicate via a backscatter path near the MUF. See **Figure 19.19**.

Sidescatter usually refers to a circuit that is oblique to the normal great-circle path and is sometimes referred to as *skew path*. Two stations can make use of a common side-scattering region well off the direct path, often toward the south. European and North American stations sometimes complete 28 MHz contacts via a scattering region over Africa. U.S. and Finnish 50 MHz operators observed a similar effect early one morning in November 1989 when they made contact by beaming off the coast of West Africa.

When backscattered signals cross an area where there is a sharp gradient in ionospheric density, such as between night and day, the path may take on a different geometry, as shown in **Figure 19.20**. In this case, stations can communicate because backscattered signals return via the day side ionosphere on a shorter hop than the night side. This is possible because the dayside MUF is higher and thus the skip distance shorter. The net effect is to create a backscatter path between two stations within the normal skip zone.

TRANSEQUATORIAL PROPAGATION

Discovered by Amateur Radio operators in 1947, *transequatorial propagation* (commonly abbreviated TE or TEP) supports propagation between 5000 and 8000 km (3100 and 5000 miles) across the magnetic equator from 28 MHz to as high as 432 MHz. Stations attempting TE contacts must be nearly equidistant from the geomagnetic equator. Many contacts have been made at 50 and 144 MHz between Europe and South Africa, Japan and Australia and the Caribbean region and South America. Fewer contacts have been made on the 222 MHz band, and TE signals have been heard at 432 MHz.

Unfortunately for most continental US stations, the *geomagnetic equator* dips south of the geographic equator in the Western Hemisphere, as shown in **Figure 19.21**, making only the most southerly portions of Florida and Texas within TE range. TE contacts from the southeastern part of the country may be possible with Argentina, Chile and even South Africa.

Transequatorial propagation peaks between 5 PM and 10 PM during the spring and fall equinoxes, especially during the peak years of the solar cycle. The lowest probability is during the summer. Quiet geomagnetic conditions are required for TE to form. High power and large antennas are not required to work TE, as VHF stations with 100 W and single long Yagis have been successful.

TE propagation depends on bulges of intense F_2 layer ionization on both sides of the geomagnetic equator. This field-aligned ionization forms shortly after sunset via a process known as the *fountain effect* in an area 100-200 km (60-120 miles) north and south of the geomagnetic equator and 500-3000 km (310-1900 miles) wide. It moves west with the setting Sun. The MUF may increase to twice its normal level 15° either side of the geomagnetic equator. See **Figure 19.22**. For an overview of transequatorial propagation, read *F-Region Propagation and the Equatorial Ionosphere Anomaly* with the downloadable supplemental content.

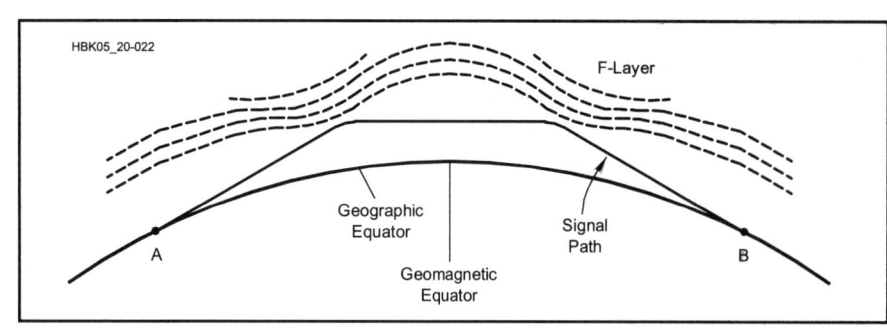

Figure 19.22 — Cross-section of a transequatorial signal path, showing the effects of ionospheric bulging and a double refraction above the normal MUF.

19.2.14 Emerging Theories of HF and VHF Propagation

Although much is known about the ionosphere and propagation, there are still many instances of unusual propagation that cannot be easily explained with our textbook knowledge. It is encouraging to note that Amateur Radio operators continue to be at the forefront of trying to understand many of these unusual modes. Several recent studies have included:

1) The tie between polar mesospheric summer echoes and 6 meter propagation in "Polar Mesospheric Summer Echoes," **k9la.us/PMSE_and_Propagation_at_50_MHz.pdf**. These summer echoes are also called SSSP (summer solstice short path), a mode that Japanese amateurs have noted.

2) Theta aurora and 6 meter propagation across the polar cap in "More Alaska to EU on 6 m," at **k9la.us/More_Alaska_to_Europe_on_6m.pdf**.

3) The impact of galactic cosmic rays on 160 meter *ducting* in "A Theory on the Role of Galactic Cosmic Rays in 160-Meter Propagation," *CQ*, Nov 2008. *Ducting* refers to an electromagnetic wave successively refracting between a lower boundary and an upper boundary (for example, between the top of the E region and the bottom of the F region for 160 meters at night)

4) Discovery of single-day enhancements in the F_2 region that do not be appear to be tied to geomagnetic activity. This came from an interesting paper that was published in the *Journal of Geophysical Research* in late 2010. The paper was by Michael David and Jan J. Sojka, who were with the Center for Atmospheric and Space Sciences at Utah State University. The title of the paper is "Single-day dayside density enhancements over Europe: A survey of a half-century of ionosonde data."

5) Although not a propagation issue, there is evidence that we may have missed a small solar cycle way back in the 1790 time frame. See **k9la.us/Did_We_Lose_a_Solar_Cycle.pdf**.

6) Another topic not tied directly to propagation is the on-going research into better models of the ionosphere. We already pretty much understand solar radiation and we've recently developed a much better model of how elevated geomagnetic indices affect the ionosphere (it's not simply applying a single K index). Research is on-going to better understand the physics behind events in the lower atmosphere coupling up to the ionosphere. Understanding these three processes is leading the way towards a true daily model of the ionosphere.

19.2.15 WSJT-X

WSJT-X (Weak Signal Communication, by K1JT; see **physics.princeton.edu/pulsar/k1jt/wsjtx.html**) is a computer program mentioned in Section 15.4 (Structured Digital Modes) and again in Section 19.2.12, in relation to meteor scatter. This software provides a wide variety of modes tailored for specific types of propagation. For example, FT8 is optimized for use at HF and 50 MHz; JT65 for EME on the VHF and UHF bands; JT4 for microwave bands; and JT9 especially for LF and MF. Any of these modes can be used on the HF bands to make worldwide contacts with a few watts and compromise antennas. The WSPR mode implements a protocol specially designed for probing potential propagation paths with low power transmissions.

19.3 MUF Predictions

F layer MUF prediction is key to forecasting HF communications paths at particular frequencies, dates and times, but forecasting is complicated by several variables. Solar radiation varies over the course of the day, season, year and solar cycle. Additionally, the ionization at any given point in the world depends on geomagnetic field activity and events in the lower atmosphere coupling up to the ionosphere. These regular intervals provide the main basis for prediction, yet recurrence is far from reliable. In addition, forecasts are predicated on a quiet geomagnetic field, but the condition of the Earth's magnetic field is most difficult to predict weeks or months ahead. For professional users of HF communications, uncertainty is a nuisance for maintaining reliable communications paths, while for many amateurs it provides an aura of mystery and chance that adds to the fun of DXing. Nevertheless, many amateurs want to know what to expect on the HF bands to make best use of available on-the-air time, plan contest strategy, ensure successful net operations or engage in other activities.

19.3.1 MUF Forecasts

Long-range forecasts several months ahead provide only the most general form of prediction. A series of 48 charts on the members-only ARRL website (**www.arrl.org/propagation**), similar to **Figure 19.23**, forecast average propagation for a one-month period over specific paths. The charts assume a single average solar flux value for the entire month and they assume that the geomagnetic field is undisturbed.

The uppermost curve in Figure 19.23 shows the highest frequency that will be propagated on at least 10% of the days in the month. The given values might be exceeded considerably on a few rare days. On at least half the days, propagation should be possible on frequencies as high as the middle curve. Propagation will exceed the lowest curve on at least 90% of the days. The exact MUF on any particular day cannot be determined from these statistical charts, but you can determine when you should start monitoring a band to see if propagation actually does occur that day — particularly at frequencies above 14 MHz.

Short-range forecasts of a few days ahead are marginally more reliable than long-range forecasts, because underlying solar indices and geomagnetic conditions can be anticipated with greater confidence. The tendency for solar disturbances to recur at 27-day intervals may enhance short-term forecasts. Daily forecasts may not be any better, as the ionosphere does not instantly react to small changes in solar flux (or sunspot number) and geomagnetic field indices. Regardless of these limitations, it is always good to know the current solar and geophysical data, as well as understanding warnings provided by observations of the

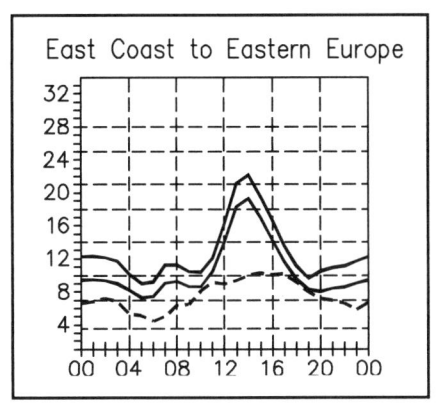

Figure 19.23 — Propagation prediction chart for East Coast to Eastern Europe from the ARRL web members-only site for April 2001. An average 2800 MHz (10.7 cm) solar flux of 159 was assumed for the month. On 10% of the days, the highest frequency propagated is predicted to be at least as high as the uppermost curve (the Highest Possible Frequency, or HPF, approximately 33 MHz), and for 50% of the days as high as the middle curve, the MUF. The lowest curve shows the Lowest Usable Frequency (LUF) for a 1500-W CW transmitter.

Sun in the visual to X-ray range.

The CD-ROM bundled with *The ARRL Antenna Book* contains even more detailed propagation-prediction tables from more than 150 locations around the world for six levels of solar activity, for the 12 months of the year. Again, keep in mind that these long-range forecasts assume quiet geomagnetic conditions. Real-time MUF forecasts are also available in a variety of text and graphical forms on the web. Forecasts can also be made by individuals using one of several popular programs for personal computers, including *ASAPS*, *VOACAP*, and *W6ELProp*. (See the sidebar, "MUF Prediction on the Home Computer.")

19.3.2 Statistical Nature of Propagation Predictions

The model of the ionosphere in propagation prediction software is a monthly median model — thus the results (usually MUF and signal strength) are statistical over a month's time frame. The median aspect means that the predicted value will actually occur on at least half the days of the month — but unfortunately it's tough to tell which are the "better" days and which are the "worse" days.

This monthly median model came about due to the efforts of scientists to correlate what the ionosphere was doing to what the Sun was doing. The best correlation was between a smoothed solar index (smoothed sunspot number or smoothed 10.7 cm solar flux) and monthly median ionospheric parameters. Thus our propagation prediction software was never intended to give daily predictions. One good way to achieve somewhat better short-term predictions is to use the concept of an effective sunspot number — SSNe.

EFFECTIVE SUNSPOT NUMBER (SSNe)

The concept of SSNe is quite simple. The F_2 layer critical frequency data from worldwide ionosondes is monitored, and then the sunspot number in an F_2 layer model of the ionosphere is varied until it provides a best fit to the monitored data. The current SSNe comes from Northwest Research Associates in Tucson (AZ), and can be found at **www.nwra.com/spawx/ssne.html**. By plugging the current SSNe into your favorite propagation prediction program, you will have a better (but not perfect) picture of what the ionosphere is doing "now."

19.3.3 Direct Observation

Propagation conditions can be determined directly by listening to the HF bands. The simplest method is to tune higher in frequency until no more long-distance stations are heard. This point is roughly just above the MUF to anywhere in the world at that moment. The highest usable amateur band would be the next lowest one. If HF stations seem to disappear around 23 MHz, for example, the 15 meter band at 21 MHz might make a good choice for DXing. By carefully noting station locations as well, the MUF in various directions can also be determined quickly.

The shortwave broadcast bands (see **Table 19.5**) are most convenient for MUF browsing, because there are many high-powered stations on regular schedules. Take care to ensure that programming is actually transmitted from the originating country. A Radio Moscow or BBC program, for example, may be relayed to a transmitter outside Russia or England for retransmission. An excellent guide to shortwave broadcast stations is the *World Radio TV Handbook*, available through the ARRL.

Table 19.5
Shortwave Broadcasting Bands

Frequency (MHz)	Band (meters)
2.300-2.495	120
3.200-3.400	90
3.900-4.000	75
4.750-5.060	60
5.959-6.200	49
7.100-7.300	41
9.500-9.900	31
11.650-12.050	25
13.600-13.800	22
15.100-15.600	19
17.550-17.900	16
21.450-21.850	13
25.600-26.100	11

19.3.4 WWV and WWVH

The standard time stations WWV (Fort Collins, Colorado) and WWVH (Kauai, Hawaii), which transmit on 2.5, 5, 10, 15 and 20 MHz, are also popular for propagation monitoring. They transmit 24 hours a day. Daily monitoring of these stations for signal strength and quality can quickly provide a good basic indication of propagation conditions. In addition, each hour they broadcast the geomagnetic A and K indices, the 2800 MHz (10.7 cm) solar flux, and a short forecast of conditions for the next day. These are heard on WWV at 18 minutes past each hour and on WWVH at 45 minutes after the hour. The same information, along with a lot more space weather information, is available at various websites, such as **www.swpc.noaa.gov** or **www.spaceweather.com**. The K index is updated every three hours, while the A index and solar flux are updated after 2100 UTC. These data are useful for making predictions on home computers, especially when averaged over several days of solar flux observations.

19.3.5 Beacons

Automated *beacons* in the higher amateur bands can also be useful adjuncts to propagation watching. Beacons are ideal for this purpose because most are designed to transmit 24 hours a day.

One of the best organized beacon systems is the International Beacon Project, sponsored by the Northern California DX Foundation (NCDXF) and International Amateur Radio Union (IARU). The beacons operate 24 hours a day at 14.100, 18.110, 21.150, 24.930 and 28.200 MHz. Eighteen beacons on five continents transmit in successive 10-second intervals (each beacon transmits once every 3 minutes). More on this system can be found at the Northern California DX Foundation website **www.ncdxf.org** (click on the *Beacons* link on the left).

A network of automated SDR receivers called the Reverse Beacon Network (**www.reversebeacon.net**) has been created to monitor the HF CW subbands for signals that are automatically decoded by *CW Skimmer* software by VE3NEA (**www.dxatlas.com/cwskimmer**). The network logs signal strength and location for the received signals, providing real-time information on HF propagation.

A list of many 28 MHz beacons can be found on the 10-10 International website, **www.ten-ten.org** (look for *Beacons* under the Resources link). Beacons often include location as part of their automated message, and many can be located from their call sign. Thus, even casual scanning of beacon subbands can be useful. **Table 19.6** provides the frequencies where beacons useful to HF propagation are most commonly placed.

There are also many beacons on VHF and higher bands. "G3USF's Worldwide List of

MUF Prediction on the Home Computer

Like predicting the weather, predicting HF propagation — even with the best computer software available — is not an exact science. The processes occurring as a signal is propagated from one point on the Earth to another are enormously complicated and subject to an incredible number of variables. Experience and knowledge of propagation conditions (as related to solar activity, especially unusual solar activity, such as flares or coronal mass ejections) are needed when you actually get on the air to check out the bands. Keep in mind, too, that ordinary computer programs are written mainly to calculate propagation for great-circle paths via the F layer. Scatter, skew-path, auroral and other such propagation modes may provide contacts when computer predictions indicate no contacts are possible.

What follows is some brief information about commercially available propagation-prediction programs for the IBM PC and compatible computers. See **Table 19.A**. These programs generally allow predictions from 3 to 30 MHz. Unfortunately prediction programs are not available on 160 meters (because of an incomplete understanding of the lower ionosphere and ducting mechanisms that contribute to propagation on that band) and on 6 meters (because of an incomplete understanding of openings when the MUF is not predicted to be high enough). As a general guideline, you should look for 160 meter openings when the path to your target station is in darkness and around sunrise/sunset, and you should look for 6 meter F_2 openings in the daytime during winter months near solar maximum.

You may find an article that appeared in the Summer 2008 issue of *CQ VHF* to be helpful with your 6m endeavors: "Predicting 6-meter F_2 Propagation," by Carl Luetzelschwab, K9LA.

ASAPS Version 7

An agency of the Australian government has developed the *ASAPS* program, which stands for Advanced Stand-Alone Prediction System. It rivals *IONCAP* (see below) in its analysis capability and in its prediction accuracy. It is a *Windows* program that interacts reasonably well with the user, once you become accustomed to the acronyms used. If you change transmit power levels, antennas and other parameters, you can see the new results almost instantly without further menu entries. Available from IPS Radio and Space Services. See **www.sws.bom.gov.au/Products_and_Services/1/2**.

IONCAP and VOACAP

IONCAP, short for Ionospheric Communications Analysis and Prediction, was written by an agency of the US government and has been under development for about 30 years in one form or another. The *IONCAP* program has a well-deserved reputation for being difficult to use, since it came from the world of Fortran punch cards and mainframe computers.

VOACAP is a version of *IONCAP* adapted to Voice of America predictions, but this one includes a sophisticated Windows interface. The Voice of America (VOA) started work on *VOACAP* in the early 1990s and continued for several years before funding ran out. The program was maintained by a single, dedicated computer scientist, Greg Hand, at NTIA/ITS (Institute for Telecommunication Sciences), an agency of the US Department of Commerce in Boulder, Colorado. Greg Hand is now retired, but considerable documentation can be found at the website referenced below, along with links to other VOACAP-related websites. Although *VOACAP* is not specifically designed for amateurs (and thus doesn't include some features that amateurs are fond of, such as entry of locations by ham radio call signs and multiple receiving antennas), it is available for free by downloading from **www.its.bldrdoc.gov/resources/radio-propagation-software/high-frequency/high-frequency-propagation-models.aspx**.

W6ELProp, Version 2.70

In 2001, W6EL (SK) ported his well known *MINIPROP PLUS* program into the *Windows* world. It uses the same Fricker-based F_2 region computation engine as its predecessor. (This method was developed by Raymond Fricker of the BBC.) *W6ELProp* has a highly intuitive, ham-friendly user interface. It produces detailed output tables, along with a number of useful charts and maps, including the unique and useful "frequency map," which shows the global MUFs from a given transmitting location for a particular month/day/time and solar-activity level. *W6ELProp* is available for free by downloading from **www.qsl.net/w6elprop**.

PropLab Pro, Version 3.0

PropLab Pro by Solar Terrestrial Dispatch represents the high end of propagation-prediction programs. It is the only commercial program presently available that can do complete 3D ray tracing through the ionosphere, even taking complex geomagnetic effects and electron-neutral collisions (what causes

---

50 MHz Beacons" may be found at **www.keele.ac.uk/depts/por/50.htm**. Information on North American beacons on 144 MHz and up is maintained by Ron Klimas, WZ1V, at **www.newsvhf.com/beacons2.html**.

19.3.6 Other Methods for Real-Time Assessment of the Ionosphere

Since our propagation predictions are statistical in nature over a month's time frame, determining what the ionosphere is doing in real time can be important. In addition to using the effective sunspot number, making direct observations of our bands, monitoring WWV/WWVH on their five frequencies, and monitoring the IARU/NCDXF and other beacons as discussed previously, there are other ways to get a real-time picture of the ionosphere.

An emerging method is to use the Reverse Beacon Network (RBN — briefly discussed previously) to construct maps of F2 region critical frequencies (foF2). Applying some simple rules will allow MUFs (maximum useable frequencies) to be easily estimated. See the RBN article with the downloadable supplemental content for general information about the RBN. Also expect to see a technical article about foF2 maps generated from RBN data in the future.

Watching the worldwide spotting network is another way to assess real-time propagation. An extension of this is to plot the paths from the spots on a worldwide map. One such presentation is at **www.dxmaps.com/spots/map.php**.

Table 19.6
Popular Beacon Frequencies

(MHz)	Comments
14.100, 18.110, 21.150, 24.930, 28.200	Northern California DX Foundation beacons
28.2-28.3	Several dozen beacons worldwide
50.0-50.1	Most US beacons are within 50.06-50.08 MHz
70.03-70.13	Beacons in England, Ireland, Gibraltar and Cyprus

absorption) into account. The number of computations is huge, especially in the full-blown 3D mode and operation can be slow and tedious. The *Windows* based user interface is easier to use than previous versions, which were complex and difficult to learn.

It is fascinating to see exactly how a signal can bend off-azimuth or how it can split into the ordinary and extraordinary waves. It is best considered a propagation analysis tool, as opposed to a propagation prediction program. See **www.spacew.com/proplab**.

Table 19.A
Features and Attributes of Several Currently Available Propagation Prediction Programs

	ASAPS V. 7	VOACAP Windows	W6ELProp V. 2.70	PropLab Pro 3.1
User Friendliness	Good	Good	Good	Good
Operating System	Windows	Windows	Windows	Windows
Uses K index	No	No	Yes	Yes
User library of QTHs	Yes/Map	Yes	Yes	No
Bearings, distances	Yes	Yes	Yes	Yes
MUF calculation	Yes	Yes	Yes	Yes
LUF calculation	Yes	Yes	No	Yes
Wave angle calculation	Yes	Yes	Yes	Yes
Vary minimum wave angle	Yes	Yes	Yes	Yes
Path regions and hops	Yes	Yes	Yes	Yes
Multipath effects	Yes	Yes	No	Yes
Path probability	Yes	Yes	Yes	Yes
Signal strengths	Yes	Yes	Yes	Yes
S/N ratios	Yes	Yes	Yes	Yes
Long path calculation	Yes	Yes	Yes	No
Antenna selection	Yes	Yes	Indirectly	Yes
Vary antenna height	Yes	Yes	Indirectly	Yes
Vary ground characteristics	Yes	Yes	No	No
Vary transmit power	Yes	Yes	Indirectly	Yes
Graphic displays	Yes	Yes	Yes	2D/3D
UT-day graphs	Yes	Yes	Yes	Yes
Area Mapping	Yes	Yes	Yes	Yes
Documentation	Yes	Online	Yes	Yes
Price class	$AUD350[1]	free[2]	free[3]	$240[4]

Prices are for early 2017 and are subject to change.

[1] See **www.ips.gov.au/Products_and_Services/1/2**. Be advised that the price will depend on the exchange rate.
[2] *VOACAP* available at **www.its.bldrdoc.gov/resources/radio-propagation-software/high-frequency/high-frequency-propagation-models.aspx**
[3] *W6ELProp*, see **www.qsl.net/w6elprop**
[4] *PropLab Pro V3*, see **www.spacew.com/proplab/**

19.3.7 Space Weather Information

Living in the space age results in a wealth of information about the Sun-Earth environment. Not only do we have measurements available, but we also have extensive tutorials available on what is being measured, how it is measured, and its general impact to propagation.

SPACE WEATHER SATELLITES

Three of the most beneficial satellites for propagation information are the Advanced Composition Explorer (ACE), the Solar and Heliospheric Observatory (SOHO), and the STEREO mission.

ACE is on a line from the Earth to the Sun, and is about 1 million miles from the Earth. Its primary purpose is to measure solar wind characteristics. For example, it measures the direction of the IMF (interplanetary magnetic field), the solar wind speed, and the dynamic solar wind pressure. More detailed information about ACE can be found at **www.srl.caltech.edu/ACE/**.

SOHO moves around the Sun in step with Earth — it always faces the Sun. Its primary purpose is to study the Sun. For example, it views coronal mass ejections, and in conjunction with the Michelson Doppler Imager (MDI), allows scientists to "see" sunspots on the far side of the Sun. More detailed information about SOHO and MDI can be found at **sohowww.nascom.nasa.gov** and **soi.stanford.edu**, respectively.

The STEREO mission consists of two spacecraft that are in heliocentric orbits leading and lagging the Earth. Each spacecraft provides a unique observing vantage point, and taken together, they enable a stereoscopic view of the Sun, solar activity, and the solar environment between the Sun and Earth. More information can be found at **stereo.gsfc.nasa.gov/**.

More satellite data can be found at **www.swpc.noaa.gov** and at **www.spaceweather.com**.

19.3.8 Online Predictions

In addition to propagation predictions on your home PC, you can make predictions online. Two such websites to do this are **www.voacap.com/p2p/index.html** and **rsgb.org/main/about-us/committees/propagation-studies-committee/projects/iturhf-prop-propagation-prediction-engine/**.

The first website is by Jari Perkiömäki, OH6BG/OG6G, and uses *VOACAP*. The second web site is by Gwyn Williams, G4FKH, a member of the RSGB's Propagation Studies Committee. Both websites have instructions on how to input your data to generate the desired prediction.

19.4 Propagation in the Troposphere

All radio communication involves propagation through the troposphere for at least part of the signal path. Radio waves traveling through the lowest part of the atmosphere are subject to refraction, scattering and other phenomena, much like ionospheric effects. Tropospheric conditions are rarely significant below 30 MHz, but they are very important at 50 MHz and higher. Much of the long-distance work on the VHF, UHF and microwave bands depends on some form of tropospheric propagation. Instead of watching solar activity and geomagnetic indices, those who use tropospheric propagation are much more concerned about terrestrial weather as opposed to space weather.

19.4.1 Line of Sight

At one time it was thought that communications in the VHF range and higher would be restricted to line-of-sight paths. Although this has not proven to be the case even in the microwave region, the concept of line of sight is still useful in understanding tropospheric propagation. In the vacuum of space or in a completely homogeneous medium, radio waves do travel essentially in straight lines, but these conditions are almost never met in terrestrial propagation.

Radio waves traveling through the troposphere are ordinarily refracted slightly earthward. The normal drop in temperature, pressure and water-vapor content with increasing altitude change the index of refraction of the atmosphere enough to cause refraction. Under average conditions, radio waves are refracted toward Earth enough to make the horizon appear 1.15 times farther away than the visual horizon. Under unusual conditions, tropospheric refraction may extend this range significantly.

A simple formula can be used to estimate the distance to the radio horizon under average conditions:

$$d = \sqrt{2h}$$

where
d = distance to the radio horizon, miles
h = height above average terrain, ft.

and

$$d = \sqrt{17h}$$

where
d = distance to the radio horizon, km
h = height above average terrain, m.

The distance to the radio horizon for an antenna 30 meters (98 ft) above average terrain

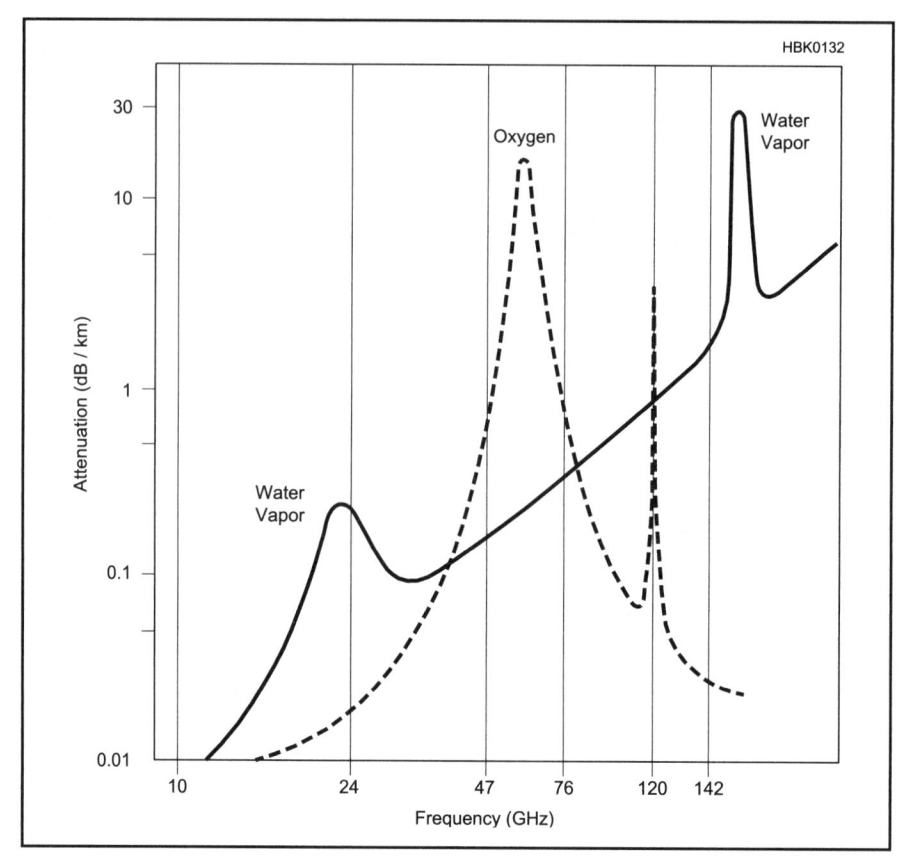

Figure 19.24 — Attenuation caused by oxygen and water vapor at 10 grams per cubic meter (equivalent to 40% humidity at 25 °C). There is little attenuation caused by atmospheric gases at 10 GHz and lower. Note that the 24 GHz band lies near the center of a peak of water vapor absorption and the 120 GHz band is near a peak of oxygen absorption.

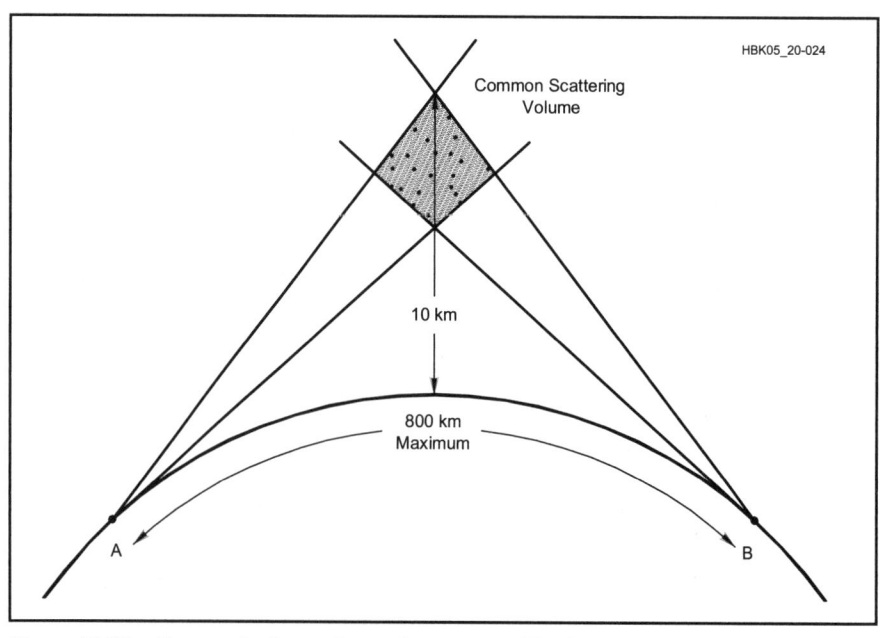

Figure 19.25 — Tropospheric-scatter path geometry. The lower boundary of the common scattering volume is limited by the take-off angle of both stations. The upper boundary of 10 km (6 miles) altitude is the limit of efficient scattering in the troposphere. Signal strength increases with the scattering volume.

is thus 22.6 km (14 miles). A station on top of a 1000 meter (3280 ft) mountain has a radio horizon of 130 km (80 miles).

ATMOSPHERIC ABSORPTION

Atmospheric gases, most notably oxygen and water vapor, absorb radio signals, but neither is a significant factor below 10 GHz. See **Figure 19.24**. Attenuation from rain becomes important at 3.3 GHz, where signals passing through 20 km (12 miles) of heavy showers incur an additional 0.2 dB loss. That same rain would impose 12 dB additional losses at 10 GHz and losses continue to increase with frequency. Heavy fog is similarly a problem only at 5.6 GHz and above.

19.4.2 Tropospheric Scatter

Contacts beyond the radio horizon out to a working distance of 100 to 500 km (60-310 miles), depending on frequency, equipment and local geography, are made every day without the aid of obvious propagation enhancement. At 1.8 and 3.5 MHz, local communication is due mostly to ground wave. At higher frequencies, especially in the VHF range and above, the primary mechanism is scattering in the troposphere, or *troposcatter*.

Most amateurs are unaware that they use troposcatter even though it plays an essential role in most local communication. Radio signals through the VHF range are scattered primarily by wavelength sized gradients in the index of refraction of the lower atmosphere due to turbulence, along with changes in temperature. Radio signals in the microwave region can also be scattered by rain, snow, fog, clouds and dust. That tiny part that is scattered forward and toward the Earth creates the over-the-horizon paths. Troposcatter path losses are considerable and increase with frequency.

The maximum distance that can be linked via troposcatter is limited by the height of a scattering volume common to two stations, shown schematically in **Figure 19.25**. The highest altitude for which scattering is efficient at amateur power levels is about 10 km (6 miles). An application of the distance-to-the-horizon formula yields 800 km (500 miles) as the limit for troposcatter paths, but typical maxima are about half that. Tropospheric scatter varies little with season or time of day, but it is difficult to assess the effect of weather on troposcatter alone. Variations in tropospheric refraction, which is very sensitive to the weather, probably account for most of the observed day-to-day differences in troposcatter signal strength.

Troposcatter does not require special operating techniques or equipment, as it is used unwittingly all the time. In the absence of all other forms of propagation, especially at VHF and above, the usual working range is essentially the maximum troposcatter distance. Ordinary working range increases most dramatically with antenna height, because that lowers the take-off angle to the horizon. Working range increases less quickly with antenna gain and transmitter power. For this reason, a mountaintop is the choice location for extending ordinary troposcatter working distances.

RAIN SCATTER IN THE TROPOSPHERE

Scatter from raindrops is a special case of troposcatter practical in the 3.3 to 24 GHz range. Stations simply point their antennas toward a common area of rain. A certain portion of radio energy is scattered by the raindrops, making possible over-the-horizon or obstructed-path contacts, even with low power. The theoretical range for rain scatter is as great as 600 km (370 miles), but the experience of amateurs in the microwave bands suggests that expected distances are less than 200 km (120 miles). Snow and hail make less efficient scattering media unless the ice particles are partially melted. Smoke and dust particles are too small for extraordinary scattering, even in the microwave bands.

19.4.3 Refraction and Ducting in the Troposphere

Radio waves are refracted by natural gradients in the index of refraction of air with altitude, due to changes in temperature, humidity and pressure. Refraction under standard atmospheric conditions extends the radio horizon somewhat beyond the visual line of sight. Favorable weather conditions further enhance normal tropospheric refraction, lengthening the useful VHF and UHF range by several hundred kilometers and increasing signal strength. Higher frequencies are more sensitive to refraction, so its effects may be observed in the microwave bands before they are apparent at lower frequencies.

Ducting takes place when refraction is so great that radio waves are bent back to the surface of the Earth. When tropospheric ducting conditions exist over a wide geographic area, signals may remain very strong over distances of 1500 km (930 miles) or more. Ducting results from the gradient created by a sharp increase in temperature with altitude, quite the opposite of normal atmospheric conditions. A simultaneous drop in humidity contributes to increased refractivity.

Normally the temperature steadily decreases with altitude, but at times there is a small portion of the troposphere in which the temperature increases and then again begins decreasing normally. This is called an *inversion*. Useful temperature inversions form between 250 and 2000 meters (800-6500 ft) above ground. The elevated inversion and the Earth's surface act something like the boundaries of a natural open-ended waveguide. Radio waves of the right frequency range caught inside the duct will be propagated for long distances with relatively low losses. Several common weather conditions can create temperature inversions.

RADIATION INVERSIONS IN THE TROPOSPHERE

Radiation inversions are probably the most common and widespread of the various weather conditions that affect propagation. Radiation inversions form only over land after

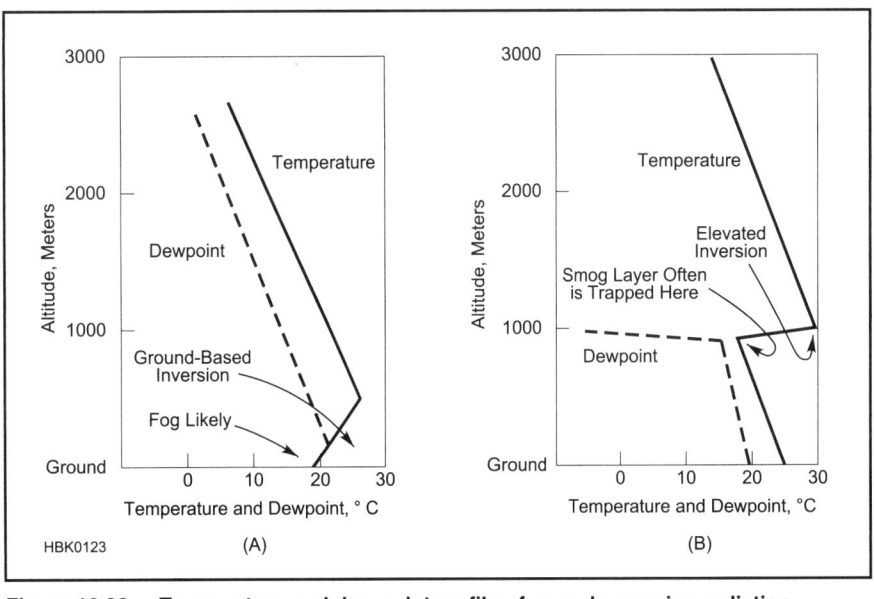

Figure 19.26 — Temperature and dew point profile of an early-morning radiation inversion is shown at A. Fog may form near the ground. The midday surface temperature would be at least 30 °C. At B, temperature and humidity profile across an elevated duct at 1000 meters altitude. Such inversions typically form in summertime high-pressure systems. Note the air is very dry in the inversion.

sunset as a result of progressive cooling of the air near the Earth's surface. As the Earth cools by radiating heat into space, the air just above the ground is cooled in turn. At higher altitudes, the air remains relatively warmer, thus creating the inversion. A typical radiation-inversion temperature profile is shown in **Figure 19.26A**.

The cooling process may continue through the evening and predawn hours, creating inversions that extend as high as 500 meters (1500 ft). Deep radiation inversions are most common during clear, calm, summer evenings. They are more distinct in dry climates, in valleys and over open ground. Their formation is inhibited by wind, wet ground and cloud cover. Although radiation inversions are common and widespread, they are rarely strong enough to cause true ducting. The enhanced conditions so often observed after sunset during the summer are usually a result of this mild kind of inversion.

HIGH-PRESSURE WEATHER SYSTEMS

Large, sluggish, high-pressure systems (or *anticyclones*) create the most dramatic and widespread tropospheric ducts due to *subsidence*. Subsidence inversions in high-pressure systems are created by air that is sinking. As air descends, it is compressed and heated. Layers of warmer air — temperature inversions — often form between 500 and 3000 meters (1500-10,000 ft) altitude, as shown in Figure 19.26B. Ducts usually intensify during the evening and early morning hours, when surface temperatures drop and suppress the tendency for daytime ground-warmed air to rise. In the Northern Hemisphere, the longest and strongest radio paths usually lie to the south of high-pressure centers. See **Figure 19.27**.

Sluggish high-pressure systems likely to contain strong temperature inversions are common in late summer over the eastern half of the US. They generally move southeastward out of Canada and linger for days over the Midwest, providing many hours of extended propagation. The southeastern part of the country and the lower Midwest experience the most high-pressure openings; the upper Midwest and East Coast somewhat less frequently; the western mountain regions rarely.

Semi-permanent high-pressure systems, which are nearly constant climatic features in certain parts of the world, sustain the longest and most exciting ducting paths. The Eastern Pacific High, which migrates northward off the coast of California during the summer, has been responsible for the longest ducting paths reported to date. Countless contacts in the 4000 km (2500 mile) range have been made from 144 MHz through 5.6 GHz between California and Hawaii. The *Bermuda High* is a nearly permanent feature of the Caribbean area, but during the summer it moves north and often covers the southeastern US. It has supported contacts in excess of 2800 km (1700 miles) from Florida and the Carolinas to the West Indies, but its full potential has not been exploited. Other semi-permanent highs lie in the Indian Ocean, the western Pacific and off the coast of western Africa.

WAVE CYCLONE

The *wave cyclone* is a more dynamic weather system that usually appears during the spring over the middle part of the American continent. The wave begins as a disturbance along a boundary between cooler northern and warmer southern air masses. Southwest of the disturbance, a cold front forms and moves rapidly eastward, while a warm front moves slowly northward on the eastward side. When the wave is in its open position, as shown in **Figure 19.28**, north-south radio paths 1500 km (930 miles) and longer may be possible in the area to the east of the cold front and south of the warm front, known as the warm sector. East-west paths nearly as long may also open in the southerly parts of the warm sector.

Wave cyclones are rarely productive for more than a day in any given place, because the eastward-moving cold front eventually closes off the warm sector. Wave-cyclone temperature inversions are created by a southwesterly flow of warm, dry air above 1000 meters (3200 ft) that covers relatively cooler and moister Gulf air flowing northward near the Earth's surface. Successive waves spaced two or three days apart may form along the same frontal boundary.

WARM FRONTS AND COLD FRONTS

Warm fronts and cold fronts sometimes bring enhanced tropospheric conditions, but rarely

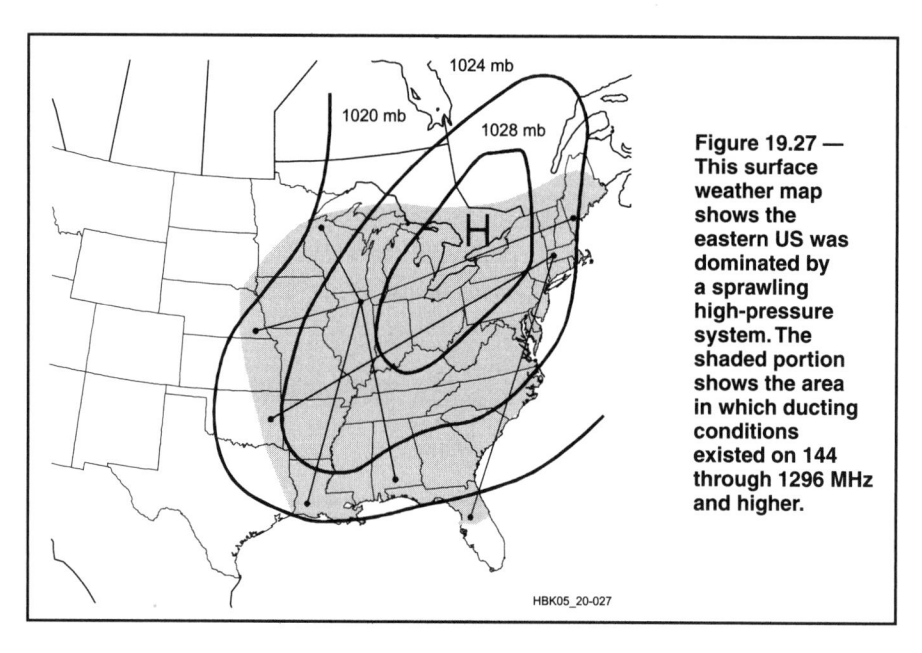

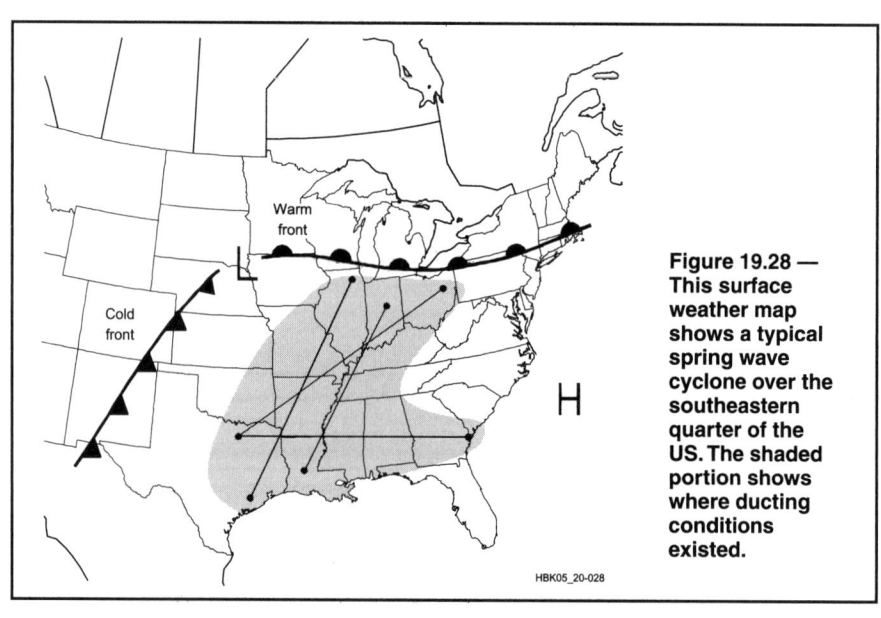

Figure 19.27 — This surface weather map shows the eastern US was dominated by a sprawling high-pressure system. The shaded portion shows the area in which ducting conditions existed on 144 through 1296 MHz and higher.

Figure 19.28 — This surface weather map shows a typical spring wave cyclone over the southeastern quarter of the US. The shaded portion shows where ducting conditions existed.

true ducting. A warm front marks the surface boundary between a mass of warm air flowing over an area of relatively cooler and more stationary air. Inversion conditions may be stable enough several hundred kilometers ahead of the warm front to create extraordinary paths.

A cold front marks the surface boundary between a mass of cool air that is wedging itself under more stationary warm air. The warmer air is pushed aloft in a narrow band behind the cold front, creating a strong but highly unstable temperature inversion. The best chance for enhancement occurs parallel to and behind the passing cold front.

OTHER CONDITIONS ASSOCIATED WITH DUCTS

Certain kinds of wind may also create useful inversions. The *Chinook* wind that blows off the eastern slopes of the Rockies can flood the Great Plains with warm and very dry air, primarily in the springtime. If the ground is cool or snow-covered, a strong inversion can extend as far as Canada to Texas and east to the Mississippi River. Similar kinds of *foehn* winds, as these mountain breezes are called, can be found in the Alps, Caucasus Mountains and other places.

The *land breeze* is a light, steady, cool wind that commonly blows up to 50 km (30 miles) inland from the oceans, although the distance may be greater in some circumstances. Land breezes develop after sunset on clear summer evenings. The land cools more quickly than the adjacent ocean. Air cooled over the land flows near the surface of the Earth toward the ocean to displace relatively warmer air that is rising. See **Figure 19.29**. The warmer ocean air, in turn, travels at 200-300 meters (600-1000 ft) altitude to replace the cool surface air. The land-sea circulation of cool air near the ground and warm air aloft creates a mild inversion that may remain for hours. Land-breeze inversions often bring enhanced conditions and occasionally allow contacts in excess of 800 km (500 miles) along coastal areas.

In southern Europe, a hot, dry wind known as the *sirocco* sometimes blows northward from the Sahara Desert over relatively cooler and moister Mediterranean air. Sirocco inversions can be very strong and extend from Israel and Lebanon westward past the Straits of Gibraltar. Sirocco-type inversions are probably responsible for record-breaking microwave contacts in excess of 1500 km (930 miles) across the Mediterranean.

MARINE BOUNDARY LAYER EFFECTS

Over warm water, such as the Caribbean and other tropical seas, *evaporation inversions* may create ducts that are useful in the microwave region between 3.3 and 24 GHz. This inversion depends on a sharp drop in water-vapor content rather than on an increase in temperature to create ducting conditions. Air just above the surface of water at least 30°C is saturated because of evaporation. Humidity drops significantly within 3 to 10 meters (10 to 30 ft) altitude, creating a very shallow but stable duct. Losses due to water vapor absorption may be intolerable at the highest ducting frequencies, but breezes may raise the effective height of the inversion and open the duct to longer wavelengths. Stations must be set up right on the beaches to ensure being inside an evaporation inversion.

TROPOSPHERIC DUCTING FORECASTS

To help decide if weather conditions may support tropospheric ducting, visit "William Hepburn's Worldwide Tropospheric Ducting Forecasts" at **www.dxinfocentre.com/tropo.html**. The principal content on this website is the forecast maps — 6-day preview as well as 42-hour preview (in 6-hour increments) maps for virtually every region of the world.

The purpose of these maps is to display potential duct paths for VHF, UHF and microwave signals, indicated by the color shading on the maps using the Hepburn Tropo Index. This index indicates the degree of tropospheric bending forecast to occur over a particular area. It is an indication of the overall tropospheric radio signal strength on a linear scale from 0 to 10 (with 10 representing an "extremely intense opening" for propagation by ducting).

Also shown on the maps are predicted "unstable signal areas" where weather conditions could potentially disrupt signal paths and cause unusual and sometimes rapid variations in signal strengths

19.4.4 Tropospheric Fading

Because the atmosphere is not homogeneous, radio signals are refracted slightly as they encounter variations in density and humidity. A signal may arrive at the receiver by two or more different paths simultaneously, causing addition or partial cancellation depending on the relative phases and amplitudes of the paths. As the wind blows, the paths change, which causes the net amplitude of the received signal to vary slowly, a process known as *scintillation fading*. This is the same process that causes the stars to twinkle in the visible portion of the electromagnetic spectrum. The higher the frequency and the longer the path length, the more pronounced the effect. While scintillation is generally not significant for short-range VHF/UHF repeater work, it can be the main limitation on power budgets for microwave point-to-point links.

Fast-flutter fading at 28 MHz and above is often the result of an airplane that temporarily creates a second propagation path. Flutter results as the phase relationship between the direct signal and that reflected by the airplane changes with the airplane's movement.

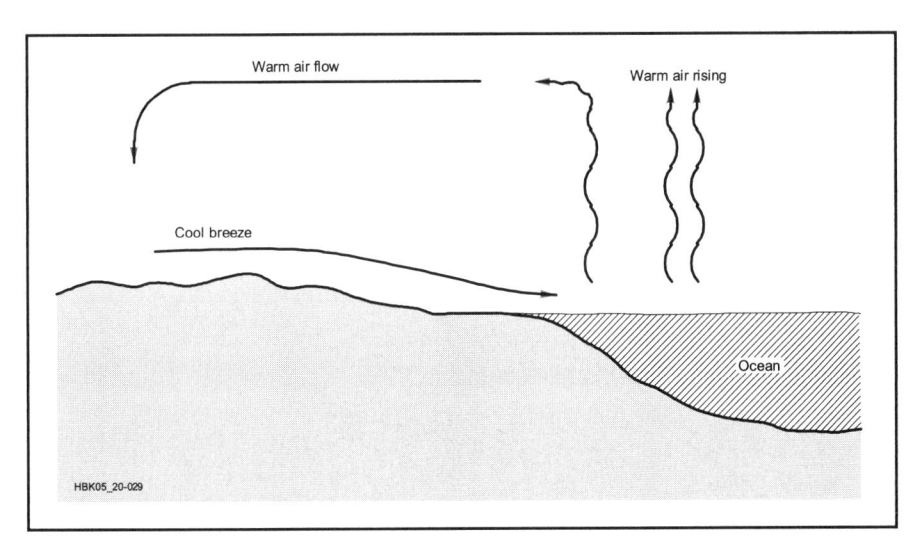

Figure 19.29 — Land-breeze convection along a coast after sunset creates a temperature inversion over the land.

19.5 VHF/UHF Mobile Propagation

Most amateurs are aware that radio signals in free space obey the inverse-square law: the received signal power is inversely proportional to the square of the distance between the transmitting and receiving antennas. That law applies *only* if the transmitting and receiving antennas have an obstruction-free radio path between them.

Imagine two operators using hand-held 144 MHz radios, each standing on a mountaintop so that they have a direct line of sight. How far apart can they be and still maintain reliable communications? Assume 5 W transmitter power, 0 dBi antenna gain (2.15 dB worse than a dipole), 5 dB receiver noise figure, 10 dB S/N ratio and 12 kHz receiver bandwidth.

Ask experienced VHF mobile operators that question and you'll generally get guesses in the range of 20 to 30 miles because their experience tells them that's about the most you can expect when not communicating through a repeater. The correct answer, however, is over 9500 km (5938 miles) based on the parameters given in the previous paragraph! This also explains how some operators have been able to work the Amateur Radio station on the International Space Station using only a handheld transceiver.

The discrepancy is explained by the fact that the line-of-sight scenario is not realistic for a mobile station located close to ground level. At distances greater than a few miles, there usually is no line of sight — the signal is reflected at least once on its journey from transmitter to receiver. As a result, path loss is typically proportional to distance to the third or fourth power, not the second power as the inverse-square law implies.

19.5.1 Rayleigh Fading

Not only is the signal reflected, but it usually arrives at the receiver by several different paths simultaneously. See **Figure 19.30**. Because the length of each path is different, the signals are not in phase. If the signals on two paths happen to be 180° out of phase and at the same amplitude, they will cancel. If they are in phase then their amplitudes will add. As the mobile station moves about, the phases of the various paths vary in a random fashion. However they tend to be uncorrelated over distances greater than λ/4 or so, which is about 20 inches on the 2 meter band. That is why if the repeater you are listening to drops out when you are stopped at a traffic light, you can often get it back again by creeping forward a few inches.

Because there are typically dozens of paths, it is rare for their amplitudes and phases to be such that they all cancel perfectly. Fades of 20 to 30 dB or more are common. The range of signal strengths has a *Rayleigh* distribution, named after the physicist/mathematician who first derived the mathematical formula. That is why the phenomenon is called *Rayleigh fading*. **Figure 19.31** shows the relative probability of various signal strengths. **Figure 19.32** is the same graph plotted on a logarithmic (dB) scale, along with a typical plot of signal strength versus time as the mobile station moves down the road.

The closer a reflecting object is to the antenna the smaller is the path loss. A reflector that is close to the transmitter or receiver antenna gives a much stronger signal than one located halfway between. Even a weak reflector, such as a tree branch or telephone pole, is significant if it is close to the mobile station.

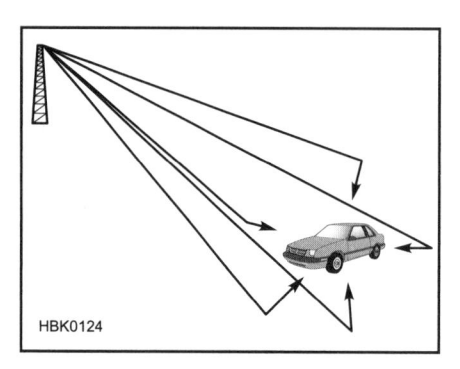

Figure 19.30 — At distances greater than a few miles, there normally is no line-of-sight path to the mobile station. Each path experiences at least one reflection. (Because the radio paths are reciprocal, propagation is the same for both receiving and transmitting.)

Because there are many such close-in reflectors, many rays arrive from all directions.

Rays arriving from in front of a forward-moving vehicle experience a positive Doppler frequency shift and rays from the rear have a negative Doppler shift. Those from the sides are somewhere in-between, proportional to the cosine of the angle of arrival. The received signal is the sum of all those rays, which results in *Doppler spreading* of the signal as illustrated in **Figure 19.33**. At normal vehicle speeds on the 2 meter band, the Doppler spread is only plus and minus 10 or 15 Hz, calculated from

Doppler frequency = F_c v/c

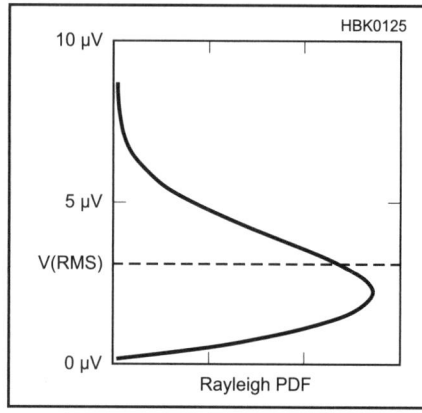

Figure 19.31 — The horizontal axis is the Rayleigh probability density function (PDF), which is the relative probability of the different signal levels shown on the vertical axis. For this graph, an RMS value of 3.16 µV has been selected to represent a typical average signal level in a marginal-coverage area.

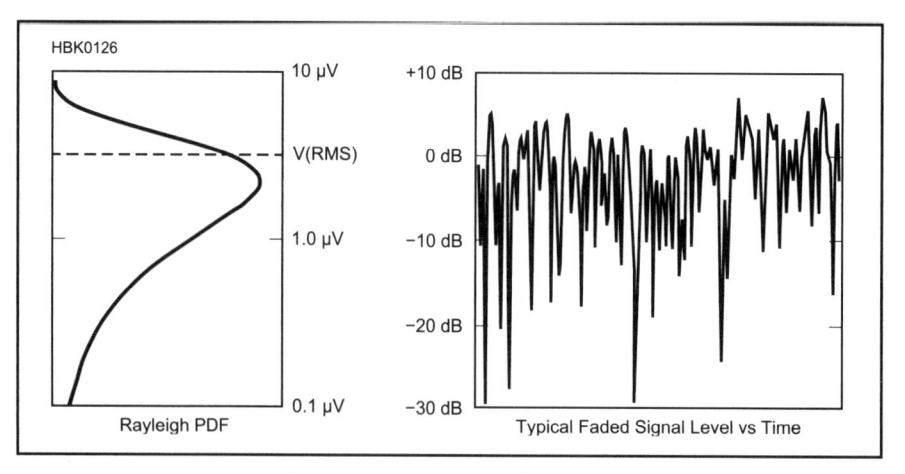

Figure 19.32 — The graph at the left is the same as Figure 19.31 except that the vertical axis is logarithmic (proportional to dB). At the right is a typical Rayleigh-faded signal of the same RMS voltage level plotted using the same vertical scale.

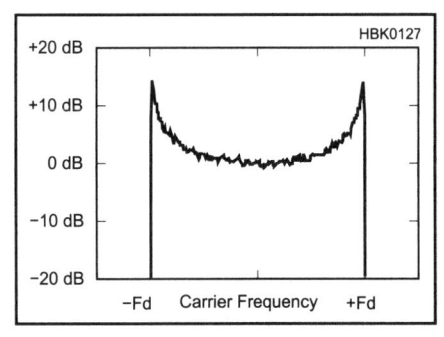

Figure 19.33 — Rayleigh fading spectrum of a CW (unmodulated) signal. The maximum deviation (F_d) from the center frequency is typically less than 10-15 Hz on the 144 MHz band.

where
F_c = the carrier frequency
v = the vehicle speed
c = the speed of light

Use the same units for v and c. On an FM voice signal the only effect is a slight distortion of the audio, but Doppler spreading can severely affect digital signals, as will be discussed later.

19.5.2 Multipath Propagation

In addition to scattering by local reflectors, it is not uncommon also to have more than one main radio path caused by strong reflectors, such as large metal buildings located some distance away. See **Figure 19.34**. Each main path typically does not reach the mobile station directly, but is separately Rayleigh-faded by the local reflectors.

As the mobile station moves around, the shadowing of various paths by intervening hills, buildings and other objects causes the average signal level to fade in and out, but at a much slower rate than Rayleigh fading. This is called *shadowing* or *slow fading*. It is also called *log-normal fading* because the distribution of average signal levels tends to follow a log-normal curve. That means that the *logarithm* of the signal level (on a dB scale, if you will) has a *normal* distribution (the famous bell-shaped curve). This effect typically causes the average signal level on each path to vary plus and minus 10-20 dB (at two standard deviations) from the mean value. This is in addition to the signal variation due to Rayleigh fading.

19.5.3 Effect on the Receiver

Radio direction finding (RDF) enthusiasts have noticed that their RDF receivers usually do not give stable or accurate indications unless located on a hilltop or other location with a clear line of sight to the transmitter because of fading and reflections. The best technique is to record the bearing to the hidden transmitter from a high location clear of nearby reflecting objects, then drive in that direction and take the next reading from another (hopefully closer) hilltop. Only when close to the transmitter will the RDF equipment typically give good readings while the vehicle is in motion.

Under weak-signal conditions Rayleigh fading causes the signal to drop out periodically even though the average signal level would be high enough to maintain reliable communications if there were no fading. *Picket fencing*, as such rapid periodic dropout is called, is a common occurrence when traveling in a weak-signal area at highway speeds. With analog modulation, normally the only solution is to stop at a location where the signal is strong. Moving the vehicle forward or backward a few inches is often enough to change an unreadable signal to solid copy.

Another possible solution is to employ *diversity reception*. If two (or more) mobile receiver antennas are spaced a half-wavelength or more apart, their Rayleigh fading will be almost entirely uncorrelated. That means it is relatively rare for both to experience a deep fade at the same time. The receiving system must have circuitry to determine which of the antennas has a stronger signal at any given time and to automatically combine the signals using some scheme that minimizes the probability of signal dropout. (One engineering text that has a fairly readable discussion of fading is *Cellular Radio Performance Engineering* by Asha Mehrotra; see the "References and Bibliography" section at the end of this chapter.)

One low-tech scheme is to use stereo headphones with each channel connected to a separate receiver and antenna. That method works better with linear modulation (AM, SSB, CW) than with FM because of the noise burst that occurs when the FM signal drops out.

Diversity antennas can also be used at a repeater site. The conditions are different because most repeater antennas are located in the clear with few local reflectors. The diversity antennas must be located much farther apart, typically on the order of 10 to 20 wavelengths, for the fading to be uncorrelated.

FADING AND DIGITAL SIGNALS

Digitally-modulated signals, such as those used in the cellular telephone industry, use several techniques to combat Rayleigh fading. One is *error-correcting coding*, which adds redundant bits to the transmitted signal in a special way such that the receiver can "fill in" missing bits to obtain error-free reception. That technique does not work if the signal drops out completely for longer than a few consecutive bits. The solution often employed is called *interleaving*. This takes data bits that represent points close together in time in the original voice signal and shuffles them into several different time slots for transmission. That way, a single brief dropout does not affect all the bits for that time period. Instead, the lost data are scattered over several different time periods. Since only a few bits are missing at any one point, the error-correcting decoder in the receiver has enough information to reconstruct the missing information.

As the signal gradually gets weaker, the error correction in a digital receiver produces nearly-perfect voice quality until the signal gets too weak for the decoder to handle. At that point reception stops abruptly and the call

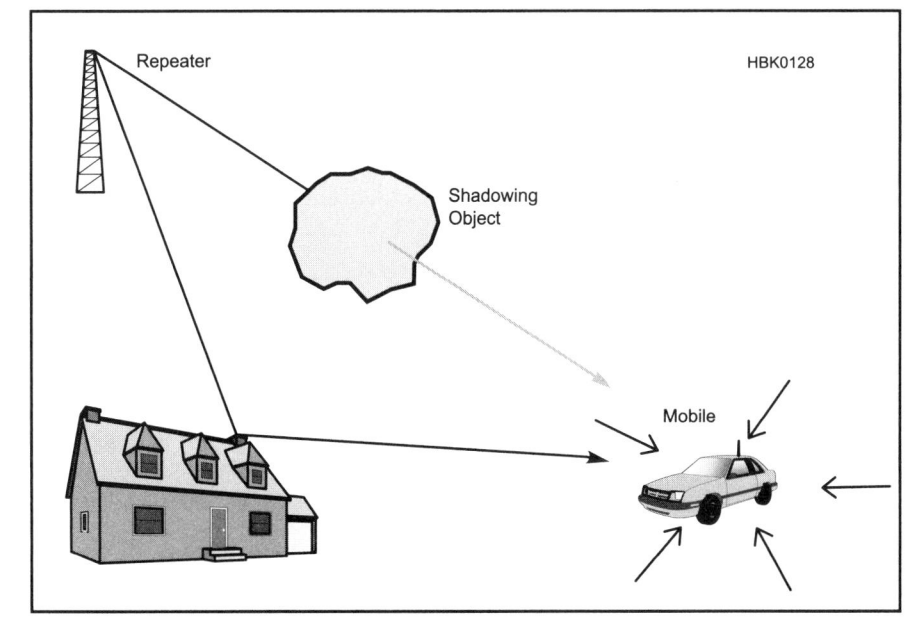

Figure 19.34 — When multipath propagation occurs, each main path is typically Rayleigh-faded by multiple reflectors close to the mobile station.

Propagation of Radio Signals   19.29

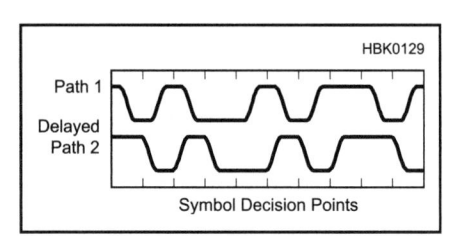

Figure 19.35 — Multipath propagation can cause inter-symbol interference (ISI). At the symbol decision points, where the receiver decoder samples the signal, the path 2 data is often opposing the data on path 1.

is dropped. With an analog signal, reception gets scratchier as the signal gets weaker; this gives advance warning before the signal drops out completely.

The main paths of a multipath-faded signal can differ in length by several miles. A 10 km (6 mile) difference in path length results in a difference in propagation delay of over 30 μs. While that is not noticeable on an FM voice signal, it can wreak havoc with digital signals by causing *intersymbol interference* (*ISI*). See **Figure 19.35**. If the delay difference is on the order of one symbol, the receiver sees adjacent symbols superimposed. In effect, the signal interferes with itself.

One solution is to use an *equalizer*. This is a special type of digital filter that filters the demodulated signal to remove the delay differences so that multiple paths become time-aligned. Since the path characteristics change as the mobile station moves around, a special *training sequence* is sent periodically so that the receiver can re-optimize the filter coefficients based on the known symbols in the training sequence.

ISI is an even bigger problem at HF than at VHF/UHF because the path lengths are much greater. It is not unusual to have path length differences up to 3000 km (1800 miles), which correspond to propagation delay differences of up to 10 ms. That is why digital modes on HF with symbol periods of less than about 10 to 20 ms (that is, with symbol rates greater than 50 to 100 baud) are not very practical without some method of equalization.

There is much more detailed information available about mobile radio propagation, but unfortunately most of it is written at an engineering level. For example, Keysight Technologies (**keysight.com**) offers fading simulator software that operates in conjunction with their N5182B MXG X-Series RF Vector Signal Generator.

For those who would like to explore the subject further, a *Mathcad* file with equations and explanatory text related to Rayleigh fading is available at **www.arrl.org/qst-in-depth**. Look in the 2006 section for Bloom0806.zip. The file was used to generate some of the graphics in this section. For those without access to *Mathcad*, a read-only PDF version of the file is available in the same directory.

19.6 Propagation for Space Communications

Communication of all sorts into space has become increasingly important. Amateurs confront extraterrestrial propagation when accessing satellite repeaters or using the moon as a reflector. (More information on these modes may be found in the **Space Communications** section with the downloadable supplemental content.) Special propagation problems arise from signals that travel from the Earth through the ionosphere (or a substantial portion of it) and back again. Tropospheric and ionospheric phenomena, so useful for terrestrial paths, are unwanted and serve only as a nuisance for space communication. A phenomenon known as *Faraday rotation* may change the polarization of radio waves traveling through the ionosphere, presenting special problems to receiving weak signals. Cosmic noise also becomes an important factor when antennas are intentionally pointed into space.

19.6.1 Faraday Rotation

Magnetic and electrical forces rotate the polarization of radio waves passing through the ionosphere. For example, signals that leave the Earth as horizontally polarized and return after a reflection from the moon may not arrive with the same polarization. Additional path loss can occur when polarization is shifted by 90°, resulting in fading of the received signal.

Faraday rotation is difficult to predict and its effects change over time and with operating frequency. At 144 MHz, the polarization of space waves may shift back into alignment with the antenna within a few minutes, so often just waiting can solve the Faraday problem. At 432 MHz, it may take half an hour or longer for the polarization to become realigned. Use of circular polarization completely eliminates this problem, but creates a new problem for EME paths. The sense of circularly polarized signals is reversed with reflection, so two complete antenna systems are normally required, one with left-hand polarization and one with right-hand polarization.

19.6.2 Scintillation

Extraterrestrial signals experience scintillation fading as they travel through the lower atmosphere, as described previously in the *Tropospheric Fading* section. However, they also experience scintillation fading as they traverse the ionosphere. The rule of thumb is that the ionosphere dominates below about 2 GHz and the atmosphere is usually more significant above 2 GHz. Scintillation in the ionosphere is more complex than in the troposphere because, unlike the troposphere, the ionosphere

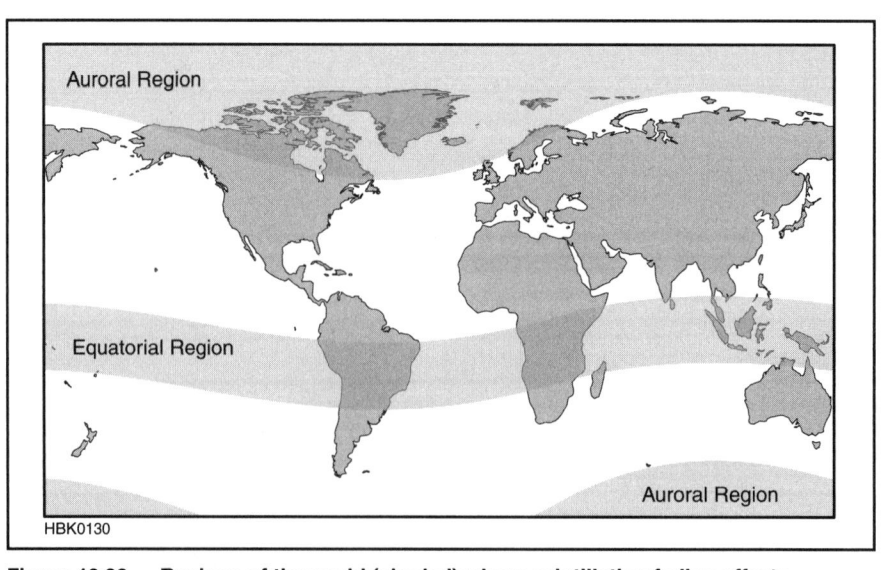

Figure 19.36 — Regions of the world (shaded) where scintillation fading effects can be especially severe.

is highly anisotropic and irregularities tend to be aligned with the Earth's magnetic field lines.

Ionospheric scintillation varies with geographical location, time of day, the 11-year sunspot cycle, and the presence of geomagnetic storms. **Figure 19.36** shows the worldwide areas where scintillation occurs. The most intense and frequent disturbances are located within about 20 degrees of the Earth's magnetic equator. Fading depth in this region can be as much as 20 to 30 dB. Scintillation fading also is common within about 30 degrees of the magnetic poles, although fade depths are generally no more than 10 dB or so. At mid latitudes ionospheric scintillation is rarely an issue. Longitude is important as well. In South America, Africa and India, the frequency of occurrence is significantly lower in the southern hemisphere winter (May-August) than during the summer, while the pattern is exactly opposite in the central Pacific.

In the polar regions disturbances occur at any time of day, but in the equatorial region they tend to start an hour or so after sunset and last a few hours, from perhaps 1900-2400 local time at the equinox. Fading events are sometimes intermittent, starting abruptly and ending abruptly some minutes later. The signal paths to slow-moving sources, such as the moon or geostationary satellites, tend to fade about once or twice a second. While not much work has been done on characterizing ionospheric scintillation fading on low Earth orbit (LEO) satellites, the fade rate should be more than an order of magnitude faster since the orbital period is typically on the order of 1.5 hours, much less than the Earth's 24-hour rotational period.

As might be expected, sunspots also are important. Ionospheric scintillation is much more severe and frequent near the peak of the 11-year solar cycle. Geomagnetic storms also have a major effect, principally in the polar regions.

19.6.3 Earth-Moon-Earth

Amateurs have used the moon as a reflector on the VHF and UHF bands since 1960. Maximum allowable power and large antennas, along with the best receivers, are normally required to overcome the extreme free-space and reflection losses involved in Earth-Moon-Earth (EME) paths. More modest stations make EME contacts by scheduling operating times when the moon is at perigee (on the horizon). The moon, which presents a target only one-half degree wide, reflects only 7% of the radio signals that reach it. Techniques have to be designed to cope with Faraday rotation, cosmic noise, Doppler shift (due to the moon's movements) and other difficulties. In spite of the problems involved, hundreds (and possibly thousands) of amateur stations have made contacts via the moon on all bands from 50 MHz to 10 GHz. The techniques of EME communication are discussed in the **Space Communications** section with the downloadable supplemental content.

19.6.4 Satellites

Accessing amateur satellites generally does not involve huge investments in antennas and equipment, yet station design does have to take into account special challenges of space propagation. Free-space loss is a primary consideration, but it is manageable when satellites are only a few hundred kilometers distant. Free-space path losses to satellites in high-Earth orbits are considerably greater, and appropriately larger antennas and higher powers are needed.

Satellite frequencies below 30 MHz can be troublesome. Ionospheric absorption and refraction may prevent signals from reaching space, especially to satellites at very low elevations. In addition, man-made and natural sources of noise are high. VHF and especially UHF are largely immune from these effects, but free-space path losses are greater. Problems related to polarization, including Faraday rotation, intentional or accidental satellite tumbling and the orientation of a satellite's antenna in relation to terrestrial antennas, are largely overcome by using circularly polarized antennas. More on using satellites can be found in the **Space Communications** section with the downloadable supplemental content.

19.7 Noise and Propagation

Noise simply consists of unwanted electromagnetic radiation that interferes with desired communications. In some instances, noise imposes the practical limit on the lowest usable frequencies. Noise may be classified by its sources: man-made, terrestrial (atmospheric) and cosmic. Interference from other transmitting stations on adjacent frequencies is not usually considered noise and may be controlled, to some degree anyway, by careful station design or by simply moving to a frequency further away from the interference. (Additional information on noise can be found in the **RF Techniques** and **Receiving** chapters.)

19.7.1 Man-Made Noise

Many unintentional radio emissions result from man-made sources. Broadband radio signals are produced whenever there is a spark, such as in contact switches, electric motors, gasoline engine spark plugs and faulty electrical connections. Household appliances, such as fluorescent lamps, microwave ovens, lamp dimmers and anything containing an electric motor may all produce undesirable broadband radio energy. Devices of all sorts, especially computers and anything controlled by microprocessors, television receivers and many other electronics also emit radio signals that may be perceived as noise well into the UHF range. In many cases, these sources are local and can be controlled with proper measures. See the **RF Interference** chapter.

High-voltage transmission lines and associated equipment, including transformers, switches and lightning arresters, can generate

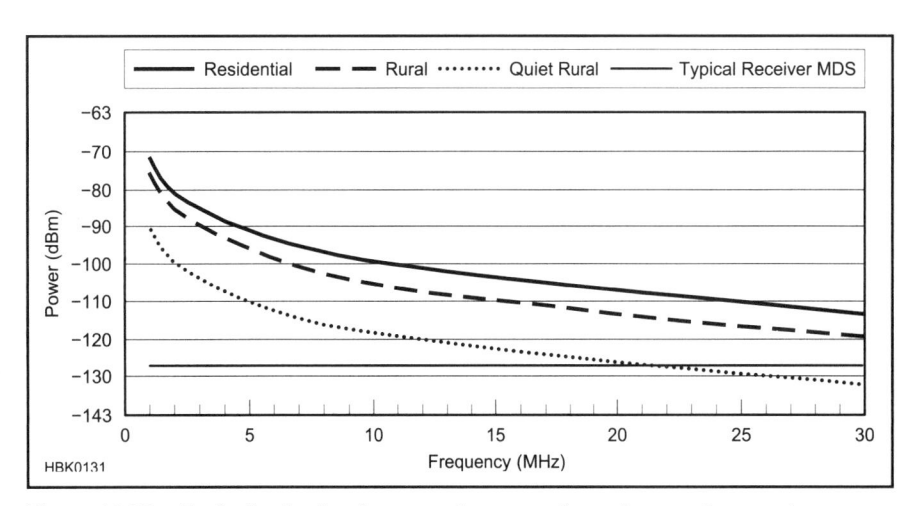

Figure 19.37 — Typical noise levels versus frequency for various environments. (This is man-made noise in a 500-Hz bandwidth, from Rec. ITU-R P.372.7, *Radio Noise*.)

high-level radio signals over a wide area, especially if they are corroded or improperly maintained. Transmission lines may act as efficient antennas at some frequencies, adding to the noise problem. Certain kinds of street lighting, neon signs and industrial equipment also contribute their share of noise.

Figure 19.37 shows typical noise levels versus frequency, in terms of power, for various noise environments. Note that man-made noise prevails below roughly 21 MHz for a Quiet Rural noise environment, and it, rather the sensitivity of your receiver (here depicted as the MDS — the minimum discernible signal), determines how weak a signal you can hear.

19.7.2 Lightning

Static is a common term given to the ear-splitting crashes of noise commonly heard on nearly all radio frequencies, although it is most severe on the lowest frequency bands. Atmospheric static is primarily caused by lightning and other natural electrical discharges. Static may result from close-by thunderstorms, but most static originates with tropical storms. Like any radio signals, lightning-produced static may be propagated over long distances by the ionosphere. Thus static is generally higher during the summer, when there are more nearby thunderstorms, and at night, when radio propagation generally improves. Static is often the limiting factor on 1.8 and 3.5 MHz, making winter a more favorable time for using these frequencies. (Note that the quiet "winter" months in the Southern Hemisphere are June through August.)

19.7.3 Precipitation Static and Corona Discharge

Precipitation static is an almost continuous hash-type noise that often accompanies various kinds of precipitation, including snowfall. Precipitation static is caused by rain drops, snowflakes or even wind-blown dust, transferring a small electrical charge on contact with an antenna. Electrical fields under thunderstorms are sufficient to place many objects such as trees, hair and antennas, into corona discharge. *Corona noise* may sound like a harsh crackling in the radio — building in intensity, abruptly ending, and then building again, in cycles of a few seconds to as long as a minute. A corona charge on an antenna may build to some critical level and then discharge in the atmosphere with an audible pop before recharging. Precipitation static and corona discharge can be a nuisance from LF to well into the VHF range.

19.7.4 Cosmic Sources

The Sun, distant stars, galaxies and other cosmic features all contribute radio noise well into the gigahertz range. These *cosmic sources* are perceived primarily as a more-or-less constant background noise at HF. In the VHF range and higher, specific sources of cosmic noise can be identified and may be a limiting factor in terrestrial and space communications. The Sun is by far the greatest source of radio noise, but its effects are largely absent at night. The center of our own galaxy is nearly as noisy as the Sun. Galactic noise is especially noticeable when high-gain VHF and UHF antennas, such as may be used for satellite or EME communications, are pointed toward the center of the Milky Way. Other star clusters and galaxies are also radio hot-spots in the sky. Finally, there is a much lower cosmic background noise that seems to cover the entire sky.

19.8 Propagation Below the AM Broadcast Band

Two bands in the LF/MF spectrum have been allocated for access by amateurs: 135.7-137.8 kHz and 472-479 kHz. It would be beneficial to review some fundamental issues with respect to propagation in these bands.

Three important parameters are involved in determining the likelihood of a signal getting from Point A to Point B. These parameters are refraction, absorption and polarization. Although propagation is certainly different on 160 meters and 6 meters, an electromagnetic wave on both of these bands follows the same laws of physics. Thus understanding how these three parameters change versus frequency will give us insight into propagation on our potentially new low frequency bands.

Figure 19.38 is a ray trace at night (0500 UTC) in mid January at moderate solar activity for frequencies from 10.65 MHz down to 150 kHz. All rays are launched at a low elevation angle of 5 degrees. (This figure was made using *Proplab Pro V3* — see the section MUF Prediction on the Home Computer for more details on this software package.)

The MUF is not high enough for 10.65 MHz under these conditions, and it goes through the ionosphere. But frequencies of 8.9 MHz and lower are successively refracted at lower heights, which results in shorter

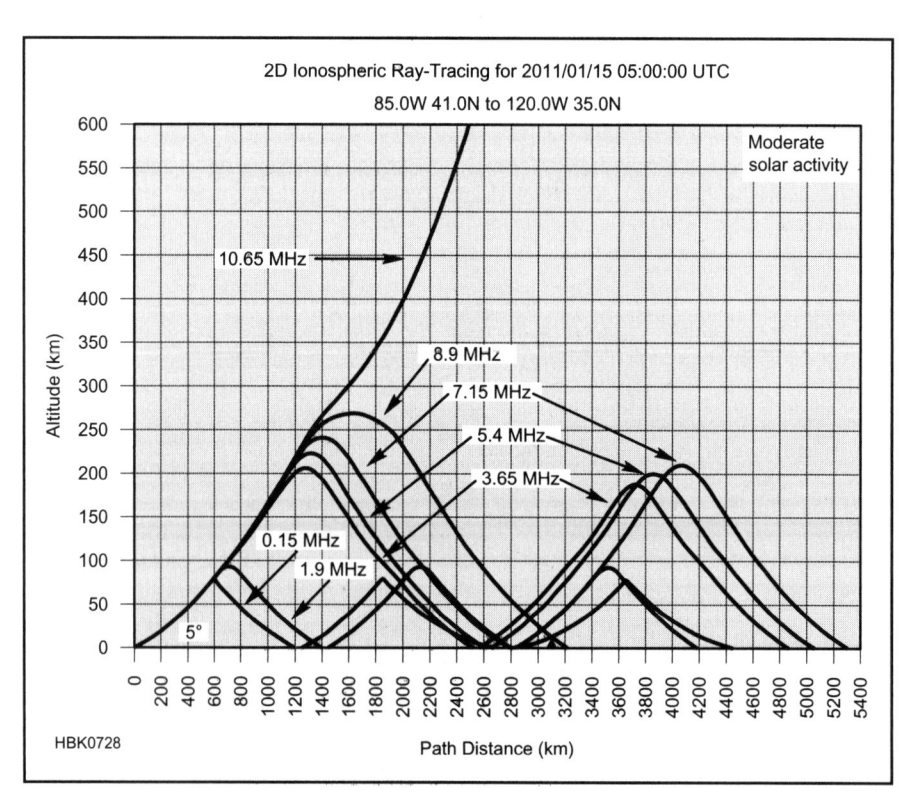

Figure 19.38 — Low frequency ray traces showing more bending as the frequency is lowered.

hops. So RF on 135.7-137.8 kHz and 472-479 kHz will take short hops.

Table 19.7 summarizes absorption (data from the ray trace) on 5.4 MHz, 3.65 MHz, 1.9 MHz and 150 kHz for a 1500 km hop under the same conditions as the ray traces in Figure 19.38. Note that as the frequency decreases from 5.4 MHz to 1.9 MHz, the loss due to ionospheric absorption increases as expected. But at 150 kHz the absorption is significantly reduced. This is due to the wave not getting very high into the ionosphere — in fact, the residual nighttime D region ionization is sufficient to refract this low frequency with minimal absorption. So RF on 135.7-137.8 kHz and 472-479 kHz will not suffer as much absorption as on 160 meters.

In theory, highly elliptical polarization will prevail for these low frequencies. It is likely that most antennas for these bands will be vertically polarized, which should be a good match to couple the most energy into the ordinary wave.

In summary, skywave propagation on 135.7-137.8 kHz and 472-479 kHz will be via short hops between the ionosphere and the D region, but with lower absorption than on 160 meters. Tempering this lower absorption are the lower antenna efficiencies and higher received noise levels. Thus these bands will be tough, but the Amateur Radio spirit will make the most of them.

This is a cursory look at propagation on our new bands. For a more detailed discussion, visit the December 2018 Monthly Feature at **k9la.us**.

Table 19.7
Absorption vs Frequency

Frequency (MHz)	Absorption per Hop (dB)
5.4	0.8
3.65	2.3
1.9	17.8
0.150	4.0

19.9 Glossary of Radio Propagation Terms

A index — An open-ended linear index that corresponds roughly to the cumulative **K index** values (it's the daily average of the eight K indices after converting the K indices to a linear scale). The A index commonly varies between 0 and 30 during quiet to active conditions, and up to 100 and higher during geomagnetic storms.

Absorption — The dissipation of the energy of a radio wave as it travels through a medium such as the ionosphere.

Antipode — Locations directly opposite each other on a globe.

Atmosphere — The mass of air surrounding the Earth. Radio signals travel through the atmosphere and different conditions in the atmosphere (in conjunction with the signal's frequency) affect how those signals travel or propagate.

Aurora — A disturbance of the atmosphere at high latitudes resulting from an interaction between electrically charged particles from the magnetosphere and the magnetic field of the Earth. *Auroral propagation* occurs when HF through UHF signals are reflected from the aurora to reach another station.

Auroral E — Sporadic E in the auroral zone.

Backscatter — Single-hop signals that have been scattered by the Earth or the ocean at some distant point back toward the transmitting station.

Beacon station — A station that transmits continuously, allowing other stations to assess propagation to and from the location of the beacon station.

Coronal hole — A region on the Sun where the magnetic field is open to the interplanetary magnetic field (IMF) and ionized particles can escape into the solar wind.

Critical angle — The largest angle at which a radio wave of a specified frequency can be returned to Earth by the ionosphere.

Critical frequency — The highest frequency that returns echoes from the E and F regions at vertical incidence.

D region — The lowest region of the ionosphere. The D region (or layer) contributes very little to short-wave radio propagation. It absorbs energy from radio waves as they pass through it. This absorption has a significant effect on signals below about 7.5 MHz during daylight.

Diffraction — Bending of waves by an edge or corner.

E region — The second lowest ionospheric region, the E region (or layer) has its highest electron density during the day and falls to a much lower electron density during the night. The E region can refract radio waves enough to return them to Earth.

Earth-Moon-Earth (EME) or *Moonbounce* — A method of communicating with other stations by reflecting radio signals off the Moon's surface.

Electromagnetic wave — A wave of energy composed of an electric and magnetic field.

Equinoxes — One of two points in the orbit of the Earth around the Sun at which the Earth crosses a horizontal plane extending through the equator of the Sun. The vernal equinox marks the beginning of spring and the autumnal equinox marks the beginning of autumn.

Faraday rotation — A rotation of the polarization of radio waves when the waves travel through an ionized medium that is immersed in a magnetic field (for example, the Earth's ionosphere).

F region — A combination of the two highest ionospheric regions (or layers), the F_1 and F_2 regions. The F region refracts radio waves and returns them to Earth. Its height varies greatly depending on the time of day, season of the year and amount of sunspot activity.

Field-aligned irregularities (FAI) — A propagation mechanism observed at 50 and 144 MHz that occurs when irregularities in the distribution of free electrons in the ionosphere are aligned parallel to the Earth's magnetic field.

Free-space attenuation — The dissipation of the energy of a radio wave that results from the spherical spreading of radio energy from its source.

Gray-line — A special form of **long-path** propagation that takes into account the unusual ionospheric configuration along the twilight region between night and day.

Ground-wave propagation — The method by which radio waves travel along the Earth's surface.

High frequency (HF) — The term used for the frequency range between 3 MHz and 30 MHz. The amateur HF bands are where you are most likely to make long-distance (worldwide) contacts.

Ionosphere — A region of electrically charged (ionized) gases high in the atmosphere. The ionosphere bends radio waves as they travel through it, returning them to Earth. Also see **sky-wave propagation**.

K index — A geomagnetic-field measurement that is updated every three hours at various observatories around the world. Changes in the K index can be used to indicate HF propagation conditions. Rising values generally indicate disturbed conditions while falling values indicate improving conditions.

Line-of-sight propagation — The term used to describe VHF and UHF propagation in a straight line directly from one station to another.

Long-path propagation — Propagation between two points on the Earth's surface that follows a path along the great circle between them, but in a direction opposite from the shortest distance between them.

Lowest usable frequency (LUF) — The frequency below the **maximum usable frequency** (MUF) at which ionospheric absorption and noise at the receiving location make the received signal-to-noise ratio too low to be usable.

M-factor — The ratio between the **maximum usable frequency** (MUF) and the critical frequency.

Maximum usable frequency (MUF) — The highest-frequency radio signal that will reach a particular destination using **sky-wave propagation**, or *skip*. The MUF may vary for radio signals sent to different destinations.

Meteor-scatter communication — A method of radio communication that uses the ionized trail of a meteor that burned up in the Earth's atmosphere to reflect, refract, or scatter radio signals back to Earth.

Microwave — Radio waves or signals with frequencies greater than 1000 MHz (1 GHz). This is not a strict definition, just a conventional way of referring to those frequencies.

Moonbounce — A common name for EME communication in which signals are bounced off the Moon before being received.

Multihop propagation — Long-distance radio propagation using several skips or hops between the Earth and the ionosphere.

Multipath — A fading effect caused by the transmitted signal traveling to the receiving station over more than one path.

Near Vertical Incidence Skywave (NVIS) propagation — A propagation mechanism that allows stations located within the **skip zone,** but too far apart for ground wave propagation, to maintain communications by going to a lower frequency.

Path loss — The total signal loss between transmitting and receiving stations relative to the total radiated signal energy.

Pedersen ray — A high-angle radio wave that penetrates deeper into the F region of the ionosphere, so the wave is bent less than a lower-angle wave, and thus for some distance parallels the Earth's surface in the F region, returning to Earth at a distance farther than normally expected for single-hop propagation.

Polarization — The orientation of the electrical-field of a radio wave. An antenna that is parallel to the surface of the Earth, such as a dipole, produces horizontally polarized waves. One that is perpendicular to the Earth's surface, such as a quarter-wave vertical, produces vertically polarized waves. An antenna that has both horizontal and vertical polarization is said to be circularly polarized.

Propagation — The process by which radio waves travel.

Radio frequency (RF) signals — RF signals are generally considered to be any electrical signals with a frequency higher than 20,000 Hz, up to 300 GHz.

Radio horizon — The position at which a direct wave radiated from an antenna becomes tangent to the surface of the Earth. Note that as the wave continues past the horizon, the wave gets higher and higher above the surface.

Radiation inversion — A weather condition that affects propagation at VHF and above. Radiation inversions form only over land after sunset as a result of progressive cooling of the air near the Earth's surface.

Rain scatter — A special case of tropospheric scatter practical in the 3.3 to 24 GHz range that is caused by scatter from raindrops.

Reflection — Signals that travel by **line-of-sight propagation** are reflected by large objects like buildings.

Refraction — Bending waves by changing the velocity of propagation. Radio waves refract as they travel through the ionosphere. If the radio waves refract enough they will return to Earth. This is the basis for long-distance communication on the HF bands.

Scattering — Radio wave propagation by means of multiple reflections in the layers of the atmosphere or from an obstruction. Scatter propagation also occurs in the ionosphere when there is not enough ionization for refraction or reflection, but enough to send weak electromagnetic waves off into varied directions.

Scintillation fading — Fading that occurs when a signal arrives at the receiver by two or more different paths simultaneously, causing addition or partial cancellation depending on the relative phases and amplitudes of the paths.

Selective fading — A variation of radio-wave intensity that changes over small frequency changes. It may be caused by changes in the medium through which the wave is traveling or changes in transmission path, among other things.

Short path — The shorter of the two great circle paths between two stations.

Skip — Propagation by means of ionospheric refraction. Traversing the distance to the ionosphere and back to the ground is called a *hop*.

Skip zone — A ring-shaped area of poor radio communication, too distant for ground waves and too close for sky waves.

Sky-wave propagation — The method by which radio waves travel through the ionosphere and back to Earth. Sometimes called *skip*, sky-wave propagation has a far greater range than **line-of-sight** and **ground-wave propagation**.

Solar cycle — The approximate 11-year period of variation in solar activity.

Solar flare — An eruption on the surface of the Sun that launches a wide spectrum of electromagnetic energy into space, disrupting communications on Earth. A large flare can also release relativistic protons that cause additional absorption in the polar cap.

Solar wind — Electrically charged particles emitted by the Sun and traveling through space. Variations in the solar wind may have a sudden impact on radio communications when they arrive at the atmosphere of the Earth.

Sporadic E — A form of enhanced radio-wave propagation that occurs when radio signals are reflected from small, thin and dense ionization patches in the E region of the ionosphere. Sporadic E is observed on the 15, 10, 6 and 2 meter bands, and occasionally on the 1.25 meter band.

Sunspot cycle — The number of **sunspots** increases and decreases in a somewhat predictable cycle that lasts about 11 years.

Sunspots — Dark spots on the surface of the Sun. When there are few sunspots, long-distance radio propagation is poor on the higher-frequency bands. When there are many sunspots, long-distance HF propagation improves.

Temperature inversion — A condition in the atmosphere in which a region of cool air is trapped beneath warmer air.

Transequatorial propagation — A form of F layer ionospheric propagation, in which signals of higher frequency than the expected MUF are propagated across the Earth's magnetic equator.

Troposphere — The region in Earth's atmosphere just above the Earth's surface and below the ionosphere.

Tropospheric bending — When radio waves are bent in the troposphere, they return to Earth farther away than the visible horizon.

Tropospheric ducting — A type of VHF propagation that can occur when warm air overruns cold air (a temperature inversion).
Tropospheric scatter — A method of radio communication at VHF and above that takes advantage of scattering in the **troposphere** to allow contacts beyond the radio horizon out to a working distance of 100 to 500 km (60 to 310 miles), depending on frequency.
Ultra high frequency (UHF) — The term used for the frequency range between 300 MHz and 3000 MHz (3 GHz). Technician licensees have full privileges on all Amateur UHF bands.
Very high frequency (VHF) — The term used for the frequency range between 30 MHz and 300 MHz. Technician licensees have full privileges on all Amateur VHF bands.
Visible horizon — The most distant point one can see by line of sight.
WWV/WWVH — Radio stations run by the US NIST (National Institute of Standards and Technology) to provide accurate time and frequencies.

19.10 References and Bibliography

A. Barter, G8ATD, ed., *International Microwave Handbook*, 2nd edition (Potters Bar: RSGB, 2008). Includes a chapter on microwave propagation.

A. Barter, G8ATD, ed., *VHF/UHF Handbook*, 2nd edition (Potters Bar: RSGB, 2008). Includes a chapter on VHF/UHF propagation.

B. R. Bean and E. J. Dutton, *Radio Meteorology* (New York: Dover, 1968).

K. Davies, *Ionospheric Radio* (London: Peter Peregrinus, 1989). Excellent though highly technical text on propagation.

R. D. Hunsucker, J.K. Hargreaves, *The High Latitude Ionosphere and Its Effect on Radio Propagation* (Cambridge University Press, 2003). Highly technical, but with an excellent chapter on fundamental physics of the ionosphere.

G. Jacobs, T. Cohen, R. Rose, *The New Shortwave Propagation Handbook*, CQ Communications, Inc. (Hicksville, NY: CQ Communications, 1995).

T. Kamp, DF5JL, "60-m-Band: Chancen für NVIS," *CQ DL*, Feb 2017, p. 48-50.

C. Luetzelschwab, K9LA, **k9la.us**. Many articles about the ionosphere and propagation as they relate to 160 meters, HF, VHF, contesting and more.

L. F. McNamara, *Radio Amateur's Guide to the Ionosphere* (Malabar, Florida: Krieger Publishing Company, 1994). Excellent, quite-readable text on HF propagation.

A. Mehrotra, *Cellular Radio Performance Engineering* (Artech House, 1994). See Chapter 4 "Propagation" and the introduction to Chapter 3 "Cellular Environment." Diversity reception techniques are covered in Chapter 8.

D. Straw, N6BV, "What's the Deal About 'NVIS'?," *QST*, Dec 2005.

J. A. White, VA7JW, and K. Tapping, "The Penticton Solar Flux receiver," *QST*, Feb 2013, pp 39-45.

Contents

20.1 Transmission Line Basics
    20.1.1 Fundamentals
    20.1.2 Matched and Mismatched Lines
    20.1.3 Reflection Coefficient and SWR
    20.1.4 Losses in Transmission Lines
20.2 Choosing a Transmission Line
    20.2.1 Effect of Loss
    20.2.2 Practical Considerations
20.3 The Transmission Line as Impedance Transformer
    20.3.1 Transmission Line Stubs
    20.3.2 Transmission Line Stubs as Filters
    20.3.3 Project: A Field Day Stub Assembly
20.4 Matching Impedances in the Antenna System
    20.4.1 Conjugate Matching
    20.4.2 Impedance Matching Networks
    20.4.3 Matching Antenna Impedance at the Antenna
    20.4.4 Matching the Line to the Transmitter
    20.4.5 Adjusting Antenna Tuners
    20.4.6 Myths About SWR

20.5 Baluns and Transmission Line Transformers
    20.5.1 Quarter-Wave Baluns
    20.5.2 Transmission Line Transformers
    20.5.3 Coiled-Coax Choke Baluns
    20.5.4 Transmitting Ferrite Choke Baluns
20.6 PC Transmission Lines
20.7 Waveguides
    20.7.1 Evolution of a Waveguide
    20.7.2 Waveguide Operation
    20.7.3 Waveguide Dimensions
    20.7.4 Waveguide Modes
    20.7.5 Waveguide Termination
    20.7.6 Practical Waveguides
20.8 Glossary of Transmission Line Terms
20.9 References and Bibliography

Chapter 20 — Downloadable Supplemental Content

Supplemental Articles
- "Multiband Operation with Open-wire Line" by George Cutsogeorge, W2VJN
- Smith Chart Supplement
- "Measuring Receiver Isolation" by George Cutsogeorge, W2VJN
- "A Commercial Triplexer Design" by George Cutsogeorge, W2VJN
- "HF Yagi Triplexer Especially for ARRL Field Day" by Gary Gordon, K6KV
- "Using *TLW* to Design Impedance Matching Networks" by George Cutsogeorge, W2VJN
- "Measuring Ferrite Chokes" by Jim Brown, K9YC
- "Microwave Plumbing" by Paul Wade, W1GHZ
- Transmission Lines in Digital Circuits
- Matching Network Material and *MATCH.EXE* by Bill Sabin, WØIYH
- "Optimizing the Placement of Stubs for Harmonic Suppression" by Jim Brown, K9YC
- "Optimizing the Performance of Harmonic Attenuation Stubs" by George Cutsogeorge, W2VJN
- "Simple Splice for ⅞" Heliax" by Ott Fiebel, W4WSR
- "Splicing Window Line" by Joel Hallas, W1ZR
- "Don't Blow Up Your Balun," by Dean Straw N6BV

Chapter 20 Software
The following software is available with the downloadable supplemental content.
- *jjSmith* from Tonne Software

Chapter 20

Transmission Lines

RF power is rarely generated right where it will be used. A transmitter and the antenna it feeds are a good example. The most effective antenna installation is outdoors and clear of ground and energy-absorbing structures. The transmitter, however, is most conveniently installed indoors, where it is out of the weather and is readily accessible. A *transmission line* is used to convey RF energy from the transmitter to the antenna. A transmission line should transport the RF from the source to its destination with as little loss as possible. Additional material on the topics covered in this chapter is available in the *ARRL Antenna Book*.

20.1 Transmission Line Basics

There are three main types of transmission lines used by radio amateurs: coaxial, open-wire and waveguide. The most common type is the *coaxial* line, usually called *coax*, shown in various forms in **Figure 20.1**. Coax is made up of a center conductor, which may be either stranded or solid wire, surrounded by a concentric outer conductor with a *dielectric* center insulator between the conductors. The outer conductor may be braided shield wire or a metallic sheath. A flexible aluminum foil or a second braided shield is employed in some coax to improve shielding over that obtainable from a standard woven shield braid. If the outer conductor is made of solid aluminum or copper, the coax is referred to as *hardline*.

The second type of transmission line uses parallel conductors, side by side, rather than the concentric ones used in coax. Typical examples of such *open-wire* lines are 300 Ω TV ribbon line or *twin-lead* and 450 Ω ladder line (sometimes called *window line*), also shown in Figure 20.1. Although open-wire lines are enjoying a sort of renaissance in recent years because of their inherently lower losses in simple multiband antenna systems, coaxial cables are far more prevalent because they are much more convenient to use.

The third major type of transmission line is the *waveguide*. While open-wire and coaxial lines are used from power-line frequencies to well into the microwave region, waveguides are used at microwave frequencies only. Waveguides will be covered at the end of this chapter.

20.1.1 Fundamentals

In either coaxial or open-wire line, currents flowing in the two conductors travel in opposite directions as shown in Figs 20.1E and 20.1I. If the physical spacing between the two parallel conductors in an open-wire line, S, is small in terms of wavelength, the phase difference between the currents will be very close to 180°. If the two currents also have equal amplitudes, the field generated by each conductor will cancel that generated by the other, and the line will not radiate energy, even if it is many wavelengths long.

The equality of amplitude and 180° phase difference of the currents in each conductor in an open-wire line determine the degree of radiation cancellation. If the currents are for some reason unequal, or if the phase difference is not 180°, the line will radiate energy. How such imbalances occur and to what degree they can cause problems will be covered in more detail later.

In contrast to an open-wire line, the outer conductor in a coaxial line acts as a shield, confining RF energy within the line as shown in Figure 20.1E. Because of *skin effect* (see the **RF Techniques** chapter), current flowing in the outer conductor of a coax does so on the inner surface of the outer conductor. The fields generated by the currents flowing on the outer surface of the inner conductor and on the inner surface of the outer conductor cancel each other out, just as they do in open-wire line.

VELOCITY FACTOR

In free space, electrical waves travel at the speed of light, or 299,792,458 meters per second. Converting to feet per second yields 983,569,082. The length of a wave in space may be related to frequency as wavelength = λ = velocity/frequency. Thus, the wavelength of a

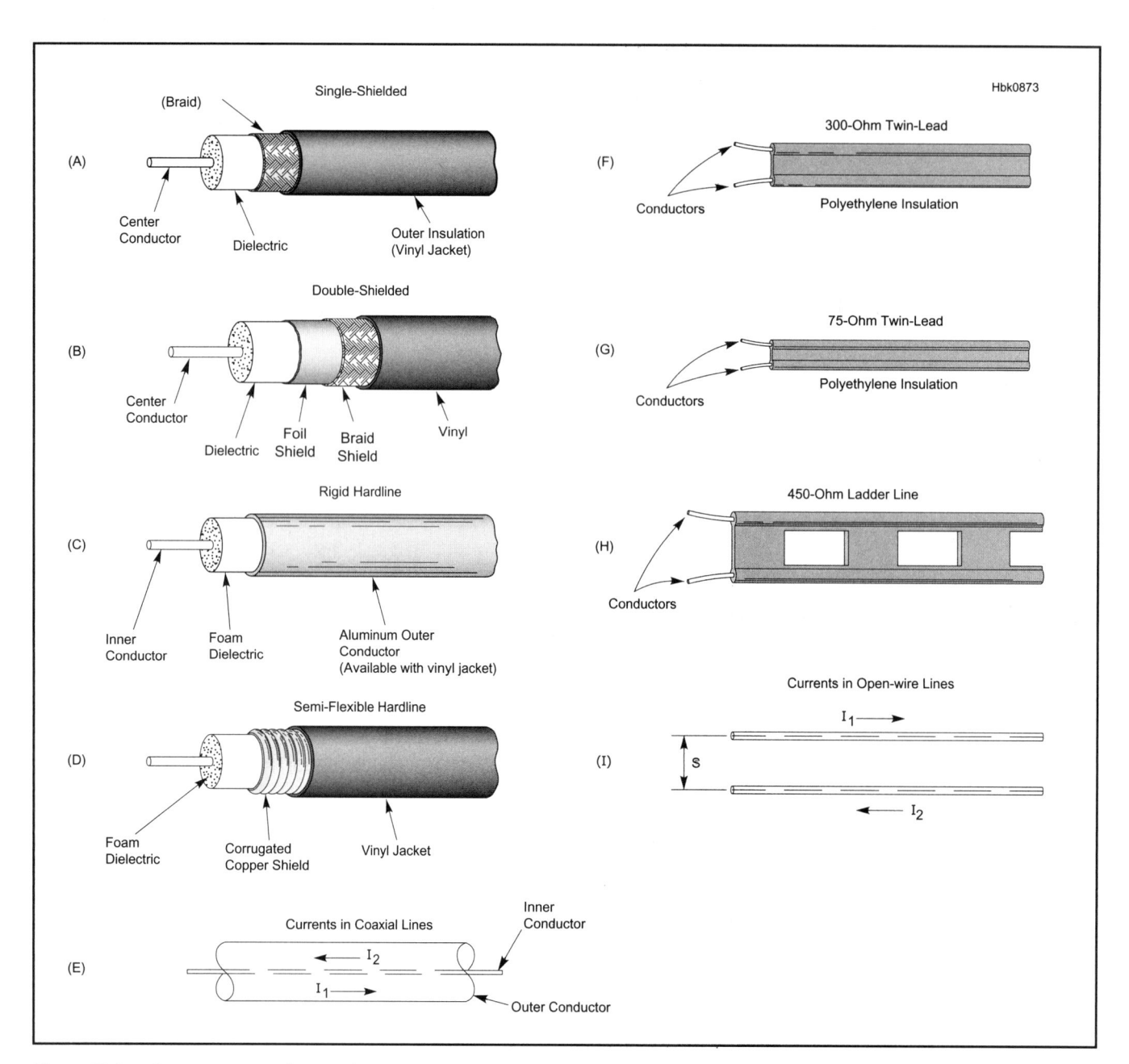

Figure 20.1 — Common types of transmission lines used by amateurs. Coaxial cable, or "coax," has a center conductor surrounded by insulation. The second conductor, called the shield, cover the insulation and is, in turn, covered by the plastic outer jacket. Various types are shown at A, B, C and D. The currents in coaxial cable flow on the outside of the center conductor and the inside of the outer shield (E). Open-wire line (F, G and H) has two parallel conductors separated by insulation. In open-wire line, the current flows in opposite directions on each wire (I). Articles on splicing hard line and window line are included in the supplmental information available online.

1 Hz signal is 983,569,082 ft. Changing to a more useful expression gives:

$$\lambda = \frac{983.6}{f} \quad (1)$$

where
λ = wavelength, in feet
f = frequency in MHz.

Thus, at 14 MHz the wavelength is 70.25 ft.

Wavelength (λ) may also be expressed in electrical degrees. A full wavelength is 360°, ½ λ is 180°, ¼ λ is 90°, and so forth.

Waves travel slower than the speed of light in any medium denser than a vacuum or free space. A transmission line may have an insulator which slows the wave travel down. The actual velocity of the wave is a function of the dielectric characteristic of that insulator. We can express the variation of velocity as the *velocity factor* for that particular type of dielectric — the fraction of the wave's velocity of propagation in the transmission line compared to that in free space. The velocity factor is related to the dielectric constant of the material in use.

$$VF = \frac{1}{\sqrt{\varepsilon}} \quad (2)$$

where
VF = velocity factor
ε = dielectric constant.

So the wavelength in a real transmission line becomes:

$$\lambda = \frac{983.6}{f} VF \quad (3)$$

As an example, many coax cables use poly-

20.2 Chapter 20

ethylene dielectric over the center conductor as the insulation. The dielectric constant for polyethylene is 2.3, so the VF is 0.66. Thus, wavelength in the cable is about two-thirds as long as a free-space wavelength.

The VF and other characteristics of many types of lines, both coax and twin lead, are shown in the table "Nominal Characteristics of Commonly used Transmission Lines" in the **Component Data and References** chapter.

There are differences in VF from batch to batch of transmission line because there are some variations in dielectric constant during the manufacturing processes. When high accuracy is required, it is best to actually measure VF by using an antenna analyzer to measure the resonant frequency of a length of cable. (The antenna analyzer's user manual will describe the procedure.)

CHARACTERISTIC IMPEDANCE

A perfectly lossless transmission line may be represented by a whole series of small inductors and capacitors connected in an infinitely long line, as shown in **Figure 20.2A**. (We first consider this special case because we need not consider how the line is terminated at its end, since there is no end.)

Each inductor in Figure 20.2A represents the inductance of a very short section of one wire and each capacitor represents the capacitance between two such short sections. The inductance and capacitance values per unit of line depend on the size of the conductors and the spacing between them. Each series inductor acts to limit the rate at which current can charge the following shunt capacitor, and in so doing establishes a very important property of a transmission line: its *surge impedance*, more commonly known as its *characteristic impedance*. This is usually abbreviated as Z_0,

$$Z_0 \approx \sqrt{\frac{L}{C}}$$

where L and C are the inductance and capacitance per unit length of line.

The characteristic impedance of an air-insulated parallel-conductor line, neglecting the effect of the insulating spacers, is given by

$$Z_0 = \frac{120}{\sqrt{\varepsilon}} \cosh^{-1} \frac{S}{d} \quad (4)$$

where
 Z_0 = characteristic impedance
 S = center to center distance between the conductors
 d = diameter of conductors in the same units as S

When S >> d, the approximation $Z_0 = 276 \log_{10}(2S/d)$ may be used but for S < 2d gives values that are significantly higher than the correct value, such as is often the case when wires are twisted together to form a transmission line for impedance transformers.

The characteristic impedance of an air-insulated coaxial line is given by

$$Z_0 = 138 \log_{10}\left(\frac{b}{a}\right) \quad (5)$$

where
 Z_0 = characteristic impedance
 b = inside diameter of outer conductors
 a = outside diameter of inner conductor (in same units as b).

It does not matter what units are used for S, d, a or b, as long as they are the *same* units. A line with closely spaced, large conductors will have a low characteristic impedance, while one with widely spaced, small conductors will have a relatively high characteristic impedance. Practical open-wire lines exhibit characteristic impedances ranging from about 200 to 800 Ω, while coax cables have Z_0 values between 25 to 100 Ω. Except in special instances, coax used in Amateur Radio has an impedance of 50 or 75 Ω.

All practical transmission lines exhibit some power loss. These losses occur in the resistance that is inherent in the conductors that make up the line, and from leakage currents flowing in the dielectric material between the conductors. We'll next consider what happens when a real transmission line, which is not infinitely long, is terminated in an actual load impedance, such as an antenna.

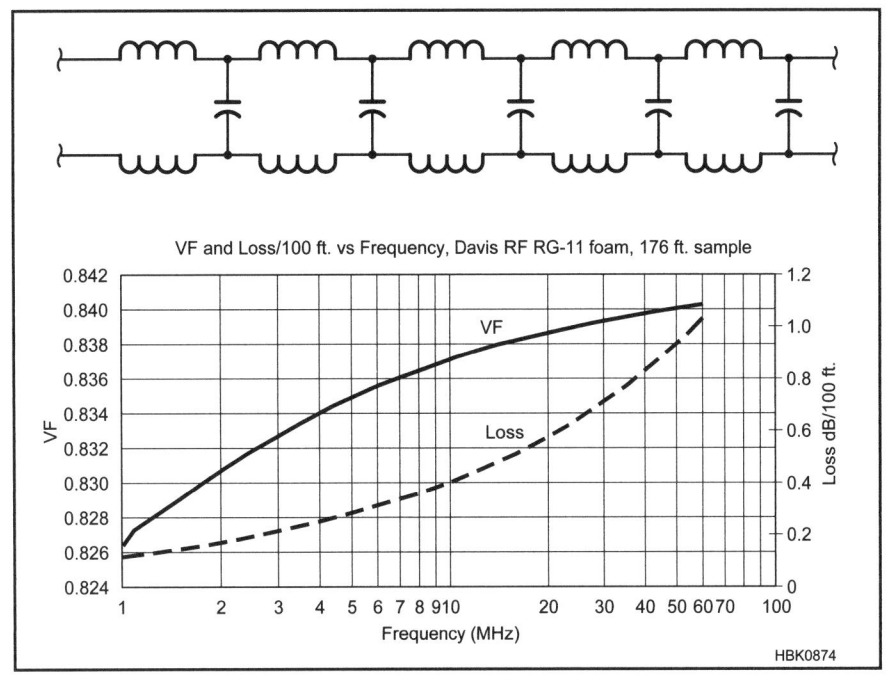

Figure 20.2 — Equivalent circuit (A) of an infinitely long lossless transmission line using lumped circuit constants. The actual performance of transmission line varies with frequency as shown in (B). For precision uses, the exact value for Z_0, VF, and loss should be determined by measuring the cable.

Practical lines also exhibit a fair amount of variation in characteristic impedance, VF, and line loss over wide frequency ranges. The simplified calculations given in this section make simplifying assumptions about conductor and insulation characteristics that give useful values at MF through low VHF. At lower and higher frequencies the actual values become significantly different. Figure 20.2B shows VF and line loss from 1-60 MHz for a RG11-type cable measured by Jim Brown, K9YC.

20.1.2 Matched and Mismatched Lines

Real transmission lines have a definite length and are connected to, or *terminate* in, a load (such as an antenna), as illustrated in **Figure 20.3A**. If the load is a pure resistance whose value equals the characteristic impedance of the line, the line is said to be *matched*. To current traveling along the line, such a load at the end of the line appears as though it were still more transmission line of the same characteristic impedance. In a matched transmission line, energy travels along the line from the source until it reaches the load, where it is completely absorbed (or radiated if the load is an antenna).

MISMATCHED LINES

Assume now that the line in Figure 20.3B is terminated in an impedance Z_a which is not equal to Z_0 of the transmission line. The line is now a *mismatched* line. Energy reaching the end of a mismatched line will not be fully

Transmission Lines 20.3

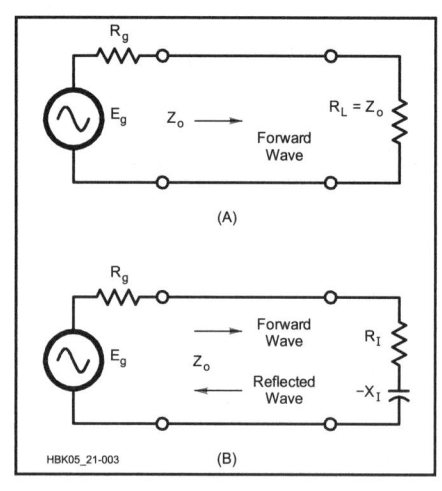

Figure 20.3 — At A the coaxial transmission line is terminated with resistance equal to its Z_0. All power is absorbed in the load. At B, coaxial line is shown terminated in an impedance consisting of a resistance and a capacitive reactance. This is a mismatched line, and a reflected wave will be returned back down the line toward the generator. The reflected wave adds to the forward wave, producing a standing wave on the line. The amount of reflection depends on the difference between the load impedance and the characteristic impedance of the transmission line.

absorbed by the load impedance. Instead, part of the energy will be reflected back toward the source. The amount of reflected versus absorbed energy depends on the degree of mismatch between the characteristic impedance of the line and the load impedance connected to its end.

The reason why energy is reflected at a discontinuity of impedance on a transmission line can best be understood by examining some limiting cases. First, consider the rather extreme case where the line is shorted at its end. Energy flowing to the load will encounter the short at the end, and the voltage at that point will go to zero, while the current will rise to a maximum. Since the short circuit does not dissipate any power, the energy will all be *reflected* back toward the source generator.

If the short at the end of the line is replaced with an open circuit, the opposite will happen. Here the voltage will rise to maximum, and the current will by definition go to zero. The phase will reverse, and again all energy will be reflected back towards the source. By the way, if this sounds to you like what happens at the end of a half-wavelength dipole antenna, you are quite correct. However, in the case of an antenna, energy traveling along the antenna is lost by radiation on purpose, whereas a good transmission line will lose little energy to radiation because the fields from the conductors cancel outside the line.

For load impedances falling between the extremes of short and open circuit, the phase and amplitude of the reflected wave will vary. The amount of energy reflected and the amount of energy absorbed in the load will depend on the difference between the characteristic impedance of the line and the impedance of the load at its end.

What actually happens to the energy reflected back down the line? This energy will encounter another impedance discontinuity, this time at the source. Reflected energy flows back and forth between the mismatches at the source and load. After a few such journeys, the reflected wave diminishes to nothing, partly as a result of finite losses in the line, but mainly because of partial absorption at the load each time it reaches the load. In fact, if the load is an antenna, such absorption at the load is desirable, since the energy is actually radiated by the antenna.

If a continuous RF voltage is applied to the terminals of a transmission line, the voltage at any point along the line will consist of a vector sum of voltages, the composite of waves traveling toward the load and waves traveling back toward the source generator. The sum of the waves traveling toward the load is called the *forward* or *incident* wave, while the sum of the waves traveling toward the generator is called the *reflected wave*.

20.1.3 Reflection Coefficient and SWR

In a mismatched transmission line, the ratio of the voltage in the reflected wave at any one point on the line to the voltage in the forward wave at that same point is defined as the *voltage reflection coefficient*. This has the same value as the current reflection coefficient. The reflection coefficient is a complex quantity (that is, having both amplitude and phase) and is generally designated by the Greek letter ρ (rho), or sometimes in the professional literature as Γ (Gamma). The relationship between R_l (the load resistance), X_l (the load reactance), Z_0 (the line characteristic impedance, whose real part is R_0 and whose reactive part is X_0) and the complex reflection coefficient ρ is

$$\rho = \frac{Z_1 - Z_0}{Z_1 + Z_0} = \frac{(R_1 \pm jX_1) - (R_0 \pm jX_0)}{(R_1 \pm jX_1) + (R_0 \pm jX_0)} \quad (6)$$

For most transmission lines the characteristic impedance Z_0 is almost completely resistive, meaning that $Z_0 = R_0$ and $X_0 \cong 0$. The magnitude of the complex reflection coefficient in equation 6 then simplifies to:

$$|\rho| = \sqrt{\frac{(R_1 - R_0)^2 + X_1^2}{(R_1 + R_0)^2 + X_1^2}} \quad (7)$$

For example, if the characteristic impedance of a coaxial line is 50 Ω and the load impedance is 120 Ω in series with a capacitive reactance of –90 Ω, the magnitude of the reflection coefficient is

$$|\rho| = \sqrt{\frac{(120-50)^2 + (-90)^2}{(120+50)^2 + (-90)^2}} = 0.593$$

Note that if R_l in equation 6 is equal to R_0 and X_l is 0, the reflection coefficient, ρ, is 0. This represents a matched condition, where all the energy in the incident wave is transferred to the load. On the other hand, if R_l is 0, meaning that the load is a short circuit and has no real resistive part, the reflection coefficient is 1.0, regardless of the value of R_0. This means that all the forward power is reflected since the load is completely reactive.

The concept of reflection is often shown in terms of the *return loss* (RL), which is given in dB and is equal to 20 times the log of the reciprocal of the reflection coefficient.

$$\text{RL(dB)} = -10\log\left(\frac{P_r}{P_f}\right) = -20\log(\rho) \quad (8)$$

In the example above, the return loss is 20 log (1/0.593) = 4.5 dB. (See Table 22.65 in the **Component Data and References** chapter.)

If there are no reflections from the load, the voltage distribution along the line is constant or *flat*. A line operating under these conditions is called either a *matched* or a *flat* line. If reflections do exist, a voltage *standing-wave* pattern will result from the interaction of the forward and reflected waves along the line. For a lossless transmission line at least ¼ λ long, the ratio of the maximum peak voltage anywhere on the line to the minimum value anywhere along the line is defined as the *voltage standing-wave ratio*, or VSWR. (The line must be ¼ λ or longer for the true maximum and minimum to be created.) Reflections from the load also produce a standing-wave pattern of currents flowing in the line. The ratio of maximum to minimum current, or ISWR, is identical to the VSWR in a given line.

In amateur literature, the abbreviation SWR is commonly used for standing-wave ratio, as the results are identical when taken from proper measurements of either current or voltage. Since SWR is a ratio of maximum to minimum, it can never be less than one-to-one. In other words, a perfectly flat line has an SWR of 1:1. The SWR is related to the magnitude of the complex reflection coefficient and vice versa by

$$\text{SWR} = \frac{1+|\rho|}{1-|\rho|} \quad (9A)$$

and

$$|\rho| = \frac{\text{SWR}-1}{\text{SWR}+1} \quad (9B)$$

The definitions in equations 8 and 9 are valid for any line length and for lines that are lossy, not just lossless lines longer than ¼ λ at the frequency in use. Very often the load impedance is not exactly known, since an antenna usually terminates a transmission line. The antenna impedance may be influenced by a host of factors, including its height above ground, end effects from insulators, and the effects of nearby conductors. We may also express the reflection coefficient in terms of forward and reflected power, quantities that can be easily measured using a directional RF wattmeter. The reflection coefficient and SWR may be computed as

$$|\rho| = \sqrt{\frac{P_r}{P_f}} \quad (10A)$$

and

$$SWR = \frac{1 + \sqrt{\frac{P_r}{P_f}}}{1 - \sqrt{\frac{P_r}{P_f}}} \quad (10B)$$

where
P_r = power in the reflected wave
P_f = power in the forward wave.

If a line is not matched (SWR > 1:1) the difference between the forward and reflected powers measured at any point on the line is the net power going toward the load from that point. The forward power measured with a directional wattmeter (often referred to as a reflected power meter or reflectometer) on a mismatched line will thus always appear greater than the forward power measured on a flat line with a 1:1 SWR.

The software program *TLW*, written by Dean Straw, N6BV, and included on the *ARRL Antenna Book* CD solves these complex equations. The characteristics of many common types of transmission lines are included in the software so that real antenna matching problems may be easily solved. Detailed instructions on using the program are included with it. *TLW* was used for the example calculations in this chapter.

20.1.4 Losses in Transmission Lines

A transmission line exhibits a certain amount of loss, caused by the resistance of the conductors used in the line and by dielectric losses in the line's insulators. The *matched-line loss* for a particular type and length of transmission line, operated at a particular frequency, is the loss when the line is terminated in a resistance equal to its characteristic impedance. The loss in a line is lowest when it is operated as a matched line.

Line losses increase when SWR is greater than 1:1. Each time energy flows from the generator toward the load, or is reflected at the load and travels back toward the generator, a certain amount will be lost along the line. The net effect of standing waves on a transmission line is to increase the average value of current and voltage, compared to the matched-line case. An increase in current raises I^2R (ohmic) losses in the conductors, and an increase in RF voltage increases E^2/R losses in the dielectric. Line loss rises with frequency, since the conductor resistance is related to skin effect, and also because dielectric losses rise with frequency.

Matched-line loss (ML) is stated in decibels per hundred feet at a particular frequency. The matched-line loss per hundred feet versus frequency for a number of common types of lines, both coaxial and open-wire balanced types, is shown graphically and as a table in the **Component Data and References** chapter. For example, RG-213 coax cable has a matched-line loss of 2.5 dB/100 ft at 100 MHz. Thus, 45 ft of this cable feeding a 50 Ω load at 100 MHz would have a loss of

$$\text{Matched line loss} = \frac{2.5 \text{ dB}}{100 \text{ ft}} \times 45 \text{ ft}$$
$$= 1.13 \text{ dB}$$

If a line is not matched, standing waves will cause additional loss beyond the inherent matched-line loss for that line.

Total Mismatched Line Loss (dB)

$$= 10 \log \left[\frac{a^2 - |\rho^2|}{a(1 - |\rho^2|)} \right] \quad (11)$$

where
$a = 10^{ML/10}$
ML = the line's matched loss in dB.

The effect of SWR on line loss is shown graphically in **Figure 20.4**. The horizontal axis is the SWR at the load end of the line. The family of curves is the matched loss of the length of transmission line in use. From the SWR value on the horizontal axis, proceed vertically to the curve representing the feed line's matched loss (loss with SWR of 1:1). At the intersection, the total loss can be read on the vertical axis.

Measuring Transmission Line Loss

The most obvious method is to use a calibrated wattmeter and dummy load. With the wattmeter at the input to the line and the dummy load at the output, apply power to the line and measure forward power, P_{IN}. (With the dummy load attached, there should be no reflected power.) Remove power and connect the input of the line directly to the power source. Connect the wattmeter between the output of the line and the dummy load. Apply the same amount of power and read forward power at the dummy load, P_{OUT}. The loss in the line is equal to 10 log (P_{OUT} / P_{IN}).

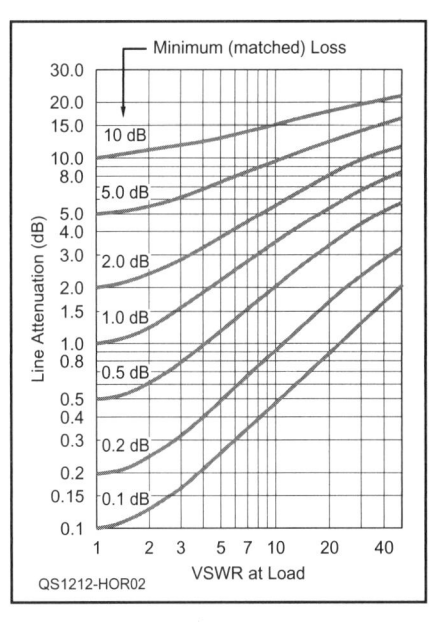

Figure 20.4 —Total insertion loss in a transmission line terminated in a mismatch. To use the chart, start with the SWR at the load. Find that value on the horizontal axis. From the SWR value on the horizontal axis, proceed vertically to the curve representing the feed line's matched loss (loss with SWR of 1:1). At the intersection, the total loss can be read on the vertical axis. (Courtesy of Joe Reisert, W1JR; see reference)

Without a wattmeter, loss can be measured by using a calibrated mismatch. Assuming a 50-Ω system, select a non-inductive resistor between 150 Ω (3:1 SWR) and 270 Ω (5.4:1 SWR). Convert the resistor's expected SWR to return loss (RL), using the table "Reflection Coefficient, Attenuation, SWR and Return Loss" in the **Component Data and References** chapter. For example, a 220-Ω resistive load results in a 4.4:1 SWR which is a return loss of 4.0 dB. Connect the resistor to the output of the line. Make sure the resistor leads are very short so that they do not add a significant amount of inductance. Measure SWR at the input to the line and convert to return loss. The line loss is the difference between return loss at the line input and return loss of the load. For example, with the 220-Ω load (4.0 dB RL) and 100 feet of RG-58 coax at 10 MHz, the input SWR might be 3.0:1 (RL = 6.0 dB). The line loss at this frequency is 6.0 dB – 4.0 dB = 2.0 dB.

Some methods use an open or short circuit at the load end of the line (an infinite SWR and RL = 0) to measure line loss. Most amateur instrumentation is not well-calibrated at high SWR and will give an unreliable reading for SWR and RL. Using a moderate mismatch improves the accuracy of the final result. You can replace the feed line with in-line attenuators to check this more accurate method with the known amounts of loss.

20.2 Choosing a Transmission Line

Making the best choice for a particular installation requires balancing the properties of the three common types of feed lines used by amateurs — coaxial, parallel-conductor or open-wire, and hardline — along with cost. The primary electrical considerations for feed line are characteristic impedance and loss. Mechanical concerns include weight, suitability for exposure to weather or soil, and interaction with other cables and conductors. When evaluating cost, be sure to include the cost of connectors and any auxiliary costs such as baluns and waterproofing materials.

The entire antenna system, composed of the feed line, tuners or matching networks and the antenna itself, must be included when evaluating what type of line to use. Along with loss, the effects of SWR on maximum voltage in the system must be considered if high power will be used, especially if high SWR is anticipated.

Multiband antenna systems, such as non-resonant wire antennas, can present quite a challenge because of the range of SWR values and the wide range of frequencies of use. As an example of the considerations involved, the article "Multiband Operation with Open-wire Line" is included with the downloadable supplemental content. By following the general process of modeling or calculation and evaluation with different types of feed line, reasonable choices can be made that result in satisfactory performance.

20.2.1 Effect of Loss

For most types of line and for modest values of SWR, the additional line loss due to SWR is of little concern. As the line's loss increases at higher frequencies, the total line loss (the sum of matched-line loss and additional loss due to SWR) can be surprisingly large at high values of SWR.

Because of losses in a transmission line, the measured SWR at the input of the line is lower than the SWR measured at the load end of the line. This does *not* mean that the load is absorbing any more power. Line loss absorbs power as it travels to the load and again on its way back to the generator, so the difference between the generator output power and the power returning from the load is higher than for a lossless line. Thus, P_r/P_f is smaller than at the load and so is the measured SWR.

For example, RG-213 solid-dielectric coax cable exhibits a matched-line loss at 28 MHz of 1.14 dB per 100 ft. A 250 ft length of this cable has a matched-line loss of 1.14 × 250/100 = 2.86 dB. Assume that we measure the SWR at the load as 6:1, the total mismatched line loss from equation 11 is 5.32 dB.

The additional loss due to the 6:1 SWR at 28 MHz is 5.32 – 2.86 = 2.46 dB. The SWR at the input of the 250 ft line is only 2.2:1, because line loss has masked the true magnitude of SWR (6:1) at the load end of the line.

The losses increase if coax with a larger matched-line loss is used under the same conditions. For example, RG-58A coaxial cable is about one-half the diameter of RG-213, and it has a matched-line loss of 2.81 dB/ 100 ft at 28 MHz. A 250 ft length of RG-58A has a total matched-line loss of 7.0 dB. With a 6:1 SWR at the load, the additional loss due to SWR is 3.0 dB, for a total loss of 10.0 dB. The additional cable loss due to the mismatch reduces the SWR measured at the input of the line to 1.33:1. An unsuspecting operator measuring the SWR at his transmitter might well believe that everything is just fine, when in truth only about 10% of the transmitter power is getting to the antenna! Be suspicious of very low SWR readings for an antenna fed with a long length of coaxial cable, especially if the SWR remains low across a wide frequency range. Most antennas have narrow SWR bandwidths, and the SWR *should* change across a band.

On the other hand, if expensive ⅞ inch diameter 50 Ω hardline cable is used at 28 MHz, the matched-line loss is only 0.19 dB/100 ft. For 250 ft of this hardline, the matched-line loss is 0.475 dB, and the additional loss due to a 6:1 SWR is 0.793 dB. Thus, the total loss is 1.27 dB.

At the upper end of the HF spectrum, when the transmitter and antenna are separated by a long transmission line, the use of bargain coax may prove to be a very poor cost-saving strategy. Adding a 1500 W linear amplifier (providing 8.7 dB of gain over a 200 W transmitter), to offset the loss in RG-58A compared to hardline, would cost a great deal more than higher-quality coax. Furthermore, no *transmitting* amplifier can boost *receiver* sensitivity — loss in the line has the same effect as putting an attenuator in front of the receiver.

At the lower end of the HF spectrum, say 3.5 MHz, the amount of loss in common coax lines is less of a problem for the range of SWR values typical on this band. For example, consider an 80 meter dipole cut for the middle of the band at 3.75 MHz. It exhibits an SWR of about 6:1 at the 3.5 and 4.0 MHz ends of the band. At 3.5 MHz, 250 ft of RG-58A small-diameter coax has an additional loss of 2.1 dB for this SWR, giving a total line loss of 4.0 dB. If larger-diameter RG-213 coax is used instead, the additional loss due to SWR is 1.3 dB, for a total loss of 2.2 dB. This is an acceptable level of loss for most 80 meter operators.

The loss situation gets dramatically worse as the frequency increases into the VHF and UHF regions. At 146 MHz, the total loss in 250 ft of RG-58A with a 6:1 SWR at the load is 21.4 dB, 10.1 dB for RG-213A, and 2.7 dB for ⅞ inch, 50 Ω hardline. At VHF and UHF, a low SWR is essential to keep line losses low, even for the best coaxial cable. The length of transmission line must be kept as short as practical at these frequencies.

Table 20.1 lists some commonly used coax cables showing feet per dB of loss vs frequency. The table can help with the selection of coax cable by comparing lengths that result in 1 dB of loss for different types of cable. The larger the value in the table, the less loss in the cable per unit length.

Transmission Lines for Microwave Frequencies

While low-loss waveguide is generally used to carry microwave frequency signals for long distances, *semi-rigid* coaxial cable — essentially miniature hardline — is used for connections inside and between pieces of equipment in the shack. Working with this type of cable requires special techniques, addressed in the supplemental article "Microwave Plumbing" with this book's online supplemental content. More information on microwave construction techniques is available in the **Construction Techniques** chapter and in the "Microwavelengths" columns by Paul Wade, W1GHZ in *QST*, available on-line to ARRL members.

Table 20.1
Length in Feet for 1 dB of Matched Loss

MHz	1.8	3.6	7.1	14.2	21.2	28.4	50.1	144	440	1296
RG-58	179	122	83	59	50	42	30	18	9	5
RG-8X	257	181	128	90	74	63	47	27	14	8
RG-213	397	279	197	137	111	95	69	38	19	9
LMR-400	613	436	310	219	179	154	115	67	38	21
9913	625	435	320	220	190	155	110	62	37	20
EC4-50				290		202		87		26
EC5-50				787		548		239		75
450 Ω OWL*	1065	758	547	391	322	279	213			
600 Ω OWL**	4550	3030	2130	1430	1150	980	715			

*Wireman #551, 400 Ω characteristic impedance
**Conductors #12 AWG

(See also Table 23-3 and 23-4 in the *ARRL Antenna Book* for information on more types of cable.) Determine the length of line your installation requires and the maximum acceptable amount of line loss in dB. Divide the total line length by the *maximum* acceptable loss to calculate the *minimum* acceptable length of line with 1 dB of loss. From the table, select a cable type that has a length per 1 dB of loss that is greater than the minimum acceptable length.

Example — An installation requires 400 feet of feed line at 14 MHz with a maximum acceptable value of 3 dB of loss. This requires cable with a minimum of 400 / 3 = 133 feet per dB of loss. Find a cable in Table 20.1 that shows more than 133 feet for 1 dB of loss at 14.2 MHz. RG-213 has the highest acceptable loss at this frequency: 137 ft / dB of loss.

Don't forget that you can combine types of cable and accessories to lower the total system cost while still meeting performance requirements. For example, it is common to use a single low-loss cable from the shack to a distant tower with multiple antennas. At the tower, an antenna switch then selects short runs of less-expensive cable to the various antennas.

20.2.2 Practical Considerations

Either coaxial cable or open-wire transmission or feed line is used to connect the transmitter and antenna. There are pros and cons for each type of feed line. Coax is the common choice because it is readily available, its characteristic impedance is close to that of a center-fed dipole, and it may be easily routed through or along walls and among other cables. Where a very long feed line is required or the antenna is to be used at frequencies for which the feed point impedance is high, the increased RF loss and low working voltage (compared to that of open-wire line) make it a poor choice. Hardline is the preferred choice at VHF and higher frequencies when the line losses for flexible coax would be too high. It is often used for very long line lengths at HF, as well. Refer to the **Component Data and References** chapter for information that will help you evaluate the RF loss of coaxial cable at different lengths and SWR.

Note that most traditional RG-type designations are no longer MIL-spec and are only general references to the cable's construction and characteristics. For example, cable advertised as RG-213 is actually "RG-213 Type" and may have characteristics quite different from the original RG-213 specification. Use the manufacturer's part number to determine the actual performance specifications.

COAXIAL CABLE

Coaxial cable is mechanically much easier to use than open-wire line. Because of the excellent shielding afforded by its outer shield, coax can be installed along a metal tower leg or taped together with numerous other cables, with virtually no interaction or crosstalk. Coax can be used with a rotatable antenna without worrying about shorting or twisting the conductors, which might happen with an open-wire line.

Coaxial cable used in the amateur service is, for the most part, made with solid polyethylene (PE), extended or "foamed" polyethylene (FPE), and solid Teflon (TFE) center insulation. (Teflon dielectric coax is often used at VHF and UHF frequencies due to its low loss characteristics.)

Class 2 PVC (P2) noncontaminating outer jackets are designed for long-life outdoor installations. Class 1 PVC (P1) outer jackets are not recommended for outdoor installations. (See the table of coaxial cables in the **Component Data and References** chapter.) Coax and hardline can be buried underground, especially if run in plastic piping (with suitable drain holes) so that ground water and soil chemicals cannot easily deteriorate the cable. A cable with an outer jacket of polyethylene (PE) rather than polyvinyl chloride (PVC) is recommended for direct-bury installations.

Respect coax's power-handling ratings. Cables such as RG-58 and RG-59 are suitable for power levels up to 300 W with low SWR. RG-8X cable can handle higher power and there are a number of variations of this type of cable. For legal-limit power or moderate SWR, use the larger diameter cables that are 0.4 inches in diameter or larger. Subminiature cables, such as RG-174, are useful for very short lengths at low power levels, but the high RF losses associated with these cables make them unsuitable for most uses as antenna feed lines. In these applications, a PTFE (Teflon) insulated cable is a better choice.

Bending Coax

Bending coax is acceptable as long as the radius of the bend is larger than the specified minimum bending radius. For example, a common minimum bending radius specification for RG-8 is 4 inches (8 times the cable diameter). Coax with more rigid shield materials will have a larger bending radius.

Bending the coax tighter than the minimum bending radius can cause impedance "bumps" in the line by distorting the geometry of the conductors. It can also cause the center conductor to migrate through the plastic insulation and eventually short to the outer shield. This is caused by several preventable conditions.

A major culprit for foam-insulation coax is bending the cable with a tight radius. Baluns are often made by wrapping several turns of coax into a tight bundle with a tight radius, either as a coiled-coax choke or through ferrite cores. Coaxial cable stubs might be wrapped into a coil of small radius to keep them small overall and out of the way. Coax is sometimes coiled up just to use up extra length.

The forces pushing on the center conductor from coiling are aggravated by self-heating from cable loss — a direct function of the amount of power applied and SWR. RG-8X is not rated for 1500 W but lots of amateurs use it successfully at that power level. RG-8X gets warm to the touch at 1500 W. Increasing internal temperature softens the foam which facilitates center conductor migration. Tight radius bends taken together with heating are a recipe for an eventual short circuit. Tightly coiled baluns used outdoors receive solar heating in addition to self-heating and a tight bend radius. A balun made and used this way has a very high probability of shorting out over time — particularly when used at high power.

Avoiding center conductor migration is easy: don't use sharp bends, particularly at high power. Use solid dielectric coax to make tightly coiled coaxial baluns and if stubs must be coiled up, use solid dielectric coax for those too. Use up spare foam coax length by laying it flat on the floor and avoiding sharp radius turns or bends.

Burying Coax

There are several reasons why you might choose to bury coax. One is that direct burial cable is virtually free from storm and UV damage, and usually has lower maintenance cost than cable that is out in the open. Another reason might be aesthetics; a buried cable will be acceptable in almost all communities. Also, being underground reduces common-mode feed line current on the outside of the shield, helping to reduce inter-station interference and RFI. Buried cable is also less susceptible to lightning.

Although any cable can be buried, a cable that is specifically designed for direct burial will have a longer life. The best cable to use is one that has a high-density polyethylene jacket because it is both nonporous and will take a relatively high amount of compressive loads. "Flooded" direct burial cables contain an additional moisture barrier of non-con-

---

Using 75 Ω Hardline in 50 Ω Systems

Surplus CATV hardline is usually 75 Ω but can be used in 50 Ω systems without special impedance matching techniques. Make the 75 Ω line some integer multiple of λ/2 at the operating frequency so that the impedance at the load end of the line is reproduced at the input to the line. This can also be done when feeding a 20/15/10 meter beam, for example, by making the 75 Ω line 2 λ on 20 meters so that it is 3 λ long on 15 and 4 λ long on 10 meters. If the load is 50 Ω, the SWR in the line will still be 75/50 = 1.5:1 but the simplicity often outweighs the minimal extra loss on the HF and lower VHF bands.

ductive grease under the jacket; this allows the material to leak out, thus "healing" small jacket penetrations. (These can be messy to work with when installing connectors.)

Here are some direct burial guidelines:

1) Because the outer jacket is the cable's first line of defense, any steps that can be taken to protect it will go a long way toward maintaining the internal quality of the cable.

2) Bury the cable in sand or finely pulverized dirt, without sharp stones, cinders, or rubble. If the soil in the trench does not meet these requirements, tamp four to six inches of sand into the trench, lay the cable and tamp another six to eleven inches of sand above it. A pressure-treated board placed in the trench above the sand prior to backfilling will provide some protection against subsequent damage that could be caused by digging or driving stakes.

3) Lay the cable in the trench with some slack. A tightly stretched cable is more likely to be damaged as the fill material is tamped.

4) Examine the cable as it is being installed to be sure the jacket has not been damaged during storage or by being dragged across over sharp edges.

5) You may want to consider burying it in plastic pipe or conduit. Be careful to drill holes in the bottom of the pipe at all low spots so that any moisture can drain out. While PVC pipe or conduit provides a mechanical barrier, water incursion is practically guaranteed — you can't keep it out. It will leak in directly or condense from moisture in the air. Use the perforated type so that any water will just drain out harmlessly. Plastic drain pipe with drain holes also works well.

6) It is important that direct burial is below the frost line to avoid damage by the expansion and contraction of the earth during freezing and thawing of the soil and any water surrounding the buried cables.

Connecting to and Weatherproofing Coax

Most manufacturers use some type of feed point system that accepts a PL-259 or N connector. Some antennas require you to split the coax and attach the shield and center conductor to machine screws attachment points on the driven element. The exposed end of the coax is very difficult to seal; indeed, it's nearly impossible. Water will wick down the outer shield and into your shack unless you take great pains to weatherproof it. Coating the entire pigtail and attachment terminals with Liquid Electrical Tape or some other conformal sealant is a good approach, although UV will degrade such coatings over time. Another approach for HF beams is to use a "Budwig HQ-1" style insulator with the integral SO-239 and wires for connecting to the terminals. As always, follow the manufacturer's directions.

With many beam antennas, the feed point is out of reach from the tower and should be connected to a jumper just long enough to reach from the feed point to the antenna mast. That way, the feed line connection and waterproofing can be done at the most convenient location. If you ever have to remove the antenna in the future you can just disconnect the jumper and lower the antenna.

The biggest mistake amateurs make with coaxial cable is improper weatherproofing. (See **Figure 28.18** in the **Safety** chapter, showing one way to do it properly.) First, use high-quality electrical tape, such as 3M Scotch 33+ or Scotch 88 (same as 33+ but 1.5 mil thicker). Avoid inexpensive utility tape. Before weatherproofing, tighten the connector (use pliers carefully to seat threaded connectors — hand-tight isn't good enough), and apply two wraps of tape around the joint.

When you're done making a tape wrap, sever the tape with a knife or tear it very carefully — do not stretch the tape until it breaks. This invariably leads to "flagging" in which the end of the tape loosens and blows around in the wind. Let the tape relax before applying the next layer and finishing the wrap.

Begin by applying two wraps of electrical tape around the joint. Next put a layer of butyl rubber vapor wrap over the joint. (3M Butyl Mastic Tape 2212 is one such material. This butyl rubber tape is also usually available in the electrical section of hardware and home improvement stores.) Finally, add two more layers of regular tape over the vapor wrap, creating a professional-quality joint that will never leak. Finally, if the coax is vertical, be sure to wrap the final layer so that the tape is going up the cable as shown in Figure 28.18. In that way, the layers will act like roofing shingles, shedding water off the connection. Wrapping it top to bottom will guide water between the layers of tape.

An alternative method suggested by K4ZA begins with a wrap of "military grade" Teflon tape — a thread wrapping tape thicker than what you'll find at your local hardware store. (McMaster-Carr #6802K44) Over that, install a layer of Scotch 130C (liner-less rubber sealing tape), using a 50% wrap (half the tape width is overlapped). Cover that with a layer of either Scotch 33+ or Scotch 88. Taken apart, 20-year-old joints have revealed connectors with like new appearance.

A recent product for coax joints is shrink-fit tubing impregnated with hot-melt glue along the inside. As you apply heat to the shrink-fit tubing, it shrinks while the glue melts and oozes inside between the fitting and the tubing. It not only keeps the tubing from slipping, but it also fills in the voids in the joint and provides an additional seal. It's an expensive alternative (approximately $1 per inch) but is very simple to use and remove if necessary.

Do not use silicone sealant that gives off acetic acid (a vinegary smell) and absorbs water when curing. Acid and water will migrate into the connection causing problems later. Use only aquarium-type sealants or Dow-Corning 3145 for reliable connections. Be aware that once cured, silicone sealants are very hard to remove from connectors — practically impossible.

OPEN-WIRE LINE

The most common open-wire transmission lines are *ladder line* (also known as *window line*) and *twin-lead*. Since the conductors are not shielded, two-wire lines are affected by their environment. Use standoffs and insulators to keep the line several inches from structures or other conductors. Ladder line has very low loss (twin-lead has a little more), and it can stand very high voltages (created by high SWR) as long as the insulators are clean. Twin-lead can be used at power levels up to 300 W and ladder line to the full legal power limit.

The characteristic impedance of open-wire line varies from 300 Ω for twin-lead to 450 to 600 Ω for most ladder and window line. The common 450 Ω window line with plastic insulation and 1" spacing has a characteristic impedance of approximately 360 to 405 Ω and velocity factor (VF) of approximately 91% depending on the manufacturer and materials used. The solid plastic insulation also means that rain, snow, or ice will affect the line's Z_0 and VF, typically dropping both by about 3% when the line is wet, according to a paper by Wes Stewart, N7WS (**k6mhe.com/n7ws/Ladder_Line.pdf**). This variability suggests that if precise characteristics are important, Z_0 and VF should be measured for the line to be used.

When used with 1/2 λ dipoles, the resulting moderate to high SWR requires an impedance-matching unit at the transmitter. The low RF losses of open-wire lines make this an acceptable situation on the HF bands.

Ladder line is available with both solid copperweld and stranded copper conductors. The solid conductor types tend to be less expensive but will break if flexed repeatedly, such as from being blown around in the wind. For that reason, stranded conductor ladder line is preferred, but if solid conductor ladder line is used, be sure to provide adequate mechanical support to provide stress relief and protection against flexing.

CONTROL CABLES

In addition to coaxial cables, most towers will have some sort of control cable for rotators, antenna switches, or other accessories. The manufacturer should provide the size that is necessary and again, you should follow their specifications.

Multi-conductor cables are not usually as waterproof as coaxial cable. The jacket is usually just a plastic sleeve around the inner wires. If the jacket is nicked or cut, water can easily get in and collect at the lowest point of the cable. If the water does not leak out, it will fill the cable jacket all the way into the station where it will run out the unsealed end of the cable. For this reason, it is common to make a drip loop in the cable where it enters the station and make a small slice or hole in the jacket to allow any accumulated water to leak out.

In the case of rotator cables, some rotators are sensitive to voltage drop so bigger sizes should be used. For really long runs, some amateurs use THHN house wire or UF-Romex, (with the motor start capacitor installed at the rotator) from the local hardware store to get reasonably-priced bigger wire. Only the motor and solenoid (if used) conductors typically require the larger wire.

For medium-length runs of buried cable, multi-conductor irrigation system control cable can be used in place of standard light-duty rotator cable. If the cable has extra conductors, pairs of conductors can be doubled to provide for the higher-current brake connections. For example, four conductors in a 10-conductor irrigation cable with #18 conductors can be doubled up in pairs to create two heavy conductors for the brake solenoid circuits. Irrigation cables generally have solid wires, requiring different terminals and splicing techniques than for stranded wire.

20.3 The Transmission Line as Impedance Transformer

If the complex mechanics of reflections, SWR and line losses are put aside momentarily, a transmission line can very simply be considered as an impedance transformer. A certain value of load impedance, consisting of a resistance and reactance, at the end of the line is transformed into another value of impedance at the input of the line. The amount of transformation is determined by the electrical length of the line, its characteristic impedance, and by the losses inherent in the line. The input impedance of a real, lossy transmission line is computed using the following equation

$$Z_{in} = Z_0 \times \frac{Z_L \cosh(\eta \ell) + Z_0 \sinh(\eta \ell)}{Z_L \sinh(\eta \ell) + Z_0 \cosh(\eta \ell)} \quad (12)$$

where
- Z_{in} = complex impedance at input of line = $R_{in} \pm j X_{in}$
- Z_L = complex load impedance at end of line = $R_l \pm j X_l$
- Z_0 = characteristic impedance of line = $R_0 \pm j X_0$
- η = complex loss coefficient = $\alpha + j \beta$
- α = matched line loss attenuation constant, in nepers/unit length (1 neper = 8.688 dB, so divide line loss in dB per unit length by 8.688)
- β = phase constant of line in radians/unit length (multiply electrical length in degrees by 2π radians/ 360 degrees)
- ℓ = electrical length of line in same units of length as used for α.

This and other complex equations describing the electrical behavior of transmission lines were traditionally solved through the use of Smith charts. (Smith charts are discussed in the article "Smith Chart Supplement" with the downloadable supplemental content. Many references to Smith charts and their use may be found on-line.) While the Smith chart is an extremely effective way of visualizing and understanding the transmission line, using it directly in design has been replaced by software. Programs such as those mentioned in the sidebar "Smith Chart Software" can perform the numerical calculations and display the results on a Smith chart. The software

Smith Chart Software

The standard way of visualizing transmission line and impedance matching mechanics is by using a Smith chart. (If you are unfamiliar with the Smith chart, recent editions of this book and the *ARRL Antenna Book* include a detailed tutorial on the Smith chart, either in print or on the CD-ROM.) Yesterday's paper charts, however, have been replaced by interactive computer software such as the easy-to-use *jjSmith* (*Windows* only) by Jim Tonne, W4ENE, available with the online supplemental content and *SimSmith* (www.ae6ty.com/Smith_Charts.html) by Ward Harriman, AE6TY. *SimSmith* is written in Java and runs on a number of operating systems. Learning about the Smith chart will be a great aid in understanding the mechanics of transmission lines and impedance matching.

TLW provided with the *ARRL Antenna Book* also solves problems of this nature, although without Smith chart graphics.

20.3.1 Transmission Line Stubs

The impedance-transformation properties of a transmission line are useful in a number of applications. If the terminating resistance is zero (that is, a short) at the end of a low-loss transmission line which is less than ¼ λ long, the input impedance consists of a reactance, which is given by a simplification of equation 12.

$$X_{in} \cong Z_0 \tan \ell \quad (13)$$

If the line termination is an open circuit, the input reactance is given by

$$X_{in} \cong Z_0 \cot \ell \quad (14)$$

The input of a short (less than ¼ λ) length of line with a short circuit as a terminating load appears as an inductance, while an open-circuited line appears as a capacitance. This is a useful property of a transmission line, since it can be used as a low-loss inductor or capacitor in matching networks. Such lines are often referred to as stubs.

A line that is electrically ¼ λ long is a special kind of a stub. When a ¼ λ line is short circuited at its load end, it presents an open circuit at its input. Conversely, a ¼ λ line with an open circuit at its load end presents a short circuit at its input. Such a line inverts the impedance of a short or an open circuit at the frequency for which the line is ¼ λ long. This is also true for frequencies that are odd multiples of the ¼ λ frequency. However, for frequencies where the length of the line is ½ λ, or integer multiples thereof, the line will duplicate the termination at its end.

20.3.2 Transmission Line Stubs as Filters

The impedance transformation properties of stubs can be put to use as filters. For example, if a shorted line is cut to be ¼ λ long at 7.1 MHz, the impedance looking into the input of the cable will be an open circuit. The line will have no effect if placed in parallel with a transmitter's output terminals. However, at twice the *fundamental* frequency, 14.2 MHz, that same line is now ½ λ, and the line looks like a short circuit. The line, often dubbed a *quarter-wave stub* in this application, will act as a trap for not only the second harmonic, but also for higher even-order harmonics, such as the fourth or sixth harmonics.

This filtering action is extremely useful in multitransmitter situations, such as Field Day, emergency operations centers, portable communications facilities and multioperator contest stations. Transmission line stubs can operate at high power where lumped-constant filters would be expensive. Using stub filters reduces noise, harmonics and strong fundamental signals from the closely spaced antennas that cause overload and interference to receivers. (For information on determining isolation between radios and filter requirements, see the supplemental article "Measuring Receiver Isolation" by W2VJN with the downloadable supplemental content.)

Quarter-wave stubs made of good-quality coax, such as RG-213, offer a convenient way to lower transmitter harmonic levels. Despite the fact that the exact amount of harmonic attenuation depends on the impedance (often unknown) into which they are working at the harmonic frequency, a quarter-wave stub will

Where to Place Stubs Used as Harmonic Filters

A quarter-wave (¼ λ) shorted stub makes an effective harmonic filter that is able to handle high power without expensive components. As described in this section, it is easy to build without special components or construction techniques. In order to get the best performance from the stub filter, however, it is important to install the stub at an appropriate location in the transmission line.

This type of stub works by presenting an open circuit at the fundamental frequency and a short circuit on the harmonics where it is a multiple of one-half wavelength (½ λ). For the short circuit to be most effective, the stub should be placed at a location in the transmission line where impedance is high *at the harmonic frequency*. The difference in performance can be dramatic. If the stub is connected at a low-impedance point, attenuation of the harmonic can be less than 10 dB. On the other hand, connected at a high-impedance point, attenuation can be well in excess of 30 dB. Without recognizing this dependence on impedance at the point of connection, applying stub filters will result in erratic results.

A complete discussion of how to determine the optimum location for a stub is beyond the scope of this chapter but two *National Contest Journal* articles on stub placement by George Cutsogeorge, W2VJN, and Jim Brown, K9YC, have been added to the supplemental files supplied with the online supplemental content. (See the Table of Contents page at the beginning of this chapter.) A convenient rule of thumb that will result in good — if not optimum — filter performance is to first determine the output circuit of the amplifier or transmitter. In almost all tube amplifiers, the output circuit will either be a Pi or a Pi-L network. (See the chapter on RF Power Amplifiers.) Solid-state transmitters usually have a low-pass LC filter at the output. Determine whether the output component of the network or filter is a shunt (parallel) capacitor or a series inductor. (Ignore protective RF chokes or similar components.)

• If the output component is a series inductor, such as in a low-pass filter or a Pi-L network, the output impedance at the frequency of the harmonic to be attenuated will probably be higher than 50 Ω. The stub is attached at the equipment output.

• If the output component is a shunt capacitor, such as in a Pi network, the output impedance at the frequency of the harmonic to be attenuated will probably be lower than 50 Ω. The nearest high-impedance point, as a result, will be 1/4 λ from the output. Connect a 1/4 λ jumper to the output and connect the stub at the junction of the jumper and the main feed line.

This simple rule-of-thumb procedure is unlikely to result in the best performance but it is a good substitute if measuring the feed line impedance directly is not practical. Both of the referenced articles go into some detail about feed line impedance measurement and determining the optimum location for the stub taking into account the antenna impedance and length of the main feed line. These are important considerations for high-performance station design to manage interstation interference. (Also see the reference section entry for *Managing Interstation Interference* by George Cutsogeorge, W2VJN.) In addition, the article by Jim Brown, K9YC, discusses placement of stub harmonic filters for receiving.

Commercial Triplexer Design Example

Provided with the online supplemental content, the article "Commercial Triplexer Design" by George Cutsogeorge, W2VJN, discusses the issues encountered in adapting a popular *QST* article on a Field Day-style triplexer to become a commercial product. The referenced *QST* article by Gary Gordon, K6KV, is provided as well.

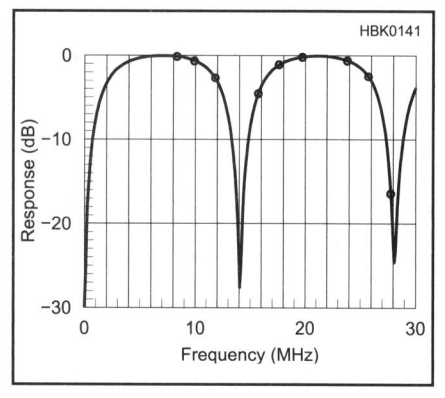

Figure 20.6 — Frequency response with a shorted stub.

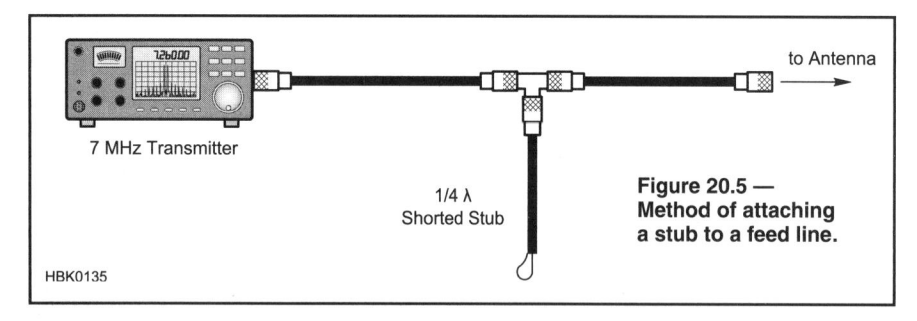

been pruned to frequency, a short jumper is soldered across the end, and the response at the second harmonic frequency is measured. **Figure 20.5** shows how to connect a shorted stub to a transmission line and **Figure 20.6** shows a typical frequency response.

The shorted quarter-wave stub shows low loss at 7 MHz and at 21 MHz where it is ¾-λ long. It nulls 14 and 28 MHz. This is useful for reducing the even harmonics of a 7 MHz transmitter. It can be used for a 21 MHz transmitter as well, and will reduce any spurious emissions such as phase noise and wideband noise which might cause interference to receivers operating on 14 or 28 MHz.

The open-circuited quarter-wave stub has a low impedance at the fundamental frequency, so it must be used at two times the frequency for which it is cut. For example, a quarter-wave open stub cut for 3.5 MHz will present a high impedance at 7 MHz where it is ½ λ long. It will present a high impedance at those frequencies where it is a multiple of ½ λ, or 7, 14 and 28 MHz. It would be connected in the same manner as Figure 20.5 shows, and the frequency plot is shown in **Figure 20.7**.

This open stub can protect a receiver operating on 7, 14, 21 or 28 MHz from interference by a 3.5 MHz transmitter. It also has nulls at 10.5, 17.5 and 24.5 MHz — the 3rd, 5th and 7th harmonics. The length of a quarter-wave stub may be calculated as follows:

$$L_e = \frac{VF \times 983.6}{4f} \qquad (15)$$

Figure 20.5 — Method of attaching a stub to a feed line.

typically yield 20 to 25 dB of attenuation of the second harmonic when placed directly at the output of a transmitter feeding common amateur antennas.

This attenuation may be a bit higher when the output impedance of the plate tuning network in an amplifier increases with frequency, such as for a pi-L network. Attenuation may be a bit lower if the tuning network's output impedance decreases with frequency, such as for a pi network.

Because different manufacturing runs of coax will have slightly different velocity factors, a quarter-wave stub is usually cut a little longer than calculated, and then carefully pruned by snipping off short pieces, while using an antenna analyzer to monitor the response at the fundamental frequency. Because the end of the coax is an open circuit while pieces are being snipped away, the input of a ¼ λ line will show a short circuit exactly at the fundamental frequency. Once the coax has

where

L_e = length in ft
VF = propagation constant for the coax in use
f = frequency in MHz.

For the special case of RG-213 (and any similar cable with VF = 0.66), equation 15 can be simplified to:

$$L_e = \frac{163.5}{f} \quad (16)$$

where

L_e = length in ft
f = frequency in MHz.

Table 20.2 solves this equation for the major contesting bands where stubs are often used. The third column shows how much of the stub to cut off if the desired frequency is 100 kHz higher in frequency. For example: To cut a stub for 14.250 MHz, reduce the overall length shown by 2.5 × 1 inches, or 2.5 inches. There is some variation in dielectric constant of coaxial cable from batch to batch or manufacturer to manufacturer, so it is always best to measure the stub's fundamental resonance before proceeding.

CONNECTING STUBS

Stubs are usually connected in the antenna feed line close to the transmitter. They may also be connected on the antenna side of a switch used to select different antennas. Some small differences in the null depth may occur for different positions.

To connect a stub to the transmission line it is necessary to insert a coaxial T (as shown in Figure 20.5). If a female-male-female T is used, the male can connect directly to the transmitter while the antenna line and the stub connect to the two females. It should be noted that the T inserts a small additional length in series with the stub that lowers the resonant frequency. The additional length for an Amphenol UHF T is about ⅜ inch. This length is negligible at 1.8 and 3.5 MHz, but on the higher bands it should not be ignored.

MEASURING STUBS WITH ONE-PORT METERS

Many of the common measuring instruments used by amateurs are *one-port devices*, meaning they have one connector at which the measurement — typically VSWR — is made. Probably the most popular instrument for this type of work is the antenna analyzer, available from a number of manufacturers.

To test a stub using an antenna analyzer, connect the stub to the meter by itself and tune the meter for a minimum impedance value, ignoring the VSWR setting. It is almost impossible to get an accurate reading on the higher HF bands, particularly with open stubs. For example, when a quarter-wave open stub cut for 20 meters was nulled on an MFJ-259 SWR analyzer, the frequency measured 14.650 MHz, with a very broad null. A recheck with a professional-quality network analyzer measured 14.018 MHz. (Resolution on the network analyzer is about ±5 kHz.) Running the same test on a quarter-wave shorted stub gave a measurement of 28.320 MHz on the MFJ-259 and 28.398 MHz on the network analyzer. (These inaccuracies are typical of amateur instrumentation and are meant to illustrate the difficulties of using inexpensive instruments for precise measurements.)

Other one-port instruments that measure phase can be used to get a more accurate reading. The additional length added by the required T adapter must be accounted for. If the measurement is made without the T and then with the T, the average value will be close to correct.

MEASURING STUBS WITH TWO-PORT INSTRUMENTS

A two-port measurement is made with a signal generator and a separate detector. A T connector is attached to the generator with the stub connected to one side. The other side is connected to a cable of any length that goes to the detector. The detector should present a 50 Ω load to the cable. This is how a network analyzer is configured, and it is similar to how the stub is connected in actual use. If the generator is calibrated accurately, the measurement can be very good. There are a number of ways to do this without buying an expensive piece of lab equipment.

An antenna analyzer can be used as the signal generator. Measurements will be quite accurate if the detector has 30 to 40 dB dynamic range. Two setups were tested by the author for accuracy. The first used a digital voltmeter (DVM) with a diode detector. (A germanium diode (1N34A or equivalent) must be used for the best dynamic range.) Tests on open and shorted stubs at 14 MHz returned readings within 20 kHz of the network analyzer. Another test was run using an oscilloscope as the detector with a 50 Ω load on the input. This test produced results that were essentially the same as the network analyzer.

A noise generator can be used in combination with a receiver as the detector. (An inexpensive noise generator kit is available from Elecraft, **www.elecraft.com**.) Set the receiver for 2-3 kHz bandwidth and turn off the AGC. An ac voltmeter connected to the audio output of the receiver will serve as a null detector. The noise level into the receiver without the stub connected should be just at or below the limiting level. With the stub connected, the noise level in the null should drop by 25 or 30 dB. Connect the UHF T to the noise generator using any necessary adapters. Connect the stub to one side of the T and connect the receiver to the other side with a short cable. Tune the receiver around the expected null frequency. After locating the null, snip off pieces of cable until the null moves to the desired frequency. Accuracy with this method is within 20 or 30 kHz of the network analyzer readings on 14 MHz stubs.

A *vector network analyzer* or VNA is another type of *two-port device*. VNAs can perform both reflection measurements as a one-port device and transmission measurements through a device or system at two locations. Once only available as expensive lab instruments, a number of inexpensive VNA designs that use a PC to perform display and calculations are now available to amateurs. The use of VNAs is discussed in the **Test Equipment and Measurements** chapter of this book.

STUB COMBINATIONS

A single stub will give 20 to 30 dB attenuation in the null. If more attenuation is needed, two or more similar stubs can be combined. Best results will be obtained if a short coupling cable is used to connect the two stubs rather than connecting them directly in parallel. The stubs may be cut to the same frequency for maximum attenuation, or to two slightly different frequencies such as the CW and SSB frequencies in one band. Open and shorted stubs can be combined together to attenuate higher harmonics as well as lower frequency bands.

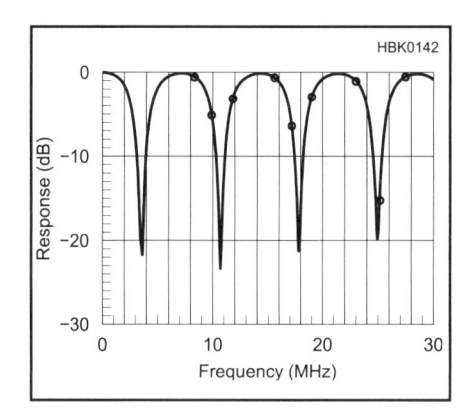

Figure 20.7 — Frequency response with an open stub.

Table 20.2
Quarter-Wave Stub Lengths for the HF Contesting Bands

Freq (MHz)	Length (L_e)*	Cut off per 100 kHz
1.8	90 ft, 10 in	57⅜ in
3.5	46 ft, 9 in	15½ in
7.0	23 ft, 4 in	4 in
14.0	11 ft, 8 in	1 in
21.0	7 ft, 9 in	7/16 in
28.0	5 ft, 10 in	¼ in

*Lengths shown are for RG-213 and any similar cable, assuming a 0.66 velocity factor (L_e = 163.5/f). See text for other cables.

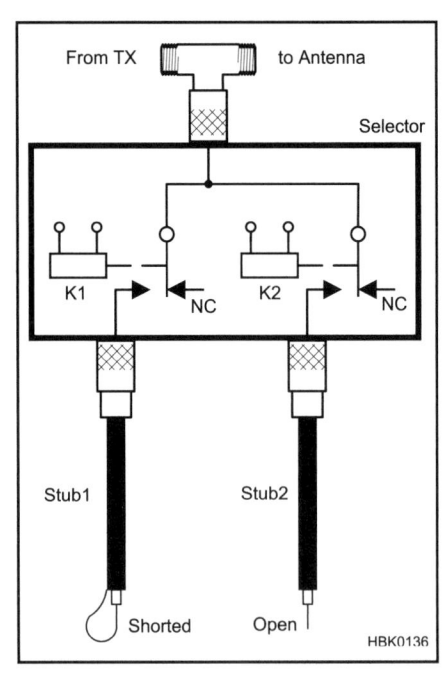

Figure 20.8 — Schematic of the Field Day stub switching relay control box. Table 20.3 shows which relays should be closed for the desired operating band.

Table 20.3
Stub Selector Operation
See Figure 20.8 for circuit details.

Relay K1 Position	Relay K2 Position	Bands Passed (meters)	Bands Nulled (meters)
Open	Open	All	None
Energized	Energized	80	40, 20, 15, 10
Energized	Open	40, 15	20, 10
Open	Energized	20, 10	40, 15

An interesting combination is the parallel connection of two ⅛ λ stubs, one open and the other shorted. The shorted stub will act as an inductor and the open stub as a capacitor. Their reactance will be equal and opposite, forming a resonant circuit. The null depth with this arrangement will be a bit better than a single quarter-wave shorted stub. This presents some possibilities when combinations of stubs are used in a band switching system.

20.3.3 Project: A Field Day Stub Assembly

Figure 20.8 shows a simple stub arrangement that can be useful in a two-transmitter Field Day station. The stubs reduce out-of-band noise produced by the transmitters that would cause interference to the other stations — a common Field Day problem where the stations are quite close together. This noise cannot be filtered out at the receiver and must be removed at the transmitter. One stub assembly would be connected to each transmitter output and manually switched for the appropriate band.

Two stubs are connected as shown. The two-relay selector box can be switched in four ways. Stub 1 is a shorted quarter-wave 40 meter stub. Stub 2 is an open quarter-wave 40 meter stub. Operation is as shown in **Table 20.3**.

The stubs must be cut and tuned while connected to the selector relays. RG-213 may be used for any amateur power level and will provide 25 to 30 dB reduction in the nulls. For power levels under 500 W or so, RG-8X may be used. It will provide a few dB less reduction in the nulls because of its slightly higher loss than RG-213.

20.4 Matching Impedances in the Antenna System

Only in a few special cases is the antenna impedance the exact value needed to match a practical transmission line. In all other cases, it is necessary either to operate with a mismatch and accept the SWR that results, or else to bring about a match between the line and the antenna.

When transmission lines are used with a transmitter, the most common load is an antenna. When a transmission line is connected between an antenna and a receiver, the receiver input circuit is the load, not the antenna, because the power taken from a passing wave is delivered to the receiver.

Whatever the application, the conditions existing at the load, and *only* the load, determine the reflection coefficient, and hence the SWR, on the line. If the load is purely resistive and equal to the characteristic impedance of the line, there will be no standing waves. If the load is not purely resistive, or is not equal to the line Z_0, there will be standing waves. No adjustments can be made at the input end of the line to change the SWR at the load. Neither is the SWR affected by changing the line length, except as previously described when the SWR at the input of a lossy line is masked by the attenuation of the line.

20.4.1 Conjugate Matching

Technical literature sometimes uses the term *conjugate match* to describe the condition where the impedance seen looking toward the load from any point on the line is the complex conjugate of the impedance seen looking toward the source. This means that the resistive and reactive magnitudes of the impedances are the same, but that the reactances have opposite signs. For example, the complex conjugate of $20 + j\,75$ is $20 - j\,75$. The complex conjugate of a purely resistive impedance, such as $50 + j\,0\,\Omega$, is the same impedance, $50 + j\,0\,\Omega$. A conjugate match is necessary to achieve the maximum power gain possible from most signal sources.

For example, if 50 feet of RG-213 is terminated in a $72 - j\,34\,\Omega$ antenna impedance, the transmission line transforms the impedance to $35.9 - j\,21.9\,\Omega$ at its input. (The *TLW* program is used to calculate the impedance at the line input.) To create a conjugate match at the line input, a matching network would have to present an impedance of $35.9 + j\,21.9\,\Omega$. The system would then become resonant, since the $\pm j\,21.9\,\Omega$ reactances would cancel, leaving $35.9 + j\,0\,\Omega$. A conjugate match is not the same as transforming one impedance to another, such as from $35.9 - j\,0\,\Omega$ to $50 + j\,0\,\Omega$. An additional impedance transformation network would be required for that step.

Conjugate matching is often used for small-signal amplifiers, such as preamps at VHF and above, to obtain the best power gain. The situation with high-power amplifiers is complex and there is considerable discussion as to whether conjugate matching delivers the highest efficiency, gain and power output. Nevertheless, conjugate matching is the model most often applied to impedance matching in antenna systems.

20.4.2 Impedance Matching Networks

When all of the components of an antenna system — the transmitter, feed line, and antenna — have the same impedance, all of the power generated by the transmitter is transferred to the antenna and SWR is 1:1. This is rarely the case, however, as antenna feed-point impedances vary widely with frequency and design. This requires some method of *impedance matching* between the various antenna system components.

Many amateurs use an *impedance-matching unit* or "antenna tuner" between their transmitter and the transmission line feeding the antenna. (This is described in a following section.) The antenna tuner's function is to transform the impedance, whatever it is, at the transmitter end of the transmission line into the 50 Ω required by the transmitter. Remember that the use of an antenna tuner at the transmitter does *not tune the antenna*, reduce SWR on the feed line or reduce feed line losses!

Some matching networks are built directly into the antenna (for example, the gamma and beta matches) and these are discussed in the chapter on **Antennas** and in *The ARRL Antenna Book*. Impedance matching networks made of fixed or adjustable components can also be used at the antenna and are particularly useful for antennas that operate on a single band.

Remember, however, that impedance can be transformed anywhere in the antenna system to match any other desired impedance. A variety of techniques can be used as described in the following sections, depending on the circumstances.

An electronic circuit designed to convert impedance values is called an *impedance matching network*. The most common impedance matching network circuits for use in systems that use coax cable are:
1) The low-pass L network.
2) The high-pass L network.
3) The low-pass pi network.
4) The high-pass T network.

Basic schematics for each of the circuits are shown in **Figure 20.9**. Properties of the circuits are shown in **Table 20.4**. As shown in Table 20.4, the L networks can be reversed if matching does not occur in one direction. L networks are the most common for single-band antenna matching. The component in parallel is the *shunt* component, so the L networks with the shunt capacitor or inductor at the input (Figs 20.9A and 20.9C) are *shunt-input* networks and the others are *series-input* networks.

Impedance matching circuits can use fixed-value components for just one band when a particular antenna has an impedance that is too high or low, or they can be made to be adjustable when matching is needed on several bands, such as for matching a dipole antenna fed with open-wire line.

Additional material by Bill Sabin, WØIYH, on matching networks can be found with the downloadable supplemental content along with his program *MATCH*. The supplemental article "Using *TLW* to Design Impedance Matching Networks" by W2VJN is also with the downloadable supplemental content.

DESIGNING AN L NETWORK

The L network, shown in Figure 20.9A through 20.9D, only requires two components and is a particularly good choice of matching network for single-band antennas. The L network is easy to construct so that it can be mounted at or near the feed point of the antenna, resulting in 1:1 SWR on the transmission line to the shack. (Note that L networks as well as pi and T networks can easily be designed with the *TLW* software.)

To design an L network, both the source and load impedances must be known. Let us assume that the source impedance, R_S, will be 50 Ω, representing the transmission line to the transmitter, and that the load is an arbitrary value, R_L.

First, determine the circuit Q.

$$Q^2 + 1 = \frac{R_L}{50} \quad (17A)$$

or

$$Q = \sqrt{\frac{R_L}{50} - 1} \quad (17B)$$

Next, select the type of L network you want from Figure 20.9. Note that the parallel component is always connected to the higher of the two impedances, source or load. Your choice should take into account whether either the source or load require a dc ground (parallel or shunt-L) and whether it is necessary to have a dc path through the network, such as to power a remote antenna switch or other such device (parallel- or shunt-C). Once you have selected a network, calculate the values of X_L and X_C:

$$X_L = Q R_S \quad (18)$$

and

$$X_C = \frac{R_L}{Q} \quad (19)$$

As an example, we will design an L network to match a 300 Ω antenna (R_L) to a 50 Ω transmission line (R_S). $R_L > R_S$ so we can select either Figure 20.9B or Figure 20.9D. The network in B is a low-pass network and will attenuate harmonics, so that is the usual choice.

$$Q = \sqrt{\frac{300}{50} - 1} = 2.236$$

$$X_L = 50 \times 2.236 = 112 \ \Omega$$

$$X_C = \frac{300}{2.236} = 134 \ \Omega$$

If the network is being designed to operate at 7 MHz, the actual component values are:

$$L = \frac{X_L}{2\pi f} = 2.54 \ \mu H$$

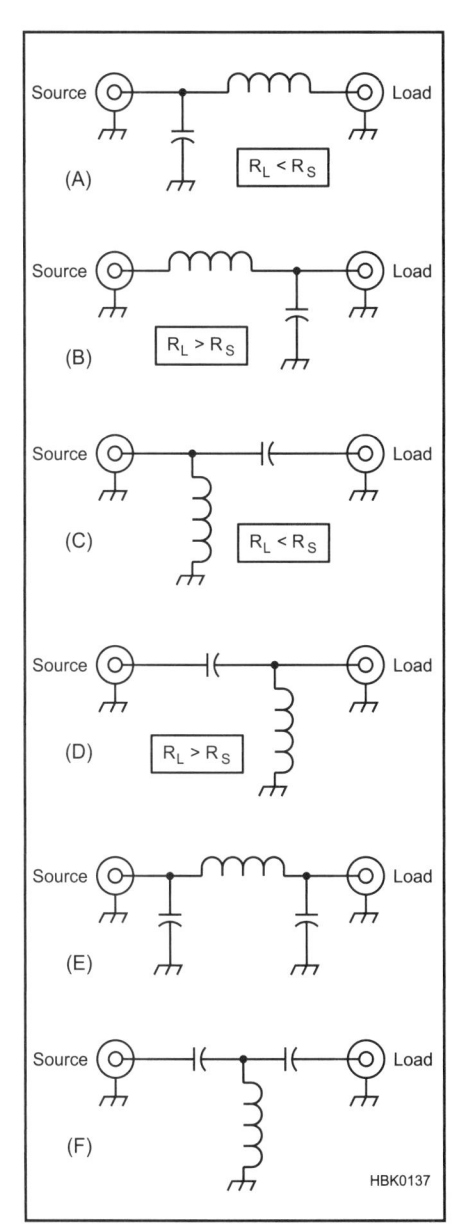

Figure 20.9 — Matching network variations. A through D show L networks. E is a pi network, equivalent to a pair of L networks sharing a common series inductor. F is a T network, equivalent to a pair of L networks sharing a common parallel inductor.

Table 20.4
Network Performance

Figure 20.9 Section	Circuit Type	Match Higher or Lower?	Harmonic Attenuation?
(A)	Low-pass L network	Lower	Fair to good
(B)	Reverse Low-pass L network	Higher	Fair to good
(C)	High-pass L network	Lower	No
(D)	Reverse high-pass L network	Higher	No
(E)	Low-pass Pi network	Lower and Higher	Good
(F)	High-pass T network	Lower and higher	No

$$C = \frac{1}{2\pi f X_C} = 170 \text{ pF}$$

The components could be fixed-value or adjustable. By running the *TLW* software, additional information is obtained: At 1500 W there will be 942 V peak across the capacitor and 5.5 A flowing in the inductor.

The larger the ratio of the impedances to be transformed, the higher Q becomes. High values of Q (10 or more) may result in impractically high or low component values. In this case, it may be easier to design the matching network as a pair of L networks back-to-back that accomplish the match in two steps. Select an intermediate value of impedance, R_{INT}, the geometric mean between R_L and the source impedance:

$$R_{INT} = \sqrt{R_L R_S}$$

Construct one L network that transforms R_L to R_{INT} and a second L network that transforms R_{INT} to R_S.

20.4.3 Matching Antenna Impedance at the Antenna

This section describes methods by which a network can be installed at or near the antenna feed point to provide matching to a transmission line. Having the matching system at the antenna rather than down in the shack at the end of a long transmission line does seem intuitively desirable, but it is not always very practical, especially in multiband antennas as discussed below.

RESONATING THE ANTENNA

If a highly reactive antenna can be tuned to resonance, even without special efforts to make the resistive portion equal to the line's characteristic impedance, the resulting SWR is often low enough to minimize additional line loss due to SWR. For example, the multiband 100 ft long flat-top antenna in **Figure 20.10** has a feed point impedance of $4.18 - j\,1590\,\Omega$ at 1.8 MHz. Assume that the antenna reactance is tuned out with a network consisting of two symmetrical inductors whose reactance is $+j\,1590/2 = j\,795\,\Omega$ each, with a Q of 200. These inductors are 70.29 μH coils in series with inherent loss resistances of $795/200 = 3.98\,\Omega$. The total series resistance is thus $4.18 + 2 \times (3.98) = 12.1\,\Omega$. If placed in series with each leg of the antenna at the feed point as in the figure, the antenna reactance and inductor reactance cancel out, leaving a purely resistive impedance at the antenna feed point.

If this tuned system is fed with 50 Ω coaxial cable, the SWR is $50/12.1 = 4.13:1$, and the loss in 100 ft of RG-213 cable would be 0.48 dB. The antenna's radiation efficiency is the ratio of the antenna's radiation resistance (4.18 Ω) to the total feed point resistance including the matching coils (12.1 Ω), so efficiency is $4.18/12.1 = 34.6\%$ which is equivalent to 4.6 dB of loss compared to a 100% efficient antenna. Adding the 0.48 dB of loss in the line yields an overall system loss of 5.1 dB. Compare this to the loss of 26 dB if the RG-213 coax is used to feed the antenna directly, without any matching at the antenna. The use of moderately high-Q resonating inductors has yielded almost 21 dB of "gain" (that is, less loss) compared to the case without the inductors. The drawback of course is that the antenna is now resonant on only one frequency, but it certainly is a lot more efficient on that one frequency!

THE QUARTER-WAVE TRANSFORMER OR "Q" SECTION

The range of impedances presented to the transmission line is usually relatively small on a typical amateur antenna, such as a dipole or a Yagi when it is operated close to resonance. In such antenna systems, the impedance-transforming properties of a ¼ λ section of transmission line are often utilized to match the transmission line at the antenna.

If the antenna impedance and the characteristic impedance of a feed line to be matched are known, the characteristic impedance needed for a quarter-wave matching section of low-loss cable is expressed by another simplification of equation 12.

$$Z = \sqrt{Z_1 Z_0} \qquad (20)$$

where
  Z = characteristic impedance needed for matching section
  Z_1 = antenna impedance
  Z_0 = characteristic impedance of the line to which it is to be matched.

Such a matching section is called a *synchronous quarter-wave transformer* or a *quarter-wave transformer*. The term synchronous is used because the match is achieved only at the length at which the matching section is exactly ¼ λ long. This limits the use of ¼ λ transformers to a single band. Different ¼ λ lengths of line are required on different bands.

Figure 20.11 shows one example of this technique to feed an array of stacked Yagis on a single tower. Each antenna is resonant and is fed in parallel with the other Yagis, using equal lengths of coax to each antenna called *phasing lines*. A stacked array is used to produce not only gain, but also a wide vertical elevation pattern, suitable for coverage of a broad geographic area. (See *The ARRL Antenna Book* for details about Yagi stacking.)

The feed point impedance of two 50 Ω Yagis fed with equal lengths of feed line connected in parallel is 25 Ω (50/2 Ω); three in parallel yield 16.7 Ω; four in parallel yield 12.5 Ω. The nominal SWR for a stack of four Yagis is 4:1 (50/12.5). This level of SWR does not cause excessive line loss, provided that low-loss coax feed line is used. However, many station designers want to be able to select, using relays, any individual antenna in the array, without having the load seen by the transmitter change. (Perhaps they might wish to turn one antenna in the stack in a different direction and use it by itself.) If the

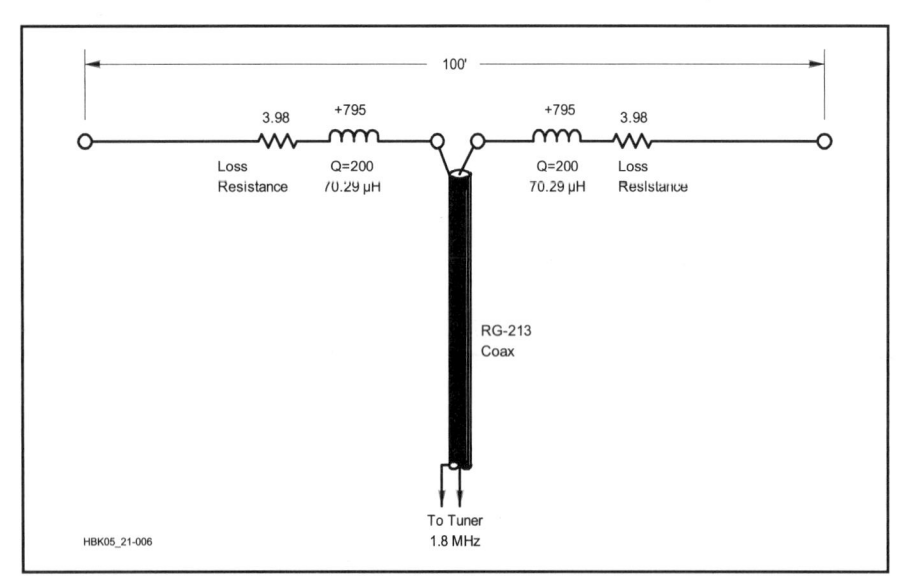

Figure 20.10 — The efficiency of a short dipole can be improved at 1.8 MHz with a pair of inductors inserted symmetrically at the feed point. Each inductor is assumed to have a Q of 200. By resonating the dipole in this fashion the system efficiency, when fed with RG-213 coax, is about 21 dB better than using this same antenna without the resonator. The disadvantage is that the formerly multiband antenna can only be used on a single band.

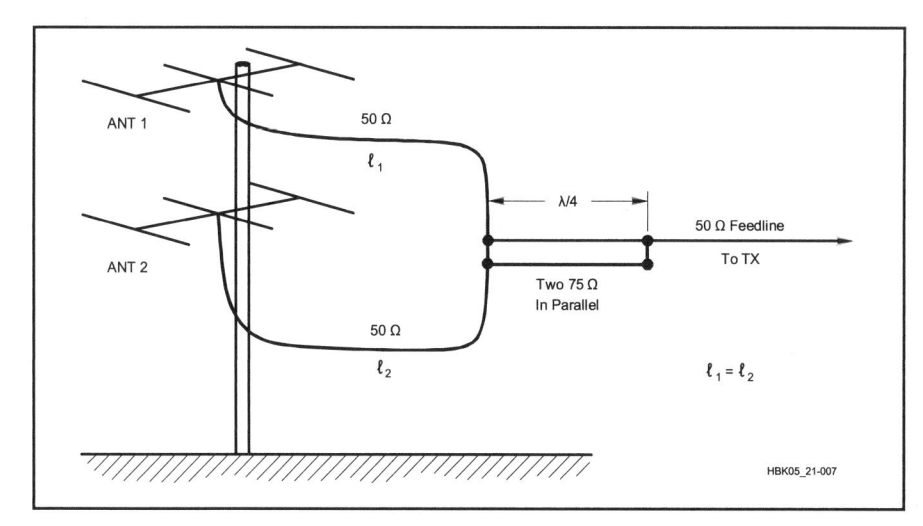

Figure 20.11 — Array of two stacked Yagis, illustrating use of ¼ λ matching sections. At the junction of the two equal lengths of 50 Ω feed line the impedance is 25 Ω. This is transformed back to 50 Ω by the two paralleled 75 Ω, ¼ λ lines, which together make a net characteristic impedance of 37.5 Ω. This is close to the 35.4 Ω value computed by the formula.

load changes, the amplifier must be retuned, an inconvenience at best.

Example: To match a 50 Ω line to a Yagi stack consisting of two antennas fed in parallel to produce a 25 Ω load, the quarter-wave matching section would require a characteristic impedance of

$$Z = \sqrt{50 \times 25} = 35.4 \; \Omega$$

RG-83 is a 35-Ω cable suitable for this application. A transmission line with a characteristic impedance of 35 Ω could be closely approximated by connecting two equal ¼ λ sections of 75 Ω cable (such as RG-11A) in parallel to yield the equivalent of a 37.5 Ω cable. Three Yagis fed in parallel would require a ¼ λ transformer made using a cable having a characteristic impedance of

$$Z = \sqrt{16.7 \times 25} = 28.9 \; \Omega$$

This is approximated by using a ¼ λ section of 50 Ω cable in parallel with a ¼ λ section of 75 Ω cable, yielding a net impedance of 30 Ω, quite close to the desired 28.9 Ω. Four Yagis fed in parallel would require a ¼ λ transformer made up using cable with a characteristic impedance of 25 Ω, easily created by using two 50 Ω cables in parallel.

The 100 foot flat-top example in the previous section with the two resonating coils has an impedance of 12 Ω at the feed point. Two RG-58A cables, each ¼ λ long at 1.8 MHz (90 ft) can be connected in parallel to feed this antenna. An additional 10 ft length of RG-213 can make up the required 100 ft. The match will be almost perfect. The disadvantage of this system is that it limits the operation to one band, but the overall efficiency will be quite good.

Another use of ¼ λ transformers is in matching the impedance of full-wave loop antennas to 50 Ω coax. For example, the driven element of a quad antenna or a full-wave 40 meter loop has an impedance of 100 to 150 Ω. Using a ¼ λ transformer made from 62, 75 or 93 Ω coaxial cable would lower the line SWR to a level where losses were insignificant.

TWELFTH-WAVE TRANSFORMERS

The Q-section is really a special case of series-section impedance matching. (See the *ARRL Antenna Book* for an extended discussion of the technique.) A particularly handy two-section variation shown in **Figure 20.12** can be used to match two different impedances of transmission line, such as 50 Ω coax and 75 Ω hardline. Sections with special impedances are not required, only sections of the two feed lines to be matched. (Also see the sidebar "Using 75 Ω Hardline in 50 Ω Systems" in the section on Choosing a Transmission Line.)

This configuration is referred to as a *twelfth-wave transformer* because when the ratio of impedances to be matched is 1.5:1 (as is the case with 50 and 75 Ω cables) the electrical length of the two matching sections between the lines to be matched is 0.0815 λ (29.3°), quite close to λ/12 (0.0833 λ or 30°). As with all synchronous transformers, the matching function works on only one band.

MATCHING TRANSFORMERS

Another matching technique uses wideband toroidal transformers. Transformers can be made that operate over very wide frequency ranges and that will match various impedances.

A very simple matching transformer consists of three windings connected in series as shown in **Figure 20.13A**. The physical arrangement of the three windings is shown in Figure 20.13B. This arrangement gives the best bandwidth. **Figure 20.14** shows a picture of this type of transformer. An IN/OUT relay

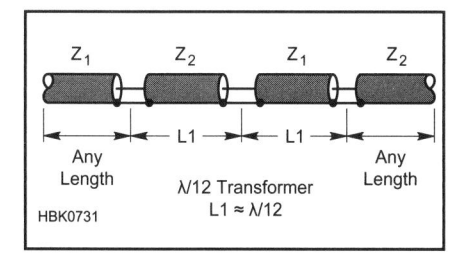

Figure 20.12 — A two-section twelfth-wave transformer can be used to match two different feed line impedances. This is a common technique for using surplus 75 Ω hardline in 50 Ω systems.

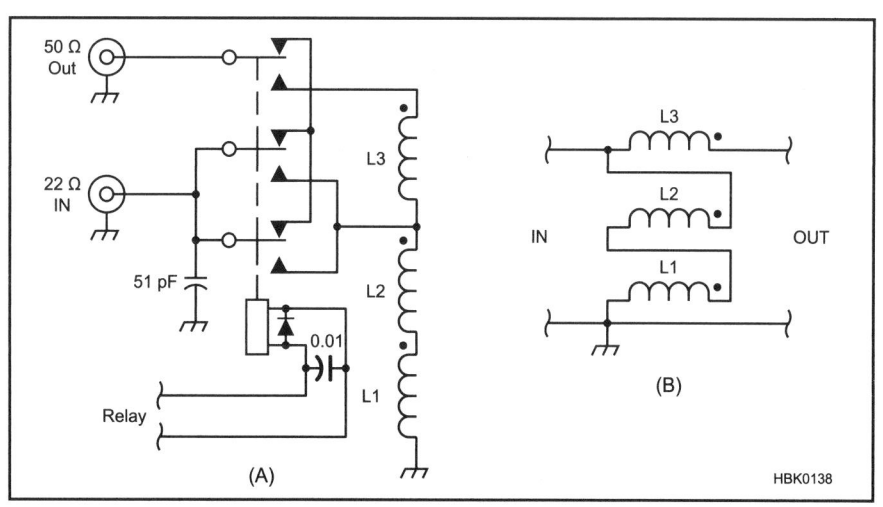

Figure 20.13 — Schematic for the impedance matching transformer described in the text. The complete schematic is shown at A. The physical positioning of the windings is shown at B.

Transmission Lines 20.15

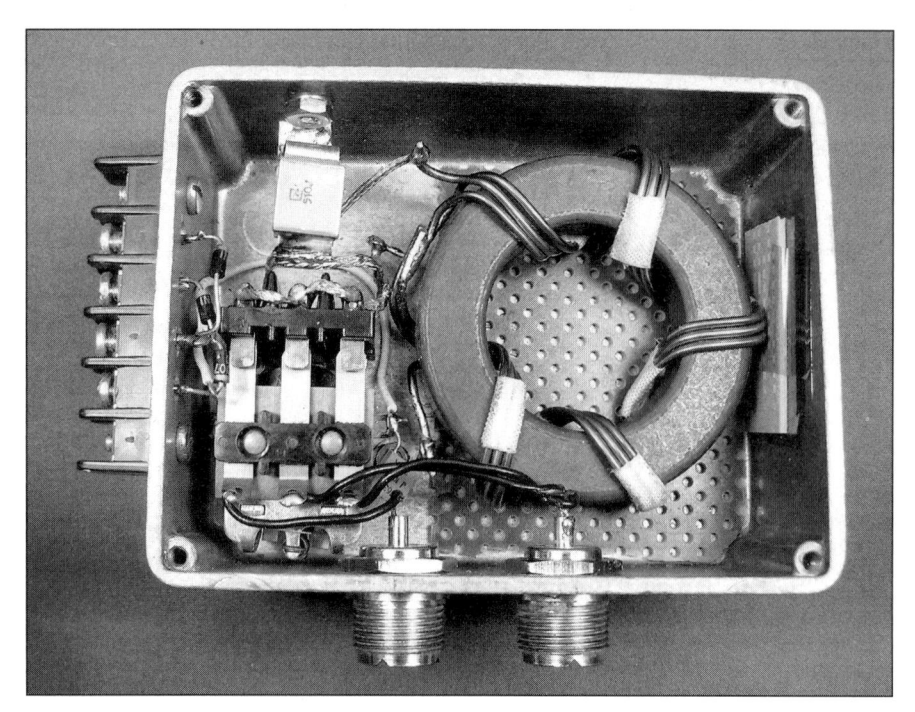

Figure 20.14 — The completed impedance matching transformer assembly for the schematic shown in Figure 20.13.

is included with the transformer. One relay pole switches the 50 Ω input port while two poles in parallel switch the 22 Ω port. Three 14 inch lengths of #14 AWG wire are taped together so they lie flat on the core. A #61 mix toroid core 2.4 inch in diameter will handle full legal power.

Use magnet wire rated for high-voltage use, such as TEMCo GP/MR-200 or Superior Essex ALLEX wire which is rated for use to 200 °C with 5.7 kV rating of the insulation. Motor repair shops may sell small quantities for single projects. Before winding on an uncoated toroid core, particularly ferrite which is abrasive, wrap the core with one or two layers of high-quality electrical tape such as Scotch 88 to avoid damaging the wire coating. When winding the toroid, it is not necessary for the wire to be pulled tight against the core, which can cause additional stresses to the insulation.

The impedance ratio of this design is 1:2.25 or 22.22-to-50 Ω. This ratio turns out to work well for two or three 50 Ω antennas in parallel. Two in parallel will give an SWR of 25/22.22 or 1.125:1. Three in parallel give an SWR of 22.22/16.67 or 1.33. The unit shown in Figure 20.14 has an SWR bandwidth of 1.5 MHz to more than 30 MHz. The 51 pF capacitor is connected to ground (shunt) at the low-impedance input to cancel unwanted stray inductive reactance.

This is a good way to stack two or three triband antennas. If they have the same length feed lines and they all point the same way, their patterns will add and some gain will result. However, they don't even need to be on the same tower or pointed in the same direction or fed with the same length lines to have some benefit. Even dissimilar antennas can sometimes show a benefit when connected together in this fashion.

20.4.4 Matching the Line to the Transmitter

So far we have been concerned mainly with the measures needed to achieve acceptable amounts of loss and a low SWR for feed lines connected to antennas. Not only is feed line loss minimized when the SWR is kept within reasonable bounds, but also the transmitter is able to perform as specified when connected to the load resistance it was designed to drive.

Most modern amateur transmitters have solid-state final amplifiers designed to work into a 50 Ω load with broadband, non-adjustable impedance matching networks. While the adjustable pi networks used in vacuum-tube amplifiers can accommodate a wide range of impedances, typical solid-state transmitters utilize built-in protection circuitry that automatically reduces output power if the SWR rises to more than about 2:1.

Besides the rather limited option of using only inherently low-SWR antennas to ensure that the transmitter sees the load for which it was designed, an *impedance-matching unit* or *antenna tuner* ("tuner" for short) can be used. The function of an antenna tuner is to transform the impedance at the input end of the transmission line, whatever that may be, to the 50 Ω value required by the transmitter for best performance.

Some solid-state transmitters incorporate (usually at extra cost) automatic antenna tuners so that they too can cope with practical antennas and transmission lines. The range of impedances that can be matched by the built-in tuners is typically rather limited, however, especially at lower frequencies. Most built-in tuners specify a maximum SWR of 3:1 that can be transformed to 1:1.

Do not forget that a tuner does *not* alter the SWR on the transmission line between

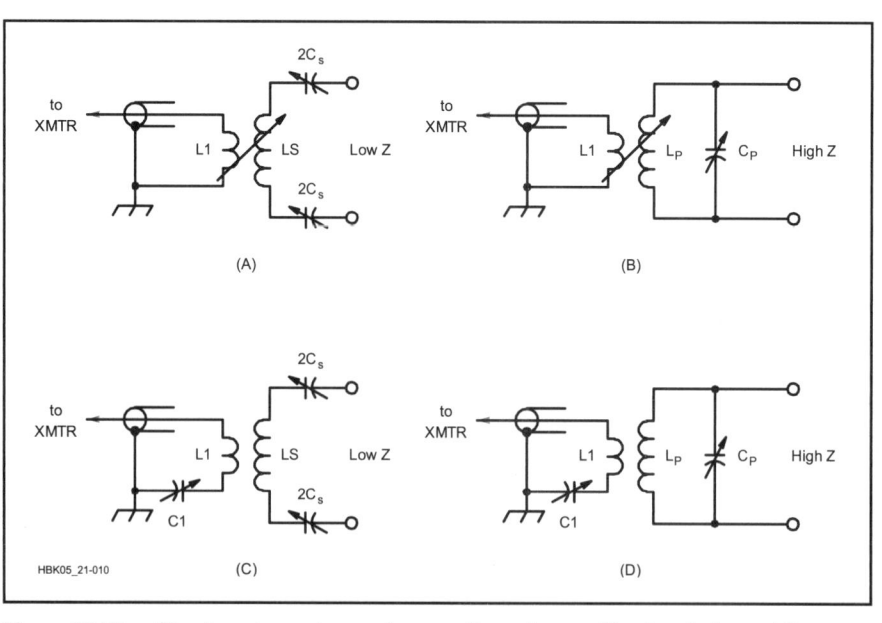

Figure 20.15 — Simple antenna tuners for coupling a transmitter to a balanced line presenting a load different from the transmitter's design load impedance, usually 50 Ω. A and B, respectively, are series and parallel tuned circuits using variable inductive coupling between coils. C and D are similar but use fixed inductive coupling and a variable series capacitor, C1. A series tuned circuit works well with a low-impedance load; the parallel circuit is better with high impedance loads (several hundred ohms or more).

the tuner and the antenna; it only adjusts the impedance at the transmitter end of the feed line to the value for which the transmitter was designed. Other names for antenna tuners include *transmatch*, *impedance matcher*, *matchbox* or *antenna coupler*. Since the SWR on the transmission line between the antenna and the output of the antenna tuner is rarely 1:1, some loss in the feed line due to the mismatch is unavoidable, even though the SWR on the short length of line between the tuner and the transmitter is 1:1.

If separate feed lines are used for different bands, the tuner can be inserted in one feed line, tuned for best VSWR, and left at that setting. If a particular antenna has a minimum VSWR in the CW portion of a band and operation in the SSB end is desired, the tuner can be used for matching and switched out when not needed. Multiband operation generally requires retuning for each band in use.

Antenna tuners for use with balanced or open-wire feed lines include a balun or link-coupling circuit as seen in **Figure 20.15**. This allows a transmitter's unbalanced coaxial output to be connected to the balanced feed line. A fully-balanced tuner has a symmetrical internal circuit with a tuner circuit for each side of the feed line and the balun at the input to the tuner where the impedance is close to 50 Ω. Most antenna tuners are unbalanced, however, with a balun located at the output of the impedance matching network, connected directly to the balanced feed line. At very high or very low impedances, the balun's power rating may be exceeded at high transmitted power levels.

Automatic antenna tuners use a microprocessor to adjust the value of the internal components. Some models sense high values of SWR and retune automatically, while others require the operator to initiate a tuning operation. Automatic tuners are available for low- and high-power operation and generally handle the same values of impedance as their manually-adjusted counterparts.

THE T NETWORK

Over the years, radio amateurs have derived a number of circuits for use as tuners. The most common form of antenna tuner in recent years is some variation of a T network, as shown in **Figure 20.16A**. Note that the choke or current balun can be used at the input or output of the tuner to match balanced feed lines.

The T network can be visualized as being two L networks back to front, where the common element has been conceptually broken down into two inductors in parallel (see Figure 20.16B). The L network connected to the load transforms the output impedance $R_a \pm j\, X_a$ into its parallel equivalent by means of the series output capacitor C2. The first L network then transforms the parallel equivalent back into the series equivalent and resonates the reactance with the input series capacitor C1.

Note that the equivalent parallel resistance R_p across the shunt inductor can be a very large value for highly reactive loads, meaning that the voltage developed at this point can be very high. For example, assume that the load impedance at 3.8 MHz presented to the antenna tuner is $Z_a = 20 - j\,1000$. If C2 is 300 pF, then the equivalent parallel resistance across L1 is 66,326 Ω. If 1500 W appears across this parallel resistance, a peak voltage of 14,106 V is produced, a very substantial level indeed. Highly reactive loads can produce very high voltages across components in a tuner.

The ARRL computer program *TLW* calculates and shows graphically the antenna-tuner values for operator-selected antenna impedances transformed through lengths of various types of practical transmission lines. (See the supplemental article "Using *TLW* to Design Impedance Matching Networks" with the downloadable supplemental content.) The **Station Accessories** chapter includes antenna tuner projects, and *The ARRL Antenna Book* contains detailed information on tuner design and construction.

ANTENNA TUNER LOCATION

The tuner is usually located near the transmitter in order to adjust it for different bands or antennas. If a tuner is in use for one particular band and does not need to be adjusted once set up for minimum VSWR, it can be placed in a weatherproof enclosure near the antenna. Some automatic tuners are designed to be installed at the antenna, for example. For some situations, placing the tuner at the base of a tower can be particularly effective and eliminates having to climb the tower to perform maintenance on the tuner.

It is useful to consider the performance of the entire antenna system when deciding where to install the antenna tuner and what types of feed line to use in order to minimize system losses. Here is an example, using the program *TLW*. Let's once again assume a flat-top antenna 50 ft high and 100 ft long and not resonant on any amateur band. As extreme examples, we will use 3.8 and 28.4 MHz with 200 ft of transmission line. There are many ways to configure this system, but three examples are shown in **Figure 20.17**.

Example 1 in Figure 20.17A shows a 200 ft run of RG-213 going to a 1:1 balun that feeds the antenna. A tuner in the shack reduces the VSWR for proper matching in the transmitter. Example 2 shows a similar arrangement

Table 20.5
Tuner Settings and Performance

Example (Figure 20.17)	Frequency (MHz)	Tuner Type	L (µH)	C (pF)	Total Loss (dB)
A	3.8	Rev L	1.46	2308	8.53
	28.4	Rev L	0.13	180.9	12.3
B	3.8	L	14.7	46	2.74
	28.4	L	0.36	15.6	3.52
C	3.8	L	11.37	332	1.81
	28.4	L	0.54	94.0	2.95

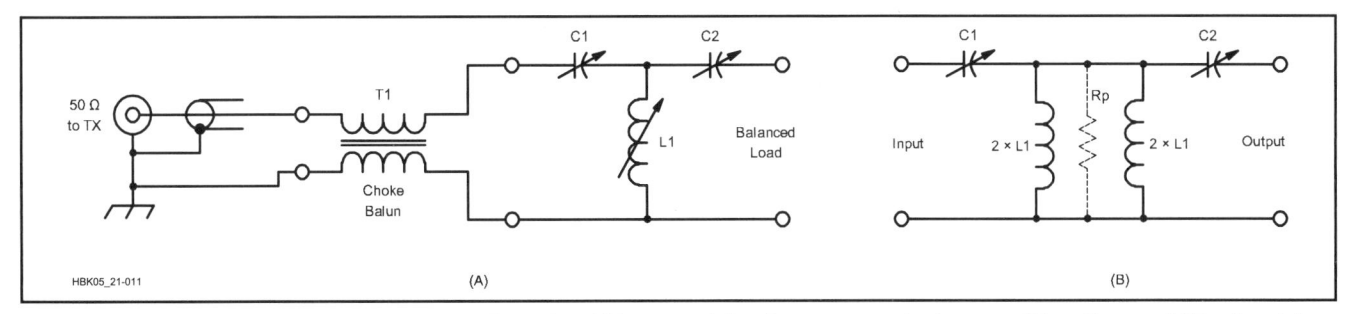

Figure 20.16 — Antenna tuner network in T configuration. This network has become popular because it has the capability of matching a wide range of impedances. At A, the balun transformer at the input of the antenna tuner preserves balance when feeding a balanced transmission line. The balun can be placed at the input or output of the tuner. At B, the T configuration is shown as two L networks back to back. (in the L network version, the two ½-value inductors replacing L1 are assumed to be adjustable with identical values).

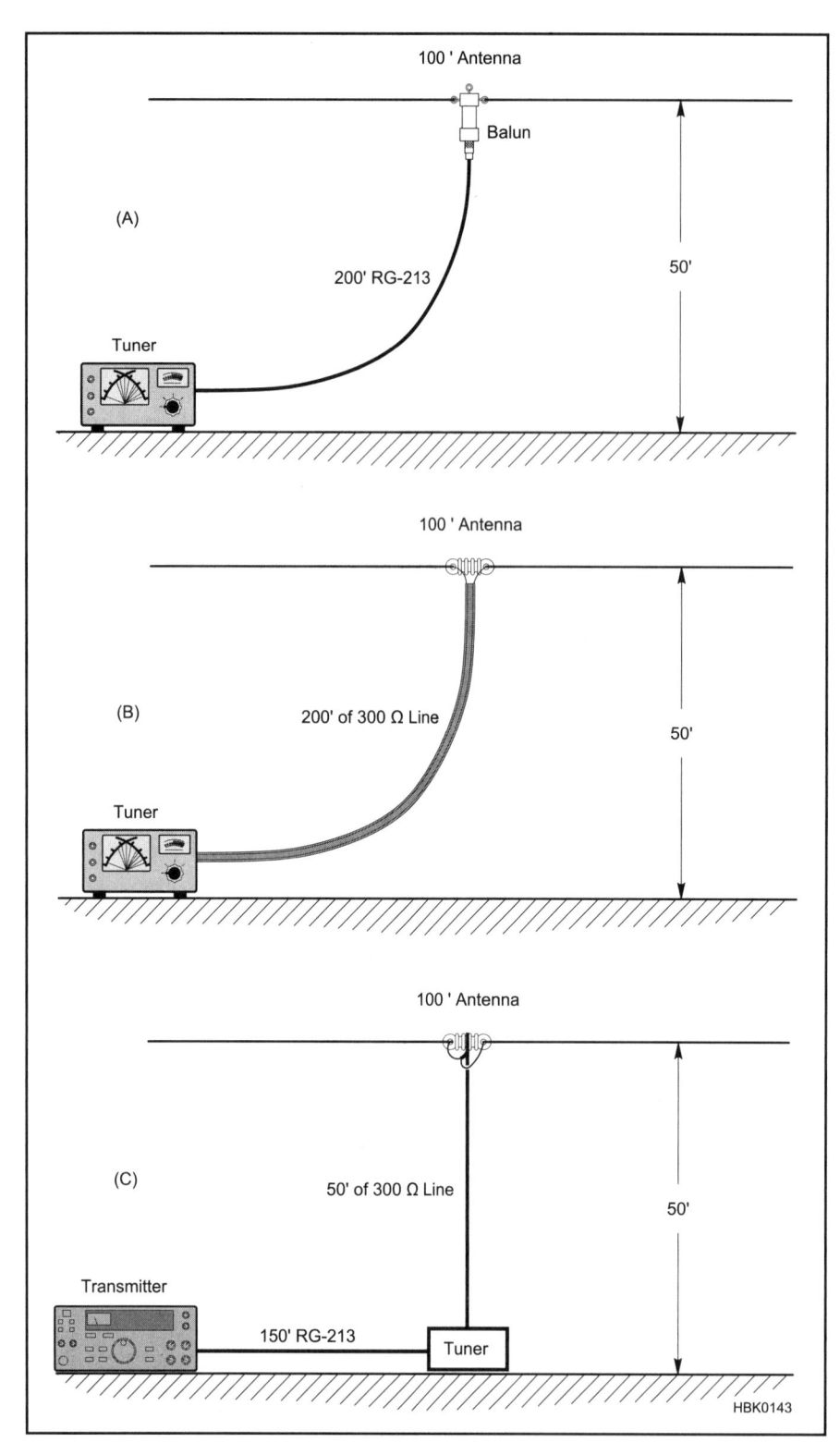

Figure 20.17 — Variations of an antenna system with different losses. The examples are discussed in the text.

using 300 Ω transmitting twin lead. Example 3 shows a 50 ft run of 300 Ω line dropping straight down to a tuner near the ground and 150 ft of RG-213 going to the shack. **Table 20.5** summarizes the losses and the tuner values required.

Some interesting conclusions can be drawn. First, direct feeding this antenna with coax through a balun is very lossy — a poor solution. If the flat-top were ½ λ long — a resonant half-wavelength dipole — direct coax feed would be a good method. In the second example, direct feed with 300 Ω low-loss line does not always give the lowest loss. The combination method in Example 3 provides the best solution.

There are other considerations as well. Supporting a balun at the antenna feed point adds stress to the wires or requires an additional support. Example 3 has some additional advantages. It feeds the antenna in a symmetrical arrangement which is best to reduce noise pickup on the shield of the feed line. The shorter feed line will not weigh down the antenna as much. The coax back to the shack can be buried or laid on the ground and it is perfectly matched. Burial of the cable will also prevent any currents from being induced on the coax shield. Once in the shack, the tuner is adjusted for minimum SWR per the manufacturer's instructions.

20.4.5 Adjusting Antenna Tuners

The process of adjusting an antenna tuner is described here and results in minimum SWR to the transmitter and also minimizes power losses in the tuner circuitry. If you have a commercial tuner and have the user's manual, the manufacturer will likely provide a method of adjustment that you should follow, including initial settings.

If you do not have a user's manual, first open the tuner and determine the circuit for the tuner. The most common circuit for commercial tuners is the high-pass T network shown in Figure 20.9F. To adjust this type of tuner:

1) Set the series capacitors to maximum value. This may not correspond to the highest number on the control scale — verify that the capacitor's plates are fully meshed.

2) Set the inductor to maximum value. This corresponds to placing a switch tap or roller inductor contact so that it is electrically closest to circuit ground.

3) If you have an antenna analyzer, connect it to the TRANSMITTER connector of the tuner. Otherwise, connect the transceiver and tune it to the desired frequency, but do not transmit.

In the following step, it is important to verify that you hear a peak in received noise before transmitting significant power through the tuner. Tuners can sometimes be adjusted to present a low SWR to the transmitter while coupling little energy to the output. Transmitting into a tuner in this configuration can damage the tuner's components.

4) Adjust the inductor throughout its range, watching the antenna analyzer for a dip in the SWR or listen for a peak in the received noise. Return the inductor to the setting for lowest SWR or highest received noise.

    4a) If no SWR minimum or noise peak is detected, reduce the value of the capacitor closest to the transmitter in steps of about 20% and repeat.

    4b) If still no SWR minimum or noise peak is detected, return the input capacitor to maximum value and reduce the output capacitor value in steps of about 20%.

    4c) If still no SWR minimum or noise peak

is detected, return the output capacitor to maximum value and reduce both input and output capacitors in 20% steps.

5) Once a combination of settings is found with a definite SWR minimum or noise peak:

5a) If you are using an antenna analyzer, make small adjustments to find the combination of settings that produce minimum SWR with the maximum value of input and output capacitance.

5b) If you do not have an antenna analyzer, set the transmitter output power to about 10 W, ensure that you won't cause interference, identify with your call sign, and transmit a steady carrier by making the same adjustments as in step 5a.

5c) For certain impedances, the tuner may not be able to reduce the SWR to an acceptable value. In this case, try adding feed line at the output of the tuner from $\frac{1}{8}$ to $\frac{1}{2} \lambda$ electrical wavelengths long. This will not change the feed line SWR, but it may transform the impedance to a value more suitable for the tuner components.

In general, for any type of tuner, begin with the maximum reactance to ground (maximum inductance or minimum capacitance) and the minimum series reactance between the source and load (minimum inductance or maximum capacitance). The configuration that produces the minimum SWR with maximum reactance to ground and minimum series reactance will generally have the highest efficiency and broadest tuning bandwidth.

To reduce on-the-air tune-up time, record the settings of the tuner for each antenna and band of operation. If the tuner requires readjustment across the band, record the settings of the tuner at several frequencies across the band. Print out the results and keep it near the tuner — this will allow you to adjust the tuner quickly with only a short transmission to check or fine tune the settings. This also serves as a diagnostic, since changes in the setting indicate a change in the antenna system.

20.4.6 Myths About SWR

This is a good point to stop and mention that there are some enduring and quite misleading myths in Amateur Radio concerning SWR.

• Despite some claims to the contrary, a high SWR does not by itself cause RFI, or TVI or telephone interference. While it is true that an antenna located close to such devices can cause overload and interference, the SWR on the feed line to that antenna has nothing to do with it, providing of course that the tuner, feed line or connectors are not arcing. The antenna is merely doing its job, which is to radiate. The transmission line is doing its job, which is to convey power from the transmitter to the radiator.

• A second myth, often stated in the same breath as the first one above, is that a high SWR will cause excessive radiation from a transmission line. SWR has nothing to do with excessive radiation from a line. Imbalances in feed lines cause radiation, but such imbalances are not related to SWR. An asymmetric arrangement of a transmission line and antenna can result in current being induced on the transmission line — on the shield of coax or as an imbalance of currents in an open-wire line. This current will radiate just as if it was on an antenna. A choke balun is used on coaxial feed lines to reduce these currents as described in the section on baluns later in this chapter.

• A third and perhaps even more prevalent myth is that you can't "get out" if the SWR on your transmission line is higher than 1.5:1, or 2:1 or some other such arbitrary figure. On the HF bands, if you use reasonable lengths of good coaxial cable (or even better yet, open-wire line), the truth is that you need not be overly concerned if the SWR at the load is kept below about 6:1. This sounds pretty radical to some amateurs who have heard horror story after horror story about SWR. The fact is that if you can load up your transmitter without any arcing inside, or if you use a tuner to make sure your transmitter is operating into its rated load resistance, you can enjoy a very effective station, using antennas with feed lines having high values of SWR on them. For example, a 450 Ω open-wire line connected to the multiband dipole in the previous sections would have a 19:1 SWR on it at 3.8 MHz. Yet time and again this antenna has proven to be a great performer at many installations.

Fortunately or unfortunately, SWR is one of the few antenna and transmission-line parameters easily measured by the average radio amateur. Ease of measurement does not mean that a low SWR should become an end in itself! The hours spent pruning an antenna so that the SWR is reduced from 1.5:1 down to 1.3:1 could be used in far more rewarding ways — making contacts, for example, or studying transmission line theory.

20.5 Baluns and Transmission Line Transformers

A center-fed dipole or a loop in free space is *balanced*, meaning electrically and physically symmetrical with respect to the feed point. In practice, very few such antennas are balanced due to the effects of ground, nearby conductive objects and surfaces, and coupling to the feed line, whether coax or open-wire line. The last can result in *common-mode* current flowing on the feed line, which affects the antenna system impedance and can radiate in unwanted directions or pick up noise. In order to minimize these effects, the feed line can be detuned or *decoupled* from the antenna.

Many amateurs use center-fed dipoles or Yagis, fed with unbalanced coaxial line. Some method should be used for connecting the line to the antenna without upsetting the symmetry of the antenna itself. This requires a circuit that will isolate the balanced load from the unbalanced line, while still providing efficient power transfer. Devices for doing this are called *baluns* (a contraction for "balanced to unbalanced"). A balanced antenna fed with balanced line, such as two-wire ladder line, will maintain its inherent balance, so long as external causes of unbalance are avoided. However, even they will require some sort of balun at the transmitter, since modern transmitters have unbalanced (coaxial) outputs.

If a balanced antenna is fed at the center by a coaxial feed line without a balun, as indicated in **Figure 20.18A**, the inherent symmetry and balance is upset because one side of the ½ λ radiator is connected to the shield while the other is connected to the inner conductor. On the side connected to the shield, current can be diverted from flowing into the antenna, and instead can flow away from the antenna on the outside of the coaxial shield. The field thus set up cannot be canceled by the field from the inner conductor because the fields inside the cable cannot escape through the shielding of the outer conductor. Hence currents flowing on the outside of the line will be responsible for some radiation from the line, just as if they were flowing on an antenna.

This is a good point at which to say that striving for perfect balance in a line and antenna system is not always absolutely mandatory. For example, if a nonresonant, center-fed dipole is fed with open-wire line and a tuner for multiband operation, the most desirable radiation pattern for general-purpose communication is actually an omnidirectional pattern. A certain amount of feed-line radiation might actually help fill in otherwise undesirable nulls in the azimuthal pattern of the antenna itself. Furthermore, the radiation pattern of a coaxial-fed dipole that is only a few tenths of a wavelength off the ground (50 feet high on the 80 meter band, for example) is not very directional anyway, because of its severe interaction with the ground.

Purists may cry out in dismay, but there are many thousands of coaxial-fed dipoles in daily use worldwide that perform very effectively without the benefit of a balun. See **Figure 20.19A** for a worst-case comparison between a dipole with and without a balun at its feed point. This is with a 1 λ feed line slanted downward 45° under one side of the antenna. *Common-mode currents* are con-

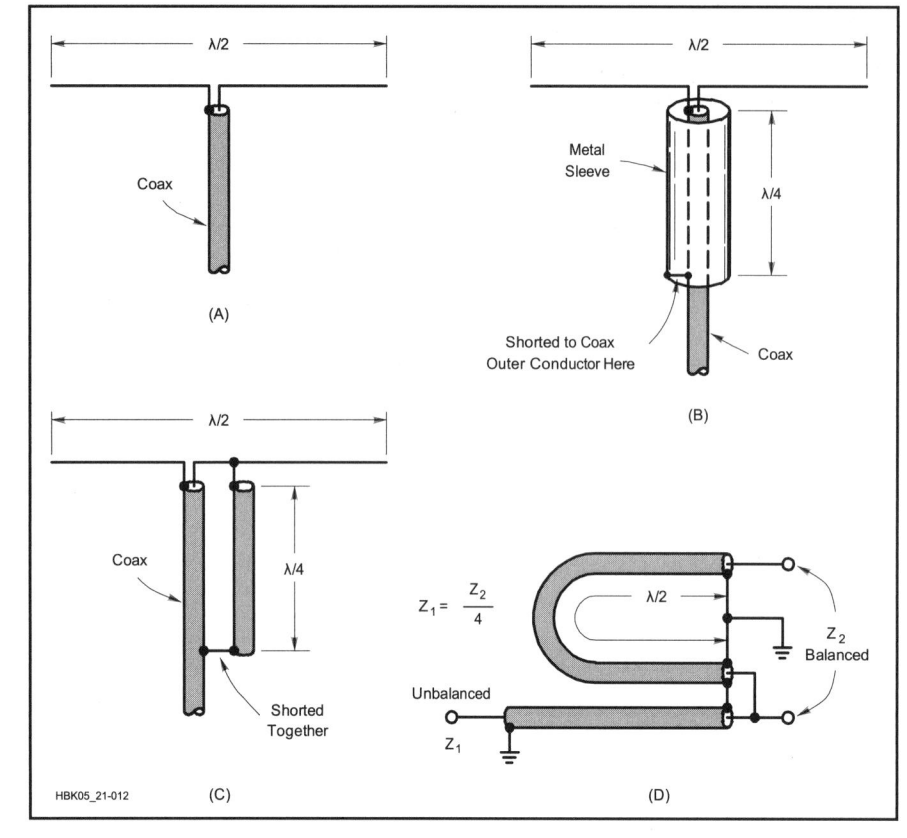

Figure 20.18 — Quarter-wavelength baluns. Radiator with coaxial feed (A) and methods of preventing unbalanced currents from flowing on the outside of the transmission line (B and C). The ½ λ phasing section shown at D is used for coupling to an unbalanced circuit when a 4:1 impedance ratio is desired or can be accepted.

ducted and induced onto the outside of the shield of the feed line, which in turn radiates. The amount of pattern distortion is not particularly severe for a dipole. It is debatable whether the bother and expense of installing a balun for such an antenna is worthwhile.

Some form of balun should be used to preserve the pattern of an antenna that is purposely designed to be highly directional, such as a Yagi or a quad. Figure 20.19B shows the distortion that can result from common-mode currents conducted and radiated back onto the feed line for a 5 element Yagi. This antenna has purposely been designed for an excellent pattern but the common-mode currents seriously distort the rearward pattern and reduce the forward gain as well. A balun is highly desirable in this case.

Choke or current baluns force equal and opposite currents to flow in the load (the antenna) by creating a high common-mode impedance to currents that are equal in both conductors or that flow on the outside of coaxial cable shields, such as those induced by the antenna's radiated field. The result of using a current balun is that currents coupled back onto the transmission line from the antenna are effectively reduced, or "choked off," even if the antenna is not perfectly balanced. Choke baluns are particularly useful for feeding asymmetrical antennas with unbalanced coax line.

The common-mode impedance of the choke balun varies with frequency, but the line's differential-mode impedance is unaffected.

Reducing common-mode current on a feed line also reduces:
• Radiation from the feed line that can distort an antenna's radiation pattern
• Radiation from the feed line that can cause RFI to nearby devices
• RF current in the shack and on power-line wiring
• Coupling of noise currents on the feed line to receivers and receiving antennas
• Coupling between different antennas via their feed lines

A single choke balun at the antenna feed point may not be sufficient to reduce common-mode current everywhere along a long feed line. If common-mode current on the line far from the antenna feed point is a problem, additional choke baluns can be placed at approximately ¼ λ intervals along the line. This breaks up the line electrically into segments too short to act as effective antennas. The chokes in this case function similarly to insulators used to divide tower guy wires into non-resonant lengths.

DETERMINING BALUN POLARITY

Many baluns, impedance transformers, line isolators, and other similar items are manufactured as sealed units and markings for output polarity with respect to the input connector are not often clear. For designs in which one or more continuous coaxial cables are connected between the input and output terminals, a resistance measurement will suffice to determine polarity. In flux-coupled designs there is no continuity between the input and output terminals at dc so a resistance measurement cannot be used. Similarly, for autotransformer designs there may be a low resistance across the input or output terminals. In these cases, it is necessary to test the units at RF.

The first method is to test the unit using a dual-trace oscilloscope. Analog scopes should be in "Chop" mode so that both traces show display waveforms synchronized in time. Digital scopes must also sample both waveforms at the same time. Do not use "Alt" or an alternating waveform display. Drive the input to the unit with a signal generator's output in the unit's specified operating frequency range. Connect one scope channel to the unit's input and the other channel to the output. If the waveforms are displayed in-phase, the connections to the scope have the same polarity.

The following procedure requires only a signal generator and RF voltmeter (see the **Test Equipment and Measurements** chapter) and is used to check two identical units. If the units are substantially different, the test may not be conclusive or reliable. The procedure assumes a 50 Ω system impedance. If the units operate at an impedance very different from 50 Ω, such as for 300, 450, or 600 Ω open-wire line, use a 6 to 10 dB attenuator in the generator output to isolate the generator from the mismatch.

Connect the signal generator output to the input of both units using a T connector and identical lengths of feed line. Connect one output terminal of unit "A" to an output terminal of unit "B" and measure the RF voltage across the combined balun outputs. Swap the output terminal connections on one of the units and measure the RF voltage again. One arrangement of connections should show a substantially higher output voltage — this is the arrangement with the same polarity for both units.

20.5.1 Quarter-Wave Baluns

Figure 20.18B shows a balun arrangement known as a *bazooka*, which uses a sleeve over the transmission line. The sleeve, together with the outside portion of the outer coax conductor, forms a shorted ¼ λ section of transmission line. The impedance looking into the open end of such a section is very high, so the end of the outer conductor of the coaxial line is effectively isolated from the part of the line below the sleeve. The length is an electrical ¼ λ, and because of the velocity factor may be physically shorter if the insulation between the sleeve and the line is not air. The bazooka has no effect on antenna impedance at the frequency where the ¼ λ sleeve is resonant. However, the sleeve adds inductive shunt reactance at frequencies lower, and capacitive shunt reactance at frequencies higher than the ¼ λ resonant frequency. The bazooka is mostly used at VHF, where its physical size does not present a major problem.

Another method that gives an equivalent effect is shown at Figure 20.18C. Since the voltages at the antenna terminals are equal and opposite (with reference to ground), equal and opposite currents flow on the surfaces of the line and second conductor. Beyond the shorting point, in the direction of the transmitter, these currents combine to cancel out each other. The balancing section acts like an open circuit to the antenna, since it is a ¼ λ parallel-conductor line shorted at the far end, and thus has no effect on normal antenna operation. This is not essential to the line-balancing function of the device, however, and baluns of this type are sometimes made shorter than ¼ λ to provide a shunt inductive reactance required in certain matching systems (such as the hairpin match described in the **Antennas** chapter).

Figure 20.18D shows a balun in which equal and opposite voltages, balanced to ground, are taken from the inner conductors of the main transmission line and a ½ λ phasing section. Since the voltages at the balanced end are in series while the voltages at the unbalanced end are in parallel, there is a 4:1 step-down in impedance from the balanced to the unbalanced side. This arrangement is useful for coupling between a 300 Ω balanced line and a 75 Ω unbalanced coaxial line.

Figure 20.20 shows a variation on the

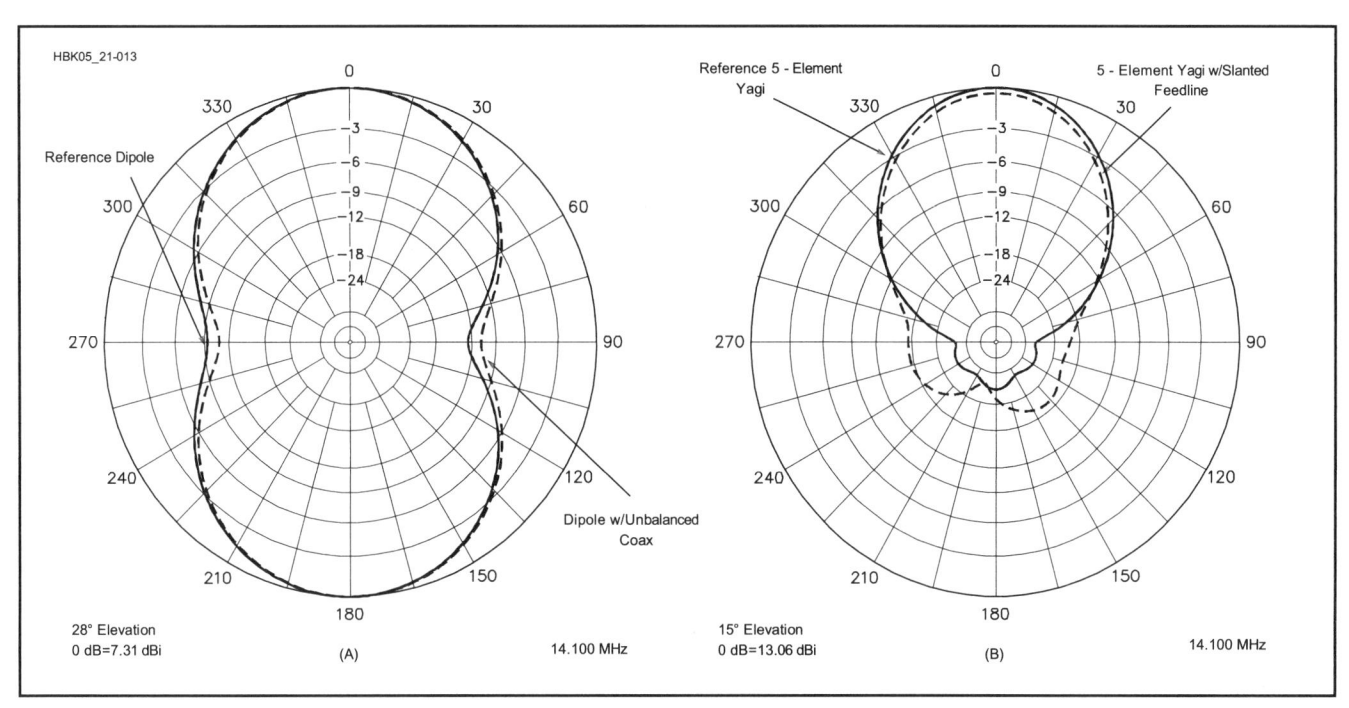

Figure 20.19 — At A, computer-generated azimuthal responses for two λ/2 dipoles placed 0.71 λ high over typical ground. The solid line is for a dipole with no feed line. The dashed line is for an antenna with its feed line slanted 45° down to ground. Current induced on the outer braid of the 1 λ long coax by its asymmetry with respect to the antenna causes the pattern distortion. At B, azimuthal response for two 5 element 20 meter Yagis placed 0.71 λ over average ground. Again, the solid line is for a Yagi without a feed line and the dashed line is for an antenna with a 45° slanted, 1 λ long feed line. The distortion in the radiated pattern is now clearly more serious than for a simple dipole. A balun is needed at the feed point, and most likely point, preferably ¼ λ from the feed point, to suppress the common-mode currents and restore the pattern.

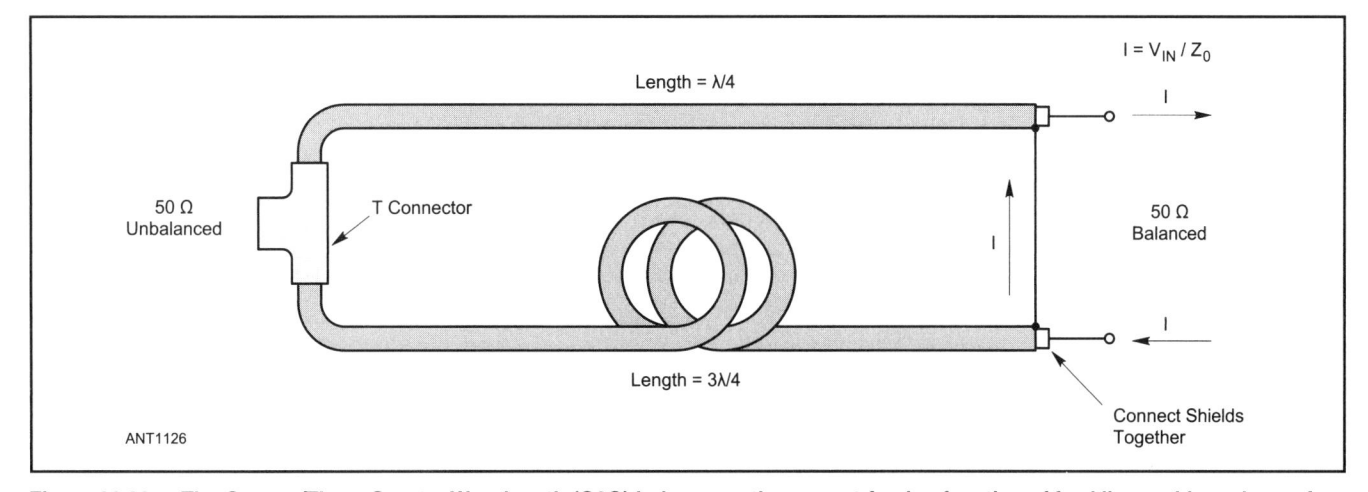

Figure 20.20 — The Quarter/Three-Quarter Wavelength (Q3Q) balun uses the current-forcing function of feed lines odd numbers of λ/4 long and the λ/2 delay of the longer line to cause equal and opposite currents to flow in the antenna terminals.

quarter-wave balun called the Quarter/Three-Quarter-Wave, or Q3Q, balun. It is a 1:1 decoupling balun made from two pieces of coaxial cable. One leg is ¼ λ long and the other is ¾ λ long. The two cables and the feed line are joined together with a T connector. At the antenna, the shields of the cables are connected together and the center conductors connected to the terminals of the antenna feed point. The balun has very little loss and is reported to have a bandwidth of more than 10%.

The balun works because of the current-forcing function of a transmission line is an odd number of λ/4 long. The current at the output of such a transmission line is V_{IN}/Z_0 regardless of the load impedance (less line losses — see the references for *QST* articles about this balun), similar to the behavior of a current source. Because both lines are fed with the same voltage, being connected in parallel, the output currents will also be equal.

The current out of the ¾ λ line is delayed by 180° from the current out of the ¼ λ line and so is out of phase. The result is that equal and opposite currents are forced into the terminals of the load.

20.5.2 Transmission Line Transformers

The basic transmission line transformer, from which other transformers are derived, is the 1:1 *choke balun* or *current balun*, shown in **Figure 20.21A**. To construct this type of balun, a length of coaxial cable or a pair of close-spaced, parallel wires forming a transmission line are wrapped around a ferrite rod or toroid or inserted through a number of beads. (The coiled feed line choke balun is discussed in the next section.) For the HF bands, use type 75 or type 31 material. Type 43 is used on the VHF bands. The Z_0 of the line should equal the load resistance, R.

Because of the ferrite, a high impedance exists between points A and C and a virtually identical impedance between B and D. This is true for parallel wire lines and it is also true for coax. The ferrite affects the A to C impedance of the coax inner conductor and the B to D impedance of the outer braid equally.

The conductors (two wires or coax braid and center-wire) are tightly coupled by electromagnetic fields and therefore constitute a good conventional transformer with a turns ratio of 1:1. The voltage from A to C is equal to and in-phase with that from B to D. These are called the *common-mode voltages* (CM).

A common-mode (CM) current is one that has the same value and direction in both wires (or on the shield and center conductor). Because of the ferrite, the CM current encounters a high impedance that acts to reduce (choke) the current. The normal *differential-mode* (DM) signal does not encounter this CM impedance because the electromagnetic fields due to equal and opposite currents in the two conductors cancel each other at the ferrite, so the magnetic flux in the ferrite is virtually zero. (See the section on Transmitting Ferrite Choke Baluns.)

The main idea of the transmission line transformer is that although the CM impedance may be very large, the DM signal is virtually unopposed, especially if the line length is a small fraction of a wavelength. But it is very important to keep in mind that the common-mode voltage across the ferrite winding that is due to this current is efficiently coupled to the center wire by conventional transformer action, as mentioned before and easily verified. This equality of CM voltages, and also CM impedances, reduces the *conversion* of a CM signal to an *undesired* DM signal that can interfere with the *desired* DM signal in both transmitters and receivers.

The CM current, multiplied by the CM impedance due to the ferrite, produces a CM voltage. The CM impedance has L and C reactance and also R. So L, C and R cause a broad parallel self-resonance at some frequency. The R component also produces some dissipation (heat) in the ferrite. This dissipation is an excellent way to dispose of a small

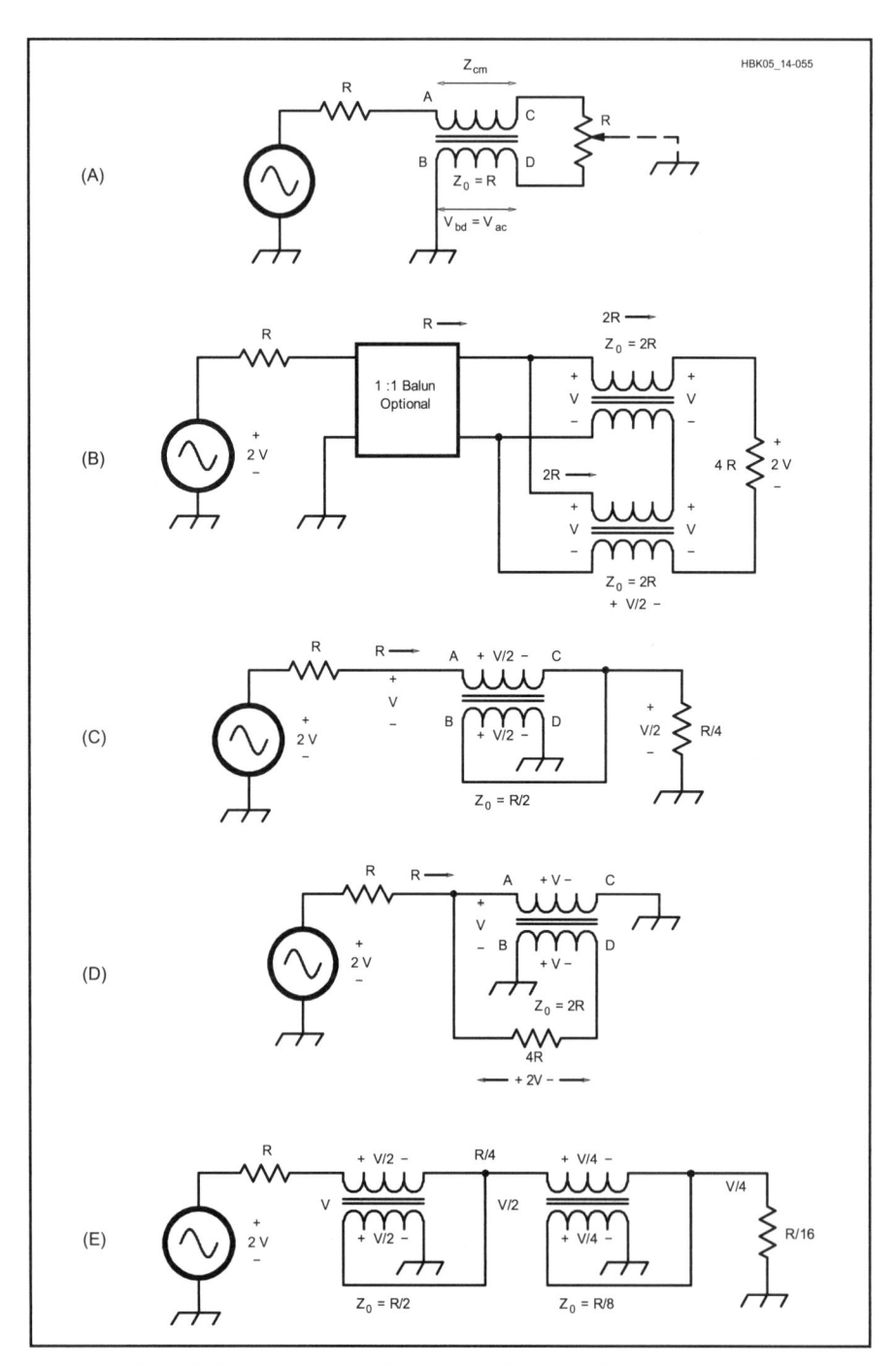

Figure 20.21 — (A) Basic current or choke balun. (B) Guanella 1:4 transformer. (C) Ruthroff 4:1 unbalanced transformer. (D) Ruthroff 1:4 balanced transformer. (E) Ruthroff 16:1 unbalanced transformer.

amount of unwanted CM power.

Because of the high CM impedance, the two output wires of the balun in Figure 20.21A have a high impedance with respect to, and are therefore "isolated" from, the generator. This feature is very useful because now any point of R at the output can be grounded. In a well-designed balun circuit almost all of the current in one conductor returns to the generator through the other conductor, despite this ground connection. Note also that the ground connection introduces some CM voltage across the balun cores and this has to be taken into account. This CM voltage is a maximum if point C is grounded. If point D is grounded and if all "ground" connections are at the same potential, which they often are not, the CM voltage is zero and the balun may no longer be needed. In a coax balun the return current flows on the inside surface of the braid.

We now look briefly at a transmission line transformer that is based on the choke balun. Figure 20.21B shows two identical choke baluns whose inputs are in parallel and whose outputs are in series. The output voltage amplitude of each balun is identical to the common input, so the two outputs add in-phase (equal time delay) to produce twice the input voltage. It is the high CM impedance that makes this voltage addition possible. If the power remains constant the load current must be one-half the generator current, and the load resistor is 2V/0.5I = 4V/I = 4R.

THE GUANELLA TRANSFORMER

The CM voltage in each balun is V/2, so there is some flux in the cores. The right side floats. This is named the *Guanella* transformer. If Z_0 of the lines equals 2R and if the load is a pure resistance of 4R then the input resistance R is independent of line length. If the lines are exactly one-quarter wavelength, then $Z_{IN} = (2R)^2 / Z_L$, an impedance inverter, where Z_{IN} and Z_L are complex. The quality of balance can often be improved by inserting a 1:1 balun (Figure 20.21A) at the left end so that both ends of the 1:4 transformer are floating and a ground is at the far left side as shown. The Guanella transformer can also be operated from a grounded right end to a floating left end. The 1:1 balun at the left then allows a grounded far left end.

THE RUTHROFF TRANSFORMER

Figure 20.21C is the *Ruthroff* transformer in which the input voltage V is divided into two equal in-phase voltages AC and BD (they are tightly coupled), so the output is V/2. And because power is constant, $I_{OUT} = 2I_{IN}$ and the load is R/4. There is a CM voltage V/2 between A and C and between B and D, so in normal operation the core is not free of magnetic flux. The input and output both return to ground so it can also be operated from right to left for a 1:4 impedance step-up.

The Ruthroff transformer is often used as an amplifier interstage transformer, for example between 200 Ω and 50 Ω. To maintain low attenuation the line length should be much less than one-fourth wavelength at the highest frequency of operation, and its Z_0 should be R/2. A balanced version is shown in Figure 20.21D, where the CM voltage is V, not V/2, and transmission is from left-to-right only. Because of the greater flux in the cores, no different than a conventional transformer, this is not a preferred approach, although it could be used with air wound coils (for example in antenna tuner circuits) to couple 75 Ω unbalanced to 300 Ω balanced. The tuner circuit could then transform 75 Ω to 50 Ω.

APPLICATIONS OF TRANSMISSION-LINE TRANSFORMERS

There are many transformer schemes that use the basic ideas of Figure 20.21. Several of them, with their toroid winding instructions, are shown in **Figure 20.22**. Two of the most commonly used devices are the 1:1 current balun and 4:1 impedance transformer wound on toroid cores as shown in **Figure 20.23**.

Because of space limitations, for a comprehensive treatment we suggest *Transmission Line Transformers* and *Building and Using Baluns and Ununs* by Jerry Sevick W2FMI (SK). For applications in solid-state RF power amplifiers, see Sabin and Schoenike, *HF Radio Systems and Circuits*, Chapter 12.

20.5.3 Coiled-Coax Choke Baluns

The simplest construction method for a 1:1 choke balun made from coaxial feed line is simply to wind a portion of the cable into a coil (see **Figure 20.24**), creating an inductor from the shield's outer surface. This type of choke balun is simple, cheap and reduces common-mode current. Currents on the outside of the shield encounter the coil's impedance, while currents on the inside are unaffected.

A scramble-wound flat coil (like a coil of rope) shows a broad resonance that easily covers three octaves, making it reasonably effective over the entire HF range. If particular problems are encountered on a single band, a coil that is resonant on that band may be added. The choke baluns described in **Table 20.6** were constructed to have a high impedance at the indicated frequencies as measured with an impedance meter. This construction technique is not effective with open-wire or twin-lead line because of coupling between adjacent turns.

The inductor formed by the coaxial cable's shield is self-resonant due to the distributed capacitance between the turns of the coil. The self-resonant frequency can be found by using a dip meter. Leave the ends of the choke open, couple the coil to the dip meter, and tune for a dip. This is the parallel resonant frequency and the impedance will be very high.

The distributed capacitance of a flat-coil choke balun can be reduced (or at least controlled) by winding the cable as a single-layer solenoid around a section of plastic pipe, an empty bottle or other suitable cylinder. **Figure 20.25** shows how to make this type

Baluns, Chokes, and Transformers

The term "balun" applies to any device that transfers differential-mode signals between a balanced (*bal-*) system and an unbalanced (*un-*) system while maintaining symmetrical energy distribution at the terminals of the balanced system. The term only applies to the function of energy transfer, not to how the device is constructed. It doesn't matter whether the balanced-unbalanced transition is made through transmission line structures, flux-coupled transformers, or simply by blocking unbalanced current flow. A common-mode *choke balun*, for example, performs the balun function by putting impedance in the path of common-mode currents and is therefore a balun.

A *current balun* forces symmetrical current at the balanced terminals. This is of particular importance in feeding antennas, since antenna currents determine the antenna's radiation pattern. A *voltage balun* forces symmetrical voltages at the balanced terminals. Voltage baluns are less effective in causing equal currents at their balanced terminals, such as at an antenna's feed point.

An *impedance transformer* may or may not perform the balun function. Impedance transformation (changing the ratio of voltage and current) is not required of a balun nor is it prohibited. There are balanced-to-balanced impedance transformers (transformers with isolated primary and secondary windings, for example) just as there are unbalanced-to-unbalanced impedance transformers (autotransformer and transmission-line designs). A *transmission-line transformer* is a device that performs the function of power transfer (with or without impedance transformation) by utilizing the characteristics of transmission lines.

Multiple devices are often combined in a single package called a "balun." For example, a "4:1 current balun" is a 1:1 current balun in series with a 4:1 impedance transformer or voltage balun. Other names for baluns are common, such as "line isolator" for a choke balun. Baluns are often referred to by their construction — "bead balun," "coiled-coax balun," "sleeve balun," and so forth. What is important is to separate the function (power transfer between balanced and unbalanced systems) from the construction.

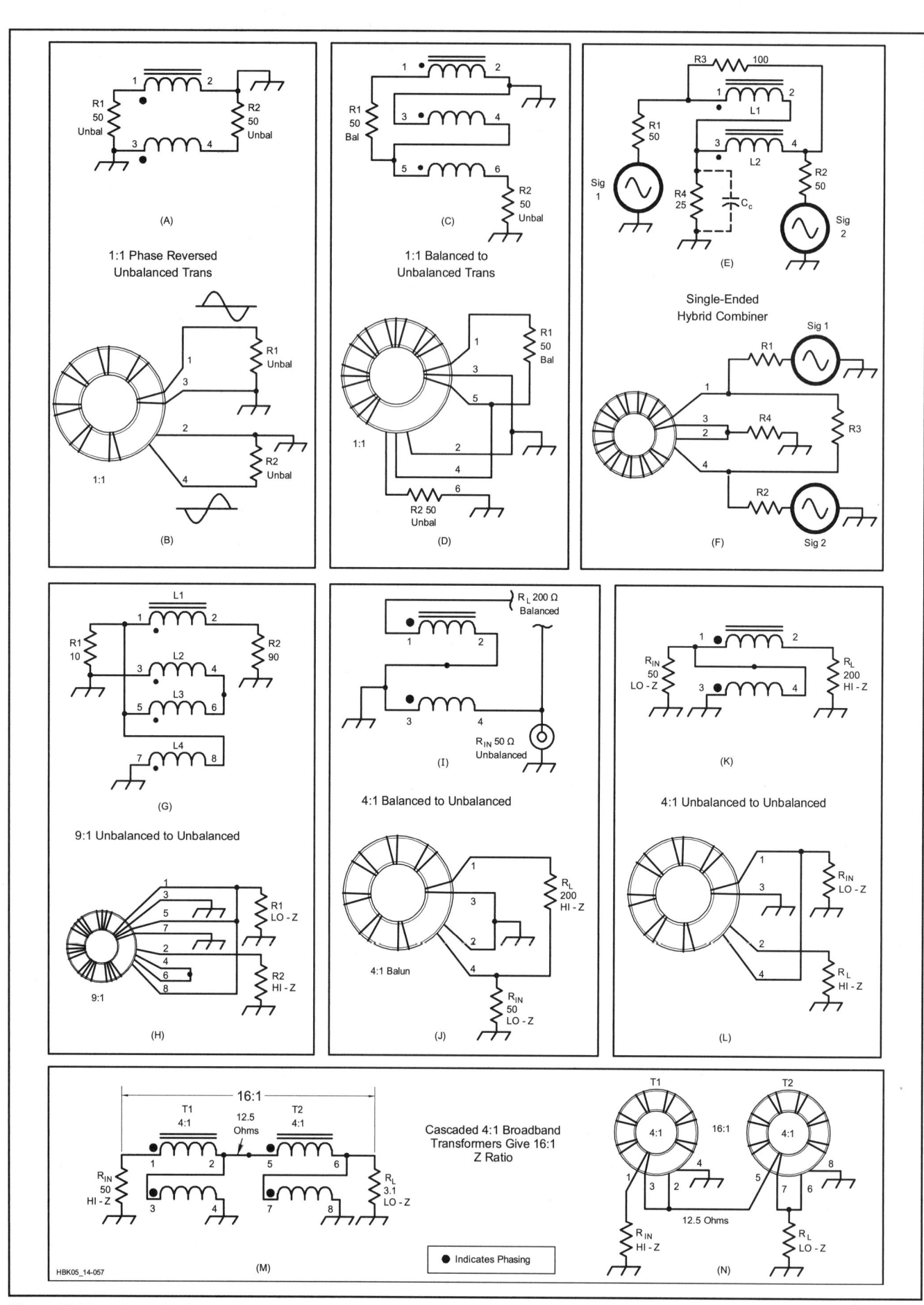

Figure 20.22 — Assembly instructions for some transmission-line transformers. See text for ferrite material type.

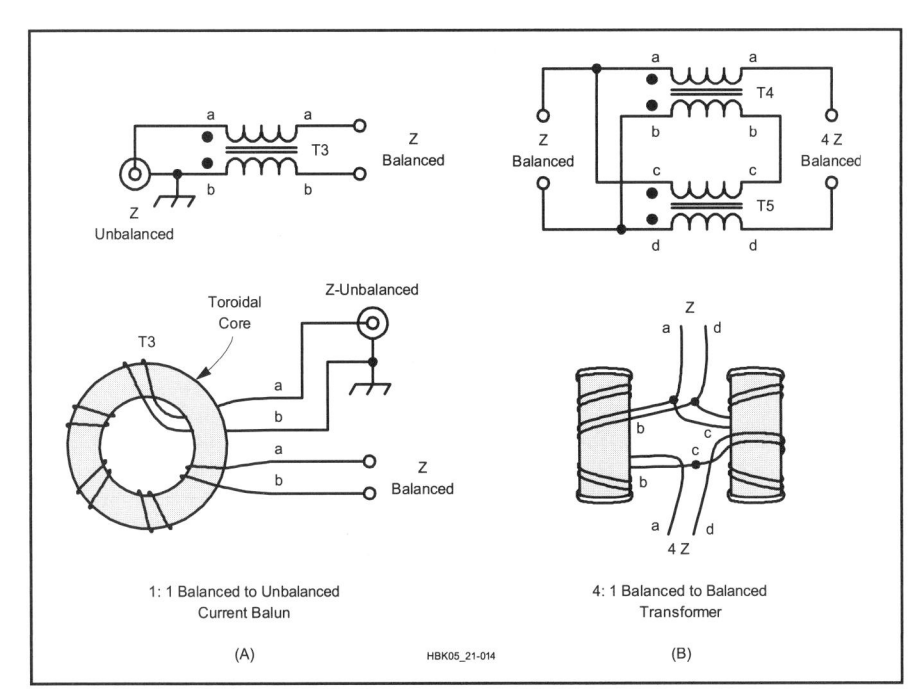

Figure 20.23 — Broadband baluns. (A) 1:1 current balun and (B) Guanella 4:1 impedance transformer wound on two cores, which are separated. Use 12 bifilar turns of #14 AWG enameled wire, wound on 2.4 inch OD cores for A and B. Distribute bifilar turns evenly around core. See text for ferrite material type.

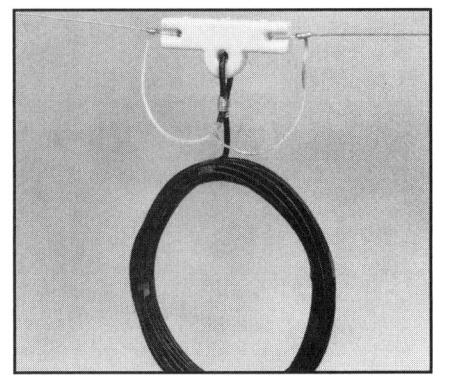

Figure 20.24 — RF choke formed by coiling the feed line at the point of connection to the antenna. The inductance of the choke isolates the antenna from the outer surface of the feed line.

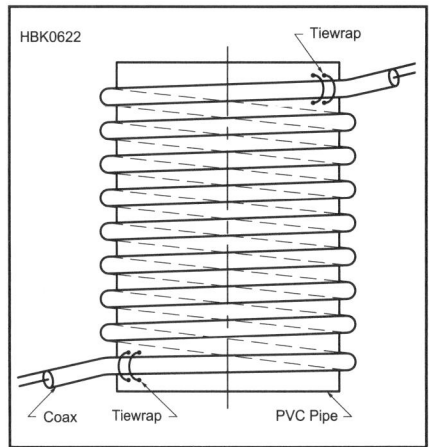

Figure 20.25 — Winding a coaxial choke balun as a single-layer solenoid typically increases impedance and self-resonant frequency compared to a flat-coil choke.

Table 20.6
Coiled-Coax Choke Baluns

Wind the indicated length of coaxial feed line into a coil (like a coil of rope) and secure with electrical tape. (Diameter 6-8 inches.)

The balun is most effective when the coil is near the antenna.

Lengths and diameter are not critical.

Single Band (Very Effective)

Freq (MHz)	RG-213, RG-8	RG-58
3.5	22 ft, 8 turns	20 ft, 6-8 turns
7	22 ft, 10 turns	15 ft, 6 turns
10	12 ft, 10 turns	10 ft, 7 turns
14	10 ft, 4 turns	8 ft, 8 turns
21	8 ft, 6-8 turns	6 ft, 8 turns
28	6 ft, 6-8 turns	4 ft, 6-8 turns

Multiple Band

Freq (MHz)	RG-8, 58, 59, 8X, 213
3.5-30	10 ft, 7 turns
3.5-10	18 ft, 9-10 turns
1.8-3.5	40 ft, 20 turns
14-30	8 ft, 6-7 turns

of choke balun. A coil diameter of about 5 inches is reasonable. This type of construction reduces the stray capacitance between the ends of the coil.

For both types of coiled-coaxial chokes, use cable with solid insulation, not foamed, to minimize migration of the center conductor through the insulation toward the shield. The diameter of the coil should be at least 10 times the cable diameter to avoid mechanically stressing the cable.

20.5.4 Transmitting Ferrite Choke Baluns

A ferrite choke is simply a very low-Q parallel-resonant circuit tuned to the frequency where the choke should be effective. Passing a conductor through most ferrite cores (that is, one turn) produces a resonance around 150 MHz. By choosing a suitable core material, size and shape, and by adding multiple turns and varying their spacing, the choke can be "tuned" (optimized) for the required frequency range. The supplemental article "Measuring Ferrite Choke Impedance" by Jim Brown, K9YC is included with the downloadable supplemental content.

Transmitting chokes differ from other common-mode chokes because they must be designed to work well when the line they are choking carries high power. They must also be physically larger so that the bend radius of the coax is large enough that the line is not deformed. Excellent common-mode chokes having very high power handling capability can be formed simply by winding multiple turns of coax through a sufficiently large ferrite core or multiple cores. (Chokes made by winding coaxial cable on ferrite cores will be referred to as "wound-coax chokes" to distinguish them from the coiled-coax chokes of the preceding section.)

In the June 2015 *QST* article, "Don't Blow Up Your Balun," Dean Straw, N6BV noted the additional differential-mode losses (and increased potential for destructive overheating) in chokes when the feed line is severely mismatched. This is in addition to the dissipation due to common-mode current. This situation is more serious in off-center-fed or asymmetrical antennas because the common-mode voltages and currents are greater. The choke must have very high choking impedance to avoid the heating caused by high common-mode voltage. The article is included in the downloadable supplemental information package for this book.

CHOKES ON TRANSMISSION LINES

A transmission line can be wound around a ferrite core to form a common-mode choke. If the line is coax, all of the magnetic flux associated with differential mode current is confined to the dielectric (the insulating material between the center conductor and the shield). The external ferrite core carries only flux associated with common-mode current.

If the line is made up of parallel wires (a bifilar winding), a significant fraction of the flux associated with differential current will leak outside the line to the ferrite core. Leakage flux can exceed 30% of the total flux for even the most tightly-spaced bifilar

Figure 20.26 — Typical transmitting wound-coax common-mode chokes suitable for use on the HF ham bands.

winding. In addition to this leakage flux, the core will also carry the flux associated with common-mode current.

When a transformer (as opposed to a choke) is wound on a magnetic core, all of the field associated with current in the windings is carried by the core. Similarly, all forms of voltage baluns require all of the transmitted power to couple to the ferrite core. Depending on the characteristics of the core, this can result in considerable heating and power loss. Only a few ferrite core materials have loss characteristics suitable for use as the cores of high power RF transformers. Type 61 material has reasonably low dissipation below about 10 MHz, but its loss tangent rises rapidly above that frequency. The loss tangent of type 67 material makes it useful in high power transformers to around 30 MHz.

Leakage flux, corresponding to 30 to 40% of the transmitter power, causes heating in the ferrite core and attenuates the transmitted signal by a dB or so. At high power levels, temperature rise in the core also changes its magnetic properties, and in the extreme case, can result in the core temporarily losing its magnetic properties. A flux level high enough to make the core hot is also likely to saturate the core, producing distortion (harmonics, splatter, clicks).

Flux produced by common-mode current can also heat the core — if there is enough common-mode current. Dissipated power is equal to I^2R, so it can be made very small by making the common-mode impedance so large that the common-mode current is very small.

DESIGN CRITERIA

It can be shown mathematically, and experience confirms, that wound-coax chokes having a resistive impedance at the transmit frequency of at least 5000 Ω and wound with RG-8 or RG-11 size cable on five toroids are conservatively rated for 1500 W under high duty-cycle conditions, such as contesting or digital mode operation. While chokes wound with smaller coax (RG-6, RG-8X, RG-59, RG-58 size) are conservatively rated for dissipation in the ferrite core, the voltage and current ratings of those smaller cables suggests a somewhat lower limit on their power handling. Since the chokes see only the common-mode voltage, the only effect of high SWR on power handling of wound-coax chokes is the peaks of differential current and voltage along the line established by the mismatch.

Experience shows that 5000 Ω is also a good design goal to prevent RFI, noise coupling and pattern distortion. While 500-1000 Ω has long been accepted as sufficient to prevent pattern distortion, W1HIS has correctly observed that radiation and noise coupling from the feed line should be viewed as a form of pattern distortion that fills in the nulls of a directional antenna, reducing its ability to reject noise and interference.

Chokes used to break up a feed line into segments too short to interact with another antenna should have a choking impedance on the order of 1000 Ω to prevent interaction with simple antennas. A value closer to 5000 Ω may be needed if the effects of common-mode current on the feed line are filling the null of directional antennas.

BUILDING WOUND-COAX FERRITE CHOKES

Coaxial chokes should be wound with a bend radius sufficiently large that the coax is not deformed. When a line is deformed, the spacing between the center conductor and the shield varies, so voltage breakdown and heating are more likely to occur. Deformation also causes a discontinuity in the impedance; the resulting reflections may cause some waveform distortion and increased loss at VHF and UHF. (Coaxial cable has a specified "minimum bend radius".)

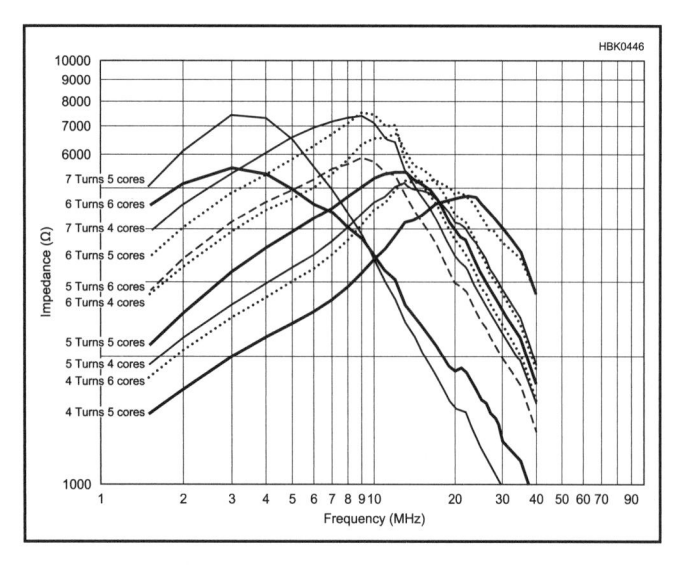

Figure 20.27 — Impedance versus frequency for HF wound-coax transmitting chokes using 2.4 inch toroid cores of #31 material with RG-8X coax.

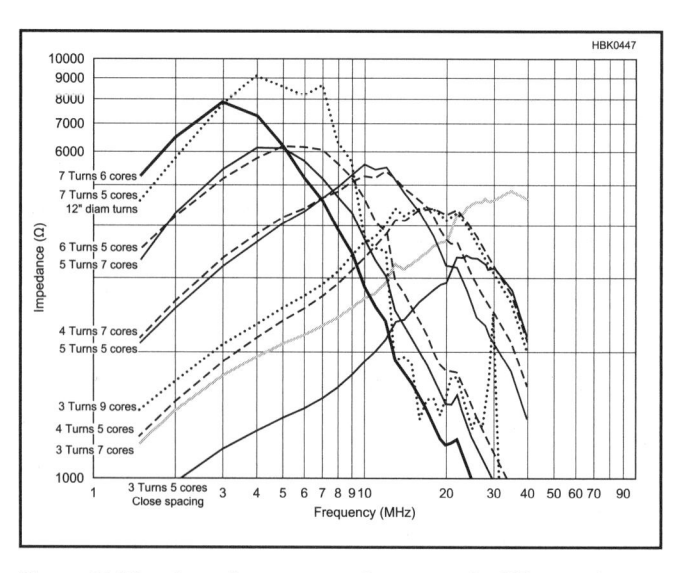

Figure 20.28 — Impedance versus frequency for HF wound-coax transmitting chokes using toroid cores of #31 material with RG-8 coax. Turns are 5 inch diameter and wide-spaced unless noted.

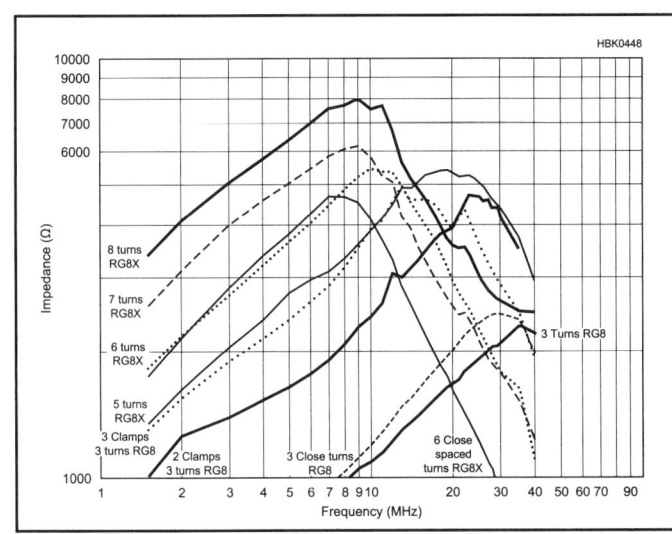

Figure 20.29 — Impedance versus frequency for HF wound-coax transmitting chokes wound on big clamp-on cores of #31 material with RG-8X or RG-8 coax. Turns are 6 inch diameter, wide-spaced except as noted.

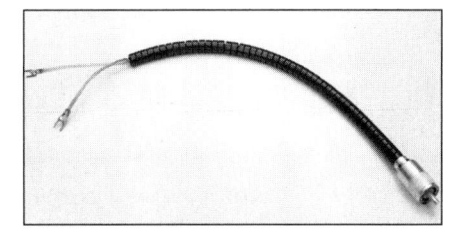

Figure 20.30 — W2DU bead balun consisting of 50 FB-73-2401 ferrite beads over a length of RG-303 coax. See text for details.

Table 20.7
Transmitting Choke Designs

Freq Band(s) (MHz)	Mix	RG-8, RG-11 Turns	Cores	RG-6, RG-8X, RG-58, RG-59 Turns	Cores
1.8, 3.8	#31	7	5 toroids	7	5 toroids
				8	Big clamp-on
3.5-7		6	5 toroids	7	4 toroids
				8	Big clamp-on
10.1	#31 or #43	5	5 toroids	8	Big clamp-on
				6	4 toroids
7-14		5	5 toroids	8	Big clamp-on
14		5	4 toroids	8	2 toroids
		4	6 toroids	5-6	Big clamp-on
21		4	5 toroids	4	5 toroids
		4	6 toroids	5	Big clamp-on
28		4	5 toroids	4	5 toroids
				5	Big clamp-on
7-28 10.1-28 or 14-28	#31 or #43	Use two chokes in series: #1 — 4 turns on 5 toroids #2 — 3 turns on 5 toroids		Use two chokes in series: #1 — 6 turns on a big clamp-on #2 — 5 turns on a big clamp-on	
14-28		Two 4-turn chokes, each w/one big clamp-on		4 turns on 6 toroids, or 5 turns on a big clamp-on	
50		Two 3-turn chokes, each w/one big clamp-on			

Notes: Chokes for 1.8, 3.5 and 7 MHz should have closely spaced turns. Chokes for 14-28 MHz should have widely spaced turns. Turn diameter is not critical, but 6 inches is good.

Chokes wound with any large diameter cable have more stray capacitance than those wound with small diameter wire. There are two sources of stray capacitance in a ferrite choke: the capacitance from end-to-end and from turn-to-turn via the core; and the capacitance from turn-to-turn via the air dielectric. Both sources of capacitance are increased by increased conductor size, so stray capacitance will be greater with larger coax. Turn-to-turn capacitance is also increased by larger diameter turns.

At low frequencies, most of the inductance in a ferrite choke results from coupling to the core, but some is the result of flux outside the core. At higher frequencies, the core has less permeability, and the flux outside the core makes a greater contribution.

The most useful cores for wound-coax chokes are the 2.4 inch OD, 1.4 inch ID toroid of type 31 or 43 material, and the 1 inch ID × 1.125 inch long clamp-on of type 31 material. Seven turns of RG-8 or RG-11 size cable easily fit through these toroids with no connector attached, and four turns fit with a PL-259 attached. Four turns of most RG-8 or RG-11 size cable fit within the 1 inch ID clamp-on. The toroids will accept at least 14 turns of most RG-6, RG-8X or RG-59 size cables.

PRACTICAL CHOKES

Figure 20.26 shows typical wound-coax chokes suitable for use on the HF ham bands. **Figure 20.27**, **Figure 20.28**, and **Figure 20.29** are graphs of the magnitude of the impedance for HF transmitting chokes of various sizes. Fourteen close-spaced, 3 inch diameter turns of RG-58 size cable on a #31 toroid is a very effective 300 W choke for the 160 and 80 meter bands.

Table 20.7 summarizes designs that meet the 5000 Ω criteria for the 160 through 6 meter ham bands and several practical transmitting choke designs that are "tuned" or optimized for ranges of frequencies. The table entries refer to the specific cores in the preceding paragraph. If you construct the chokes using toroids, remember to make the diameter of the turns large enough to avoid deformation of the coaxial cable. Space turns evenly around the toroid to minimize inter-turn capacitance.

USING FERRITE BEADS

The early "current baluns" developed by Walt Maxwell, W2DU, formed by stringing multiple beads in series on a length of coax to obtain the desired choking impedance, are really common-mode chokes. Maxwell's designs utilized 50 very small beads of type 73 material as shown in **Figure 20.30**. Product data sheets show that a single type 73 bead has a very low-Q resonance around 20 MHz, and has a predominantly resistive impedance of 10-20 Ω on all HF ham bands. Stringing 50 beads in series simply multiplies the impedance of one bead by 50, so the W2DU "current balun" has a choking impedance of 500-1000 Ω, and because it is strongly resistive, any resonance with the feed line is minimal.

This is a fairly good design for moderate

Table 20.8
Combination Ferrite and Coaxial Coil

Freq (MHz)	7 ft, 4 turns of RG-8X	1 Core	2 Cores
1.8	—	—	520 Ω
3.5	—	660	1.4 kΩ
7	—	1.6 kΩ	3.2 kΩ
14	560 Ω	1.1 kΩ	1.4 kΩ
21	42 kΩ	500 Ω	670 Ω
28	470 Ω	—	—

-------Measured Impedance-------

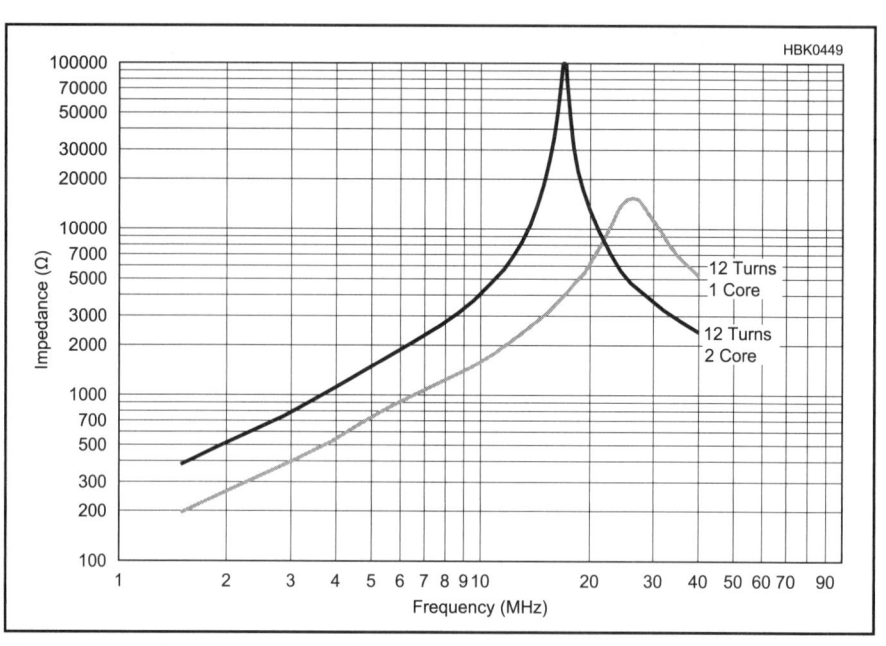

Figure 20.31 — Impedance versus frequency for HF wound-coax transmitting chokes wound with RG-142 coax on toroid cores of #61 material. For the 1 core choke: R = 15.6 kΩ, L = 25 µH, C = 1.4 pF, Q = 3.7. For the 2 core choke: R = 101 kΩ, L = 47 µH, C = 1.9 pF, Q = 20.

power levels, but suitable beads are too small to fit most coax. A specialty coaxial cable such as RG-303 must be used for high-power applications. Even with high-power coax, the choking impedance is often insufficient to limit current to a low enough value to prevent overheating. Equally important — the lower choking impedance is much less effective at rejecting noise and preventing the filling of nulls in a radiation pattern.

Newer "bead balun" designs use type 31 and 43 beads, which are resonant around 150 MHz, are inductive below resonance, and have only a few tens of ohms of strongly inductive impedance on the HF bands. Even with 20 of the type 31 or 43 beads in the string, the choke is still resonant around 150 MHz, is much less effective than a wound coaxial ferrite choke, and is still inductive on the HF bands (so it will be ineffective at frequencies where it resonates with the line).

Joe Reisert, W1JR, introduced the first coaxial chokes wound on ferrite toroids. He used low-loss cores, typically type 61 or 67 material. **Figure 20.31** shows that these high-Q chokes are quite effective in the narrow frequency range near their resonance. However, the resonance is quite difficult to measure and it is so narrow that it typically covers only one or two ham bands. Away from resonance, the choke becomes far less effective, as choking impedance falls rapidly and its reactive component resonates with the line.

Air-wound coaxial chokes are less effective than bead baluns. Their equivalent circuit is also a simple high-Q parallel resonance and they must be used below resonance. They are simple, inexpensive and unlikely to overheat. Choking impedance is purely inductive and not very great, reducing their effectiveness. Effectiveness is further reduced when the inductance resonates with the line at frequencies where the line impedance is capacitive and there is almost no resistance to damp the resonance.

Adding ferrite cores to a coiled-coax balun is a way to increase their effectiveness. The resistive component of the ferrite impedance damps the resonance of the coil and increases its useful bandwidth. The combinations of ferrite and coil baluns shown in **Table 20.8** demonstrate this very effectively. Eight feet of RG-8X in a 5 turn coil is a great balun for 21 MHz, but it is not particularly effective on other bands. If one type 43 core (Fair-Rite 2643167851) is inserted in the same coil of coax, the balun can be used from 3.5 to 21 MHz. If two of these cores are spaced a few inches apart on the coil as in **Figure 20.32**,

Figure 20.32 — Choke balun that includes both a coiled cable and ferrite beads at each end of the cable.

the balun is more effective from 1.8 to 7 MHz and usable to 21 MHz. If type 31 material was used (the Fair-Rite 2631101902 is a similar core), low-frequency performance would be even better. The 20-turn, multiple-band, 1.8-3.5 MHz coiled-coax balun in Table 20.6 weighs 1 pound, 7 ounces. The single ferrite core combination balun weighs 6.5 ounces and the two-core version weighs 9.5 ounces.

20.6 PC Transmission Lines

PC board material can be used to create a transmission line. There are several variations in which the PC trace forms one of the conductors and ground plane layers form the other. These are summarized in **Figure 20.33**, where ε_r is the dielectric constant of the PC board material. (FR4 is the most common material at and above VHF.)

Microstrip (Figure 20.33A) is the most common of the PC transmission lines, consisting of an isolated trace above a ground plane.

Stripline (Figure 20.33B) is also common in multilayer boards with the PC trace embedded in the PC board material and centered between two ground plane layers.

Offset stripline (not shown) is a variation of stripline in which the PC trace is not centered between the ground plane layers.

Coplanar waveguide (Figure 20.33C) is feasible at microwave frequencies.

In microstrip and stripline the RF energy is mostly (but not completely) confined to the region between the large surface of the PC trace and the ground plane. Current is spread across the surface of the PC trace at a depth determined by the skin effect (see the **RF Techniques** chapter).

In contrast, the RF energy in coplanar waveguide is contained between the edges of the PC trace and the edges of the adjacent ground plane. The middle surfaces of the PC trace carry little, if any, current. This increases resistive losses because the current is concentrated in a smaller region but the waves travel mostly in air and so have lower losses. This becomes an important tradeoff at microwave frequencies.

Table 20.9
50-Ω Transmission Line Dimensions

Type of Line	Dielectric (ε_r)	Layer Thickness in mils (mm)	Center Conductor in mils (mm)	Gap Gap	Characteristic Impedance (Ω)
Microstrip	Prepreg (3.8)	6 (0.152)	11.5 (0.292)	n/a	50.3
	Prepreg (3.8)	10 (0.254)	20 (0.508)	n/a	50.0
Stripline	FR4 (4.5)	12 (0.305)	3.7 (0.094)	n/a	50.0
Coplanar WG	Prepreg (3.8)	6 (0.152)	14 (0.35)	20 (0.50)	49.7

Information from Maxim Integrated, Tutorial 5100:
www.maximintegrated.com/en/app-notes/index.mvp/id/5100

Since most designs work with 50-Ω impedances, combinations of common copper foil thicknesses, trace widths, and board layer thicknesses have been calculated to produce 50 Ω. Several are shown in **Table 20.9**. For the interested reader, see Wadell's book in the Reference section of this chapter. The free program *AppCAD* (**www.hp.woodshot.com**) can handle many PC transmission line design calculations, along with S parameters and balun calculations.

With high-volume commercial and consumer electronics operating at microwave frequencies, connectors for PC transmission lines have become widely available. See the **Component Data and References** chapter's table of connector styles for possible candidates. These small connectors cannot handle a lot of power but are adequate for receiving and low-power transmitting applications. Adapters and adapter cables are available to convert these connectors to the more common SMA, UHF, BNC, N, and other styles used by amateurs.

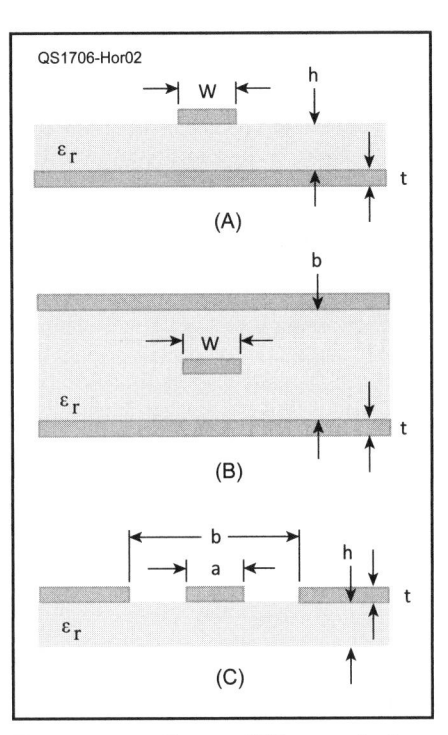

Figure 20.33 — Types of PC transmission line: microstrip (A), stripline (B), and coplanar waveguide (C). Dimensions shown are used by online calculators to determine the line's characteristic impedance. The PCB material's relative permittivity is ε_r.

20.7 Waveguides

So far, the transmission lines in this chapter have propagated a signal in an electric field established by the potential difference between two conductors, and a corresponding magnetic field, perpendicular to the electric field, resulting from the currents in the conductors. This mode of propagation is called the TEM, or *Transverse ElectroMagnetic* mode.

A waveguide is different — it acts as a transmission line by guiding and containing a electromagnetic field traveling at the speed of light. Common waveguides are hollow metal pipes, usually rectangular but sometimes round. With no lossy dielectric and solid metal conducting surfaces, waveguides have much lower losses than other transmission lines. (There are other waveguide structures — two parallel metal plates can act as a waveguide, or even a dielectric rod with no metallic conductors. The parallel plate waveguide can be used in a metal-plate lens antenna.)

This section covers the basic operation of waveguides. More information on waveguide is available at **www.wa1mba.org**.

20.7.1 Evolution of Waveguide

Suppose an open-wire line is used to carry UHF or microwave energy from a generator to a load. Imagine the transmission line is supported with quarter-wave stubs, shorted at the far end. The open end of such a stub presents an infinite impedance to the transmission line, provided that the shorted stub is non-reactive. Thus, the stub acts as an insulating support. Since the stubs act as an open-circuit, an infinite number of them may be connected in parallel without affecting the open-wire line.

Because the shorting link has finite length it also has some inductance. This inductance can be minimized by making the RF current flow on the surface of a plate rather than through a thin wire. If the plate is large enough, it will prevent the magnetic lines of force from encircling the RF current.

The transmission line may be supported from the top as well as the bottom and when infinitely many supports are added, they form the walls of a waveguide at its *cutoff frequency*. **Figure 20.34** illustrates how a rectangular waveguide evolves from a two-wire parallel transmission line.

20.7.2 Waveguide Operation

As a signal propagates along a waveguide, the metal walls contain the electric and magnetic fields. We'll concentrate on the electric field here, because the dominant mode of propagation for waveguide is a mode called TE or *Transverse Electric*. **Figure 20.35B** shows the electric field intensity in the rectangular waveguide, which is oriented parallel to the shorter side walls. The electric field is strongest in the center and must be zero at the side walls, since the walls are short circuits. The field strength distribution is half of a sine wave at the operating frequency, and propagates down the waveguide as if it were bouncing off the side walls. For this to work, the width of the waveguide must be at least one-half the wavelength of the propagating signal. At lower frequencies with longer wavelengths, the field cannot be zero at both walls so these signals will not propagate in the waveguide.

20.7.3 Waveguide Dimensions

CUTOFF AND UPPER FREQUENCIES

The minimum frequency of operation for a waveguide is that at which the waveguide width is a half-wavelength. This is called the waveguide's *cutoff frequency*, f_c.

$$f_c = c/\lambda_c$$

where c = the speed of light in free space, 2.9979×10^8 meters per second.

A wavelength in the waveguide, λ_g, is longer than a wavelength in free space, λ_0. This implies a velocity faster than the speed of light. But only the *phase velocity* exceeds the speed of light — energy cannot travel faster. The waveguide wavelength varies with frequency as a function of the cutoff frequency:

$$\lambda_g = \frac{\lambda_0}{\sqrt{1-\left(\frac{\lambda_0}{\lambda_c}\right)^2}}$$

Near the cutoff frequency, λ_g is much longer than the free-space wavelength λ_0, becoming closer to λ_0 as frequency increases.

Waveguide operating frequencies are usually well above the cutoff frequency — near (and below) the cutoff frequency, losses increase and the guide wavelength changes rapidly with frequency causing dispersion of the transmitted waveform. This is why a wave-

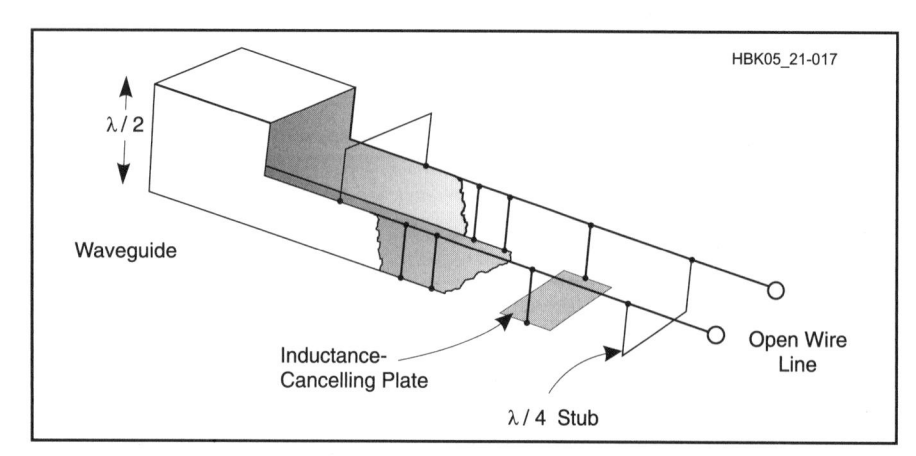

Figure 20.34 — At its cutoff frequency a rectangular waveguide can be analyzed as a parallel two-conductor transmission line supported from top and bottom by an infinite number of quarter-wave stubs.

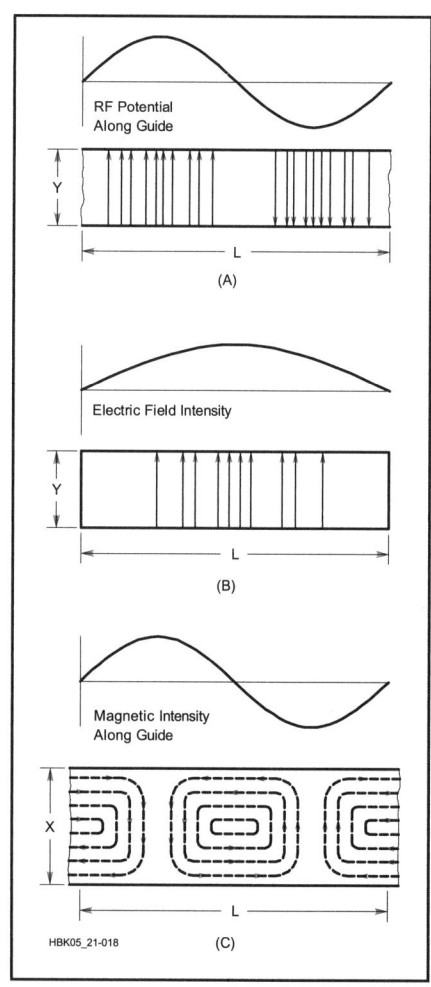

Figure 20.35 — Field distribution in a rectangular waveguide. The $TE_{1,0}$ mode of propagation is depicted.

guide makes an excellent high-pass filter.

The height of a rectangular waveguide, between top and bottom walls, determines both the upper frequency limit and the characteristic impedance. The upper limit is the frequency at which the waveguide height is ½ λ — above this frequency, the electric field may change orientation and other modes may propagate.

CHARACTERISTIC IMPEDANCE

The characteristic impedance is usually much higher than 50 ohms and is calculated for TE modes using this formula:

$$Z_0 = 377 \left(\frac{\lambda_g}{\lambda_0}\right)\left(\frac{2b}{a}\right)$$

where a and b are the large and small dimensions, respectively, of the rectangular waveguide. 377 Ω is the approximate impedance of free space.

For example, at 10 GHz, WR90 waveguide is often used. The width is 0.9 inch, or 22.86 mm, and the height is 0.4 inch, or 10.16 mm. The cutoff frequency is 6.56 GHz, but the recommended operating frequency range is 8 to 12.4 GHz. At 10.368 GHz, the free space wavelength is λ_0 = 28.915 mm, the guide wavelength is λ_g = 37.33 mm and the characteristic impedance is Z_0 = 433 ohms. Several common waveguides are pictured in cross-section in **Figure 20.36**.

For circular waveguide, the cutoff wavelength is λ_c = 1.706 × diameter and the characteristic impedance is Z_0 = 377 l_g/l_0.

20.7.4 Waveguide Modes

The operating mode described above is for the dominant mode, TE_{10} (or TE_{11} in circular waveguide). This is the lowest frequency mode at which a given waveguide will operate, and is the preferred mode for waveguide transmission.

If there is no upper limit to the frequency to be transmitted, there are an infinite number of ways in which the fields can arrange themselves in a guide. Each field configuration is called a *mode*. All modes may be separated into two general groups. One group, designated TM (Transverse Magnetic), has the magnetic field entirely crosswise to the direction of propagation, but has a component of electric field in the propagation direction. The other group, designated TE (Transverse Electric) has the electric field entirely crosswise to the direction of propagation, but has a component of magnetic field in the direction of propagation. TM waves are sometimes called E-waves in older references and TE waves are sometimes called H-waves. The TM and TE designations are preferred, however. The particular mode of transmission is identified by the group letters followed by subscript numbers; for example TE_{11}, TM_{11} and so on. The number of possible modes increases with frequency for a given size of guide.

Higher-order modes are useful in certain applications, for instance, in multimode feed horns, where the additional modes can shape the radiation pattern, special high-power waveguides, and in certain cavity filters.

20.7.5 Waveguide Termination

If a waveguide is not terminated in its characteristic impedance, there will be an elevated SWR on the line as there is on any other transmission line. A typical termination is a horn antenna, which flares out from the end of the waveguide to match the waveguide's characteristic impedance to the impedance of free space, 377 Ω.

Excitation at the other end of the waveguide is often from a coaxial line. One type of adapter, shown in **Figure 20.37**, is a probe like a monopole antenna in the center of a wide wall of the waveguide. If the probe were very thin and had no capacitance or inductance, it would be ¼ λ long and spaced ¼ λ from a short circuit — the closed end of the waveguide. Actual dimensions compensate for the probe inductance and capacitance.

Waveguide connections are made by bolting their flanges together firmly. Several flanges are shown in **Figure 20.38**. There

Figure 20.36 — Typical waveguide sizes from WR229 on the left to WR42 on the right.

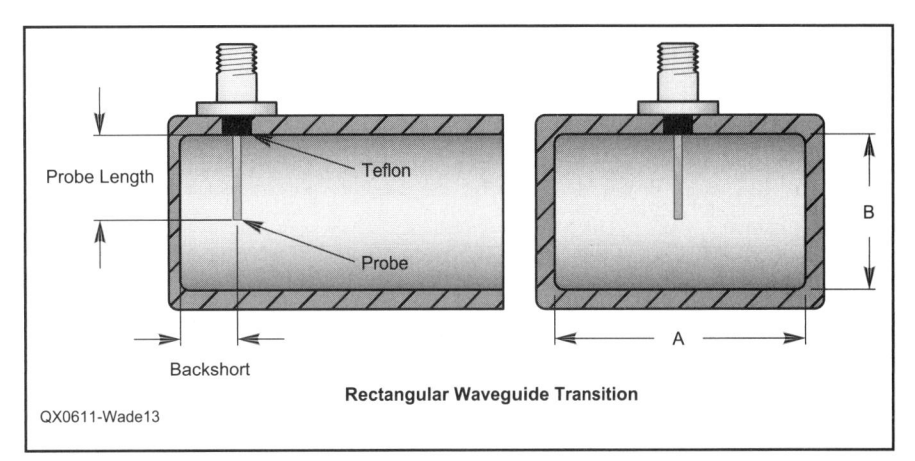

Figure 20.37 — Sketch of rectangular waveguide to coax transition, showing dimensions.

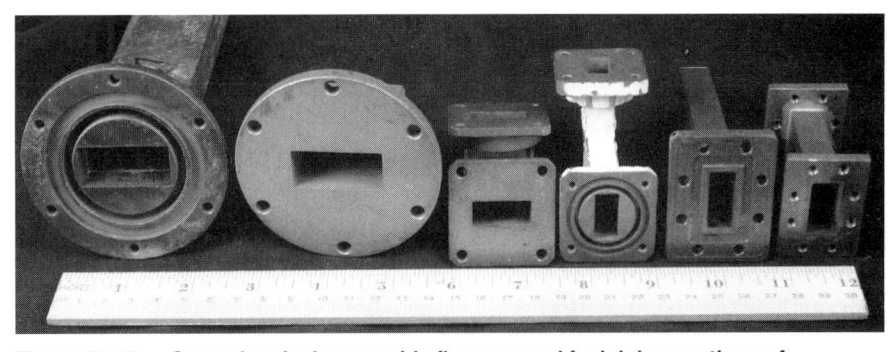

Figure 20.38 — Several typical waveguide flanges used for joining sections of waveguide. The deep grooves in choke flanges place a high-impedance in the path of any RF leakage out of the flange.

Table 20.10
Waveguide Dimensions and Coax Transitions

Waveguide	Dimensions (mm)	Freq Range (GHz)	Freq (GHz)	Probe Diam (mm)	Probe Len (mm)	Backshort (mm)	Bandwidth
WR42	10.668 × 4.318	18-26.5	24.192	1.27	2.413	2.489	>17%
WR75	19.05 × 9.525	10.0-15	10.368	1.27	5.49	5.26	14%
WR90	22.86 × 10.16	8.2-12.4	10.368	1.27	5.89	5.46	7%
WR112	28.24 × 12.62	7.05-10	10.368	1.27	6.5	6.6	15%
WR112			5.76	1.27	8.8	9.8	7%
WR137	35.85 × 15.80	5.85-8.2	5.76	1.27	10.5	8.5	10%
WR159	40.39 × 20.19	4.9-7.05	5.76	1.27	11.17	10.0	11%
WR187	47.55 × 22.15	3.95-5.85	5.76	2.36	11.3	11.0	16%
WR187			3.456	2.36	14.5	18.0	5%
WR229	58.17 × 29.08	3.3-4.9	3.456	1.27	18.2	15.0	8%
WR229			3.456	2.36	17.4	15.06	11%
WR229			3.456	3.175	17	15.6	11%
WR229			3.456	4.76	16.2	16.2	14%
WR229			3.456	6.35	15.5	16.75	17%
WR284	72.14 × 34.04	2.6-3.95	3.456	6.35	17.5	17.8	27%
WR284			2.304	6.35	20	28	9%
WR340	86.36 × 43.18	2.2-3.2	2.304	6.35	25	23	11%

are two types of flanges, *flat flanges* and *choke flanges*, which have a groove around the waveguide. Choke flanges should be mated with flat flanges, but two flat flanges may be mated together.

Waveguides of two different sizes may be mated, but there should be a transition between them since different waveguide sizes have different Z_0. Just as in coaxial lines, impedance discontinuities such as at a transition will cause reflections.

20.7.6 Practical Waveguides

Standard waveguide sizes dating to World War II are still in use today. The standard designator is WR*xx*, where *xx* is the wide dimension in hundredths of an inch; for instance, WR90, often used at 10 GHz, has a wide dimension of 90 hundredths of an inch, or 0.9 inch. There are no standards for circular waveguide, so common copper plumbing is often used — ¾ inch tubing works well at 10 GHz. Practical dimensions for standard waveguides at amateur microwave calling frequencies are shown in **Table 20.10**.

Table 20.10 includes dimensions for the waveguide sizes likely to be encountered in microwave work; while a waveguide would work very well at lower frequencies, it would be very large — one meter wide for the 2 meter band! The recommended frequency range for each type is also shown in the table.

Figure 20.39 — Special sections called bends make right- and 45-degree angles to avoid introducing impedance discontinuities where the waveguide has to change direction.

For narrowband amateur work, we can stretch the frequency range a bit to take advantage of available waveguide — some of the waveguide sizes are usable on more than one band. Many smaller size guides are used at mm-wave frequencies.

Losses in waveguide are very low, much less than coaxial transmission line, but not negligible at the higher frequencies. For example, WR90 loss is approximately 10 dB per 100 feet at 10 GHz. Power handling is not a problem; even the smallest waveguide is rated at far more than the amateur power limit.

Where the waveguide has to change direction, special fittings called *bends* are used, shown in **Figure 20.39**. These are constructed so that impedance discontinuities from the change in direction are minimized.

Waveguide transmission lines used outdoors will suffer from internal water condensation, as will closed metal container with temperature variations. Even a short length used in a portable station can collect condensation. Commercial installations often pressurize the waveguide with dry air. Otherwise, a drain hole should be provided at the bottom of a run.

20.8 Glossary of Transmission Line Terms

Antenna tuner — A device that matches the antenna system input impedance to the transmitter, receiver or transceiver output impedance. Also called an *antenna-matching network, impedance matcher, transmatch, ATU, matchbox.*

Balanced line — A symmetrical two-conductor feed line that has uniform voltage and current distribution along its length.

Balun — Contraction of "balanced to unbalanced." A device to couple a balanced load to an unbalanced feed line or device, or vice versa. May be in the form of a choke balun, or a transformer that provides a specific impedance transformation (including 1:1). Often used in antenna systems to interface a coaxial transmission line to the feed point of a balanced antenna, such as a dipole.

Characteristic impedance — The ratio of voltage to current in a matched feed line, it is determined by the physical geometry and materials used to construct the feed line. Also known as *surge impedance* since it represents the impedance electromagnetic energy encounters when entering a feed line.

Choke balun — A balun that prevents current from flowing on the outside of a coaxial cable shield when connected to a balanced load, such as an antenna.

Coax — See **coaxial cable**.

Coaxial cable — Transmission lines that have the outer shield (solid or braided) concentric with the same axis as the inner or center conductor. The insulating material can be a gas (air or nitrogen) or a solid or foam insulating material.

Common-mode current — Current that flows equally and in phase on all conductors of a feed line or multiconductor cable.

Conductor — A metal body such as tubing, rod or wire that permits current to travel continuously along its length.

Conjugate match — Creating a purely resistive impedance by connecting an impedance with an equal-and-opposite reactive component.

Current balun — see **Choke balun**.

Decibel — A logarithmic power ratio, abbreviated dB. May also represent a voltage or current ratio if the voltages or currents are measured across (or through) identical impedances. Suffixes to the abbreviation indicate references: dBi, isotropic radiator; dBm, milliwatt; dBW, watt.

Dielectrics — Various insulating materials used in antenna systems, such as found in insulators and transmission lines.

Dielectric constant (k) — Relative figure of merit for an insulating material used as a dielectric. This property determines how much electric energy can be stored in a unit volume of the material per volt of applied potential.

Electric field — An electric field exists in a region of space if an electrically charged object placed in the region is subjected to an electrical force.

Electromagnetic wave — A wave of energy composed of an electric and magnetic field.

Feed line — See **transmission line**.

Feed point — The point at which a feed line is electrically connected to an antenna.

Feed point impedance — The ratio of RF voltage to current at the feed point of an antenna.

Ferrite — A ceramic material with magnetic properties.

Hardline — Coaxial cable with a solid metal outer conductor to reduce losses compared to flexible cables. Hardline may or may not be flexible.

Impedance match — To adjust impedances to be equal or the case in which two impedances are equal. Usually refers to the point at which a feed line is connected to an antenna or to transmitting equipment. If the impedances are different, that is a **mismatch**.

Impedance matcher — See **Antenna tuner**.

Impedance matching (circuit) — A circuit that transforms impedance from one value to another. Adjustable impedance matching circuits are used at the output of transmitters and amplifiers to allow maximum power output over a wide range of load impedances.

Impedance transformer — A transformer designed specifically for transforming impedances in RF equipment.

L network — A combination of two reactive components used to transform or match impedances. One component is connected in series between the source and load and the other shunted across either the source or the load. Most L networks have one inductor and one capacitor, but two-inductor and two-capacitor configurations are also used.

Ladder line — see **Open-wire line**.

Lambda (λ) — Greek symbol used to represent wavelength.

Line loss — The power dissipated by a transmission line as heat, usually expressed in decibels.

Load — (noun) The component, antenna, or circuit to which power is delivered; (verb) To apply a load to a circuit or a transmission line.

Loading — The process of a transferring power from its source to a load. The effect a load has on a power source.

Magnetic field — A region through which a magnetic force will act on a magnetic object.

Matched-line loss — The line loss in a feed line terminated by a load equal to its characteristic impedance.

Matching — The process of effecting an impedance match between two electrical circuits of unlike impedance. One example is matching a transmission line to the feed point of an antenna. Maximum power transfer to the load (antenna system) will occur when a matched condition exists.

Microstrip — A transmission line made from a strip of printed-circuit board conductor above a ground plane, used primarily at UHF and microwave frequencies.

Open-wire line — Parallel-conductor feed line with parallel insulators at regular intervals to maintain the line spacing. The dielectric is principally air, making it a low-loss type of line. Also known as *ladder line* or *window line*.

Output impedance — The equivalent impedance of a signal source.

Parallel-conductor line — A type of transmission line that uses two parallel wires spaced from each other by insulating material. Also known as *open-wire, ladder* or *window line*.

Phasing lines — Sections of transmission line that are used to ensure the correct phase relationship between the elements of a driven array, or between bays of an array of antennas. Also used to effect impedance transformations while maintaining the desired phase.

Q section — Term used in reference to transmission-line matching transformers and phasing lines.

Reflection coefficient (ρ) — The ratio of the reflected voltage at a given point on a transmission line to the incident voltage at the same point. The reflection coefficient is also equal to the ratio of reflected and incident currents. The Greek letter rho (ρ) is used to represent reflection coefficient.

Reflectometer — see **SWR bridge**

Resonance — (1) The condition in which a system's natural response and the frequency of an applied or emitted signal are the same. (2) The frequency at which a circuit's capacitive and inductive reactances are equal and cancel.

Resonant frequency — The frequency at which the maximum response of a circuit occurs. In an antenna, the resonant frequency is one at which the feed point impedance is purely resistive.

Return loss — The absolute value of the ratio in dB of the power reflected from a load to the power delivered to the load.

Rise time — The time it takes for a waveform to reach a maximum value.

Series-input network — A network such as a filter or impedance matching circuit in which the input current flows through a component in series with the input.

Shunt-input network — A network such as a filter or impedance matching circuit with a component connected directly across the input.

Skin effect — The phenomenon in which ac current at high frequencies flows in a thin layer near the surface of a conductor.

Smith chart — A coordinate system developed by Phillip Smith to represent complex impedances graphically. This chart makes it easy to perform calculations involving antenna and transmission-line impedances and SWR.

Standing-wave ratio (SWR) — Sometimes called voltage standing-wave ratio (VSWR). A measure of the impedance match between a feed line's characteristic impedance and the attached load (usually an antenna). VSWR is the ratio of maximum voltage to minimum voltage along the feed line, or of antenna impedance to feed line impedance.

Stacking — The technique of placing similar directive antennas atop or beside one another, forming a "stacked array." Stacking provides more gain or directivity than a single antenna.

Stub — A section of transmission line used to perform impedance matching or filtering.

Surge impedance — see **Characteristic impedance**.

SWR — see **Standing-wave ratio**.

SWR bridge — Device for measuring SWR in a transmission line. Also known as an SWR meter or reflectometer.

TE mode — Transverse electric field mode. Condition in a waveguide in which the E-field component of the traveling electromagnetic energy is oriented perpendicular to (transverse) the direction the energy is traveling in the waveguide.

TM mode — Transverse magnetic field mode. Condition in a waveguide in which the H-field (magnetic field) component of the traveling electromagnetic energy is oriented perpendicular to (transverse) the direction the energy is traveling in the waveguide.

Transmatch — See **Antenna tuner**.

Transmission line — The wires or cable used to connect a transmitter or receiver to an antenna. Also called **feed line**.

Twin-lead — Parallel-conductor transmission line in which both conductors are completely embedded in continuous strip of insulating material.

Unbalanced line — Feed line with one conductor at dc ground potential, such as coaxial cable.

Universal stub system — A matching network consisting of a pair of transmission line stubs that can transform any impedance to any other impedance.

Velocity factor (VF) — The speed at which an electromagnetic wave will travel through a material or feed line stated as a fraction of the speed of the wave in free space (where the wave would have its maximum velocity).

VSWR — Voltage standing-wave ratio. See **SWR**.

Waveguide — A hollow conductor through which electromagnetic energy flows. Usually used at UHF and microwave frequencies instead of coaxial cable.

Window line — see **Open-wire line**.

20.9 References and Bibliography

A. Barter, G8ATD, International Microwave Handbook, 2nd Edition, RSGB, 2008.

J. Brown, K9YC, "A Ham's Guide to RFI, Ferrites, Baluns, and Audio Interfacing," **audiosystemsgroup.com/RFI-Ham.pdf**

J. Brown, K9YC, "Optimizing the Placement of Stubs for Harmonic Suppression," *National Contest Journal*, Jul/Aug 2015, pp 8-11.

C. Counselman, W1HIS, "Common Mode Chokes," **www.yccc.org/articles/w1his/CommonModeChokesW1HIS2006Apr06.pdf**

G. Cutsogeorge, W2VJN, "Optimizing the Performance of Harmonic Attenuation Stubs," *National Contest Journal*, Jan/Feb 2015, pp 3-4.

G. Cutsogeorge, W2VJN, *Managing Interstation Interference*, Second Edition (International Radio, 2009).

H.W. Johnson and M. Graham, *High Speed Digital Design* (Prentice Hall, 1993).

R. Lewallan, W7EL, "Baluns: What They Do and How They Do It," 1985, **www.eznec.com/Amateur/Articles/Baluns.pdf**

J. Reisert, W1JR, "VHF/UHF World," *Ham Radio*, Oct 1987, pp. 27-38.

F. Regier, "Series-Section Transmission Line Impedance Matching," *QST*, Jul 1978, pp 14-16.

Sabin and Schoenike, *HF Radio Systems and Circuits*, (SciTech Publishing, 1998).

J. Sevick, W2FMI, *Transmission Line Transformers*, 4th Edition (Noble Publishing, 2001).

J. Sevick, W2FMI, *Building and Using Baluns and Ununs* (CQ Communications, 2003).

H.W. Silver, Ed., *The ARRL Antenna Book*, 22nd Edition (Newington: ARRL, 2011). Chapters 23 through 27 include material on transmission lines and related topics.

P. Smith, *Electronic Applications of the Smith Chart* (Noble Publishing, 1995).

D. Straw, N6BV, "Don't Blow Up Your Balun," *QST*, Jun 2015, pp 30-36.

P. Wade, W1GHZ, "Microwavelengths," *QST* column.

B. Wadell, *Transmission Line Design Handbook*, ISBN: 0-89006-436-9.

F. Witt, "Baluns in the Real (and Complex) World," *The ARRL Antenna Compendium Vol 5* (Newington: ARRL, 1996).

The ARRL UHF/Microwave Experimenter's Manual (Newington: ARRL, 2000). Chapters 5 and 6 address transmission lines and impedance matching. (This book is out of print.)

ONLINE RESOURCES

A collection of articles about waveguide transitions and filters — **w1ghz.org/10g/QEX_articles.htm**

A collection of Smith chart references — **http://sss-mag.com/smith.html**

Ferrite and powdered iron cores are available from **www.fair-rite.com**, **www.amidoncorp.com** and **www.cwsbytemark.com**

Microwave oriented downloads — **www.microwaves101.com/content/downloads.cfm**

Table of transmission line properties — **hf-antenna.com/trans/**

Times Microwave catalog — **www.timesmicrowave.com**

Transmission line loss factors — **www.microwaves101.com/encyclopedia/transmission_loss.cfm**

Transmission line matching with the Smith chart — **www.odyseus.nildram.co.uk/RFMicrowave_Theory_Files/SmithChartPart2.pdf**

Transmission line transformer theory — **www.bytemark.com/products/tlttheory.htm**

Waveguide tutorials — **www.microwaves101.com/encyclopedias/waveguide-primer**
www.rfcafe.com/references/electrical/waveguide.htm
www.feynmanlectures.caltech.edu/II_24.html

Contents

- 21.1 Antenna Basics
  - 21.1.1 Directivity and Gain
  - 21.1.2 Antenna Polarization
  - 21.1.3 Current and Voltage Distribution
  - 21.1.4 Impedance
  - 21.1.5 Impedance and Height Above Ground
  - 21.1.6 Antenna Bandwidth
  - 21.1.7 Effects of Conductor Diameter
  - 21.1.8 Radiation Patterns
  - 21.1.9 Elevation Angle
  - 21.1.10 Imperfect Ground
- 21.2 Dipoles and the Half-Wave Antenna
  - 21.2.1 Radiation Characteristics
  - 21.2.2 Feed Methods
  - 21.2.3 Feed Point Baluns
  - 21.2.4 Building Dipoles and Other Wire Antennas
  - 21.2.5 Dipole Configuration
  - 21.2.6 Inverted-V Dipole
  - 21.2.7 Sloping Dipole and End-Fed Half-Wave (EFHW)
  - 21.2.8 Shortened Dipoles
  - 21.2.9 Half-Wave Vertical Dipole (HVD)
  - 21.2.10 Folded Dipoles
  - 21.2.11 Multiband Dipole Systems
  - 21.2.12 NVIS Antennas
    - *Project*: Multiband Center-Fed Dipole
    - *Project*: 40-15 Meter Dual-Band Dipole
    - *Project*: W4RNL Rotatable Dipole Inverted-U Antenna
    - *Project*: Two W8NX Multiband, Coax-Trap Dipoles
    - *Project*: Triband Dipole for 30, 17 and 12 Meters
- 21.3 Vertical (Ground-Plane) Antennas
  - 21.3.1 Ground Systems
  - 21.3.2 Full-Size Vertical Antennas
  - 21.3.3 Physically Short Verticals
    - *Project*: Top-Loaded Low-Band Antenna
  - 21.3.4 Cables and Control Wires on Towers
  - 21.3.5 Multiband Trap Verticals
- 21.4 T and Inverted-L Antennas
- 21.5 Slopers and Vertical Dipoles
  - 21.5.1 The Half-Sloper Antenna
    - *Project*: Half-Wave Vertical Dipole (HVD)
    - *Project*: Compact Vertical Dipole (CVD)
    - *Project*: All-Wire 30 Meter CVD
- 21.6 Yagi Antennas
  - 21.6.1 Parasitic Excitation
  - 21.6.2 Yagi Gain, Front-to-Back Ratio, and SWR
  - 21.6.3 Two-Element Beams
  - 21.6.4 Three-Element Beams
  - 21.6.5 Construction of Yagi Antennas
    - *Project*: Family of Computer-Optimized HF Yagis
- 21.7 Quad and Loop Antennas
  - *Project*: Five-Band, Two-Element HF Quad
  - 21.7.1 Loop Antennas
    - *Project*: Low-Band Quad and Delta Loops
    - *Project*: Two-Band Loop for 30 and 40 Meters
    - *Project*: Multiband Horizontal Loop Antenna
- 21.8 HF Mobile Antennas
  - 21.8.1 Simple Whips
  - 21.8.2 Coil-Loaded Whips
  - 21.8.3 Base vs Center vs Continuous Loading
  - 21.8.4 Top-Loaded Whips
  - 21.8.5 Remotely Controlled HF Mobile Antennas
  - 21.8.6 Ground Losses
  - 21.8.7 Antenna Mounting
  - 21.8.8 Mobile HF Antenna Matching
  - 21.8.9 Remotely-Tuned Antenna Controllers
  - 21.8.10 Efficiency
    - *Project*: Mounts for Remotely-Tuned Antennas
    - *Project*: Retuning a CB Whip Antenna
- 21.9 VHF/UHF Mobile Antennas
  - 21.9.1 VHF/UHF Mobile Antenna Mounts
  - 21.9.2 VHF/UHF Mobile Antennas for SSB and CW
- 21.10 VHF/UHF Antennas
  - 21.10.1 Gain
  - 21.10.2 Radiation Pattern
  - 21.10.3 Height Gain
  - 21.10.4 Physical Size
  - 21.10.5 Polarization
  - 21.10.6 Circular Polarization
  - 21.10.7 Transmission Lines
  - 21.10.8 Impedance Matching
  - 21.10.9 Baluns and Impedance Transformers
    - *Project*: Simple, Portable Ground-Plane Antenna
    - *Project*: Coaxial Dipole for VHF or UHF
- 21.11 VHF/UHF Beams
  - 21.11.1 Stacking Yagis
    - *Project*: Three and Five-Element Yagis for 6 Meters
    - *Project*: Medium-Gain 2 Meter Yagi
    - *Project*: Cheap Yagis by WA5VJB
    - *Project*: Fixed Moxons for Satellite Operation
- 21.12 Direction-Finding Antennas
  - 21.12.1 RDF Antennas for HF Bands
  - 21.12.2 Methods for VHF/UHF RDF
- 21.13 Rotators
- 21.14 Glossary
- 21.15 References and Bibliography

Chapter 21

Antennas

In the world of radio, the antenna is "where the rubber meets the road!" With antennas so fundamental to communication, it is important that the amateur have a basic understanding of their function. That understanding enables effective selection and application of basic designs to whatever communications task is at hand. In addition, the amateur is then equipped to engage in one of the most active areas of amateur experimentation, antenna design. The goal of this chapter is to define and illustrate the fundamentals of antennas and provide a selection of basic designs; simple verticals and dipoles, quads and Yagi beams, and other antennas, plus a section on rotator use and selection. The reader will find additional in-depth coverage of these and other topics in the *ARRL Antenna Book* and other references provided. This chapter was originally written by Chuck Hutchinson, K8CH, and has been updated by Ward Silver, NØAX. Steve Stearns, K6OIK, contributed a correction in the 2019 edition of the long-used graph of the effect of antenna diameter on half-wave resonant length. Alan Applegate, KØBG, maintains the material on mobile antennas. The section on Radio Direction Finding Antennas was written by Joe Moell, KØOV.

Chapter 21 — Downloadable Supplemental Content

Supplemental Articles
- "Direction Finding Techniques" by Joe Moell, KØOV
- "A Simple Direction-Finding Receiver for 80 Meters" by Dale Hunt, WB6BYU
- "Weatherizing Outdoor Inductors and Traps" by Dick Sander, K5QY
- Multiband and Half-Wave Dipole Azimuth and Elevation Patterns
- "Design of a Two-band Loaded Dipole Antenna" by David Birnbaum, K2LYV
- "Workshop Chronicles - Alloy Designations" by Don Daso, K4ZA

Projects
- "Rotatable Dipole Inverted-U Antenna" by L.B. Cebik, W4RNL
- Construction details for "Top-Loaded Low-Band Antenna" by Dick Stroud, W9SR
- "The Trimox — A Moxon Tribander for a Holiday DXpedition" by Brian Machesney, K1LI
- "Five-Band Two-Element Quad" by Al Doig, W6NBH, and William Stein, KC6T
- "Medium-Gain 2 Meter Yagi" by L.B. Cebik, W4RNL
- "K8SYL's 75 and 10-Meter Dipole" by Sylvia Hutchinson, K8SYL
- "A True Plumber's Delight for 2 Meters — An All-Copper J-Pole" by Michael Hood, KD8JB
- "Cheap Antennas for the AMSAT LEOs" by Kent Britain, WA5VJB
- "Wire Quad for 40 Meters" by Dean Straw, N6BV
- "Vertical Loop Antenna for 28 MHz"
- "Dual-Band Antenna for 146/446 MHz" by Wayde Bartholomew, K3MF
- "A Simple Fixed Antenna for VHF/UHF Satellite Work," by L.B. Cebik, W4RNL
- "Having a Field Day with the Moxon Rectangle," by L.B. Cebik, W4RNL
- "Extended Double-Zepp for 17 Meters" from 2016 *Handbook*
- "Triband Dipole for 30, 17, and 12 Meters" by Zack Lau W1VT
- "A Compact Multiband Dipole" by Zack Lau W1VT
- "The W4SSY Spudgun" by Byron Black, W4SSY (includes one Feedback article)
- "An Off-Center End-Fed Dipole for Portable Operation on 40 to 6 Meters," by Kai Siwiak, KE4PT
- "6-Meter Halo Antenna for DXing" by Jerry Clement, VE6AB
- "A New Spin on the Big Wheel" by L.B. Cebik, W4RNL, and Bob Cerreto, WA1FXT
- "Quick and Cheap Omni Antenna for 1296 MHz" by Paul Wade, W1GHZ
- Two W8NX Multiband, Coax-Trap Dipoles
- Skeleton Slot for 14 to 30 MHz

21.1 Antenna Basics

This section covers a range of topics that are fundamental to understanding how antennas work and defines several key terms. (A glossary is included at the end of the chapter.) While the discussion in this section uses the dipole as the primary example, the concepts apply to all antennas.

21.1.1 Directivity and Gain

All antennas, even the simplest types, exhibit directive effects in that the intensity of radiation is not the same in all directions from the antenna. This property of radiating more strongly in some directions than in others is called the *directivity* of the antenna. Directivity is the same for receiving as transmitting.

The directive pattern of an antenna at a given frequency is determined by the size and shape of the antenna, and on its position and orientation relative to the Earth and any other reflecting or absorbing surfaces.

The more an antenna's directivity is enhanced in a particular direction, the greater the *gain* of the antenna. This is a result of the radiated energy being concentrated in some directions at the expense of others. Similarly, gain describes the ability of the antenna to receive signals preferentially from certain directions. Gain does not create additional power beyond that delivered by the feed line — it only focuses that energy.

Gain is usually expressed in decibels, and is always stated with reference to a *standard* antenna — usually a dipole or an *isotropic radiator*. An isotropic radiator is a theoretical antenna that would, if placed in the center of an imaginary sphere, evenly illuminate that sphere with radiation. The isotropic radiator is an unambiguous standard, and for that reason frequently used as the comparison for gain measurements.

When the reference for gain is the isotropic radiator in *free space*, gain is expressed in dBi. When the standard is a dipole, also located in free space, gain is expressed in dBd. Because the dipole has some gain (2.15 dB with respect to the isotropic antenna as explained in the section on dipoles) in its favored direction, the dipole's gain can be expressed as 2.15 dBi. Gain in dBi can be converted to dBd by subtracting 2.15 dB and from dBd to dBi by adding 2.15 dB.

Gain also takes losses in the antenna or surrounding environment into account. For example, if a practical dipole antenna's wire element dissipated 0.5 dB of the transmitter power as heat, that specific dipole's gain with respect to an isotropic antenna would be 2.15 – 0.5 = 1.65 dBi.

21.1.2 Antenna Polarization

An electromagnetic wave has two components: an electric

field and a magnetic field at right angles to each other. For most antennas, the field of primary interest is the electric, or *E-field*. The magnetic field is called the *H-field*. (The abbreviations E- and H- come from Maxwell's equations that describe electromagnetic waves.) By convention, the orientation of the E-field is the reference for determining the electromagnetic wave's *polarization*. The E-field of an electromagnetic wave can be oriented in any direction, so orientation with respect to the Earth's surface is the usual frame of reference. The wave's polarization can be vertical, horizontal, or some intermediate angle. If the E- and H-field orientations rotate as the wave travels, that is elliptical or circular polarization.

Antennas are considered to have polarization, too, determined by the orientation of the E-field of the electromagnetic field radiated by the antenna. Because the E-field of the radiated wave is parallel to the direction of current flow in the antenna's elements, the polarization of the wave and the orientation of the antenna elements is usually the same. For example, the E-field radiated by an antenna with linear elements is parallel to those elements, so that the polarization of the radiated wave is the same as the orientation of the elements. (This is somewhat over-simplified and additional considerations apply for elements that are not linear.) Thus a radiator that is parallel to the earth radiates a horizontally polarized wave, while a vertical antenna radiates a vertically polarized wave. If a wire antenna is slanted, it radiates waves with an E-field that has both vertical and horizontal components.

Antennas function symmetrically — a received signal will create the strongest antenna current when the antenna's elements are parallel to the E-field of the incoming wave just as the radiated wave's E-field will be strongest parallel to current in the antenna's radiating elements. This also means that for the strongest received signal, the antenna elements should have the same polarization as that of the incoming wave. Misalignment of the receiving antenna's elements with the passing wave's E-field reduces the amount of signal received. This is called *cross-polarization*. When the polarizations of antenna and wave are at right angles, very little antenna current is created by the incoming signal.

For best results in line-of-sight communications, antennas at both ends of the circuit should have the same polarization. However, it is not essential for both stations to use the same antenna polarity for ionospheric propagation or sky wave (see the **Propagation** chapter). This is because the radiated wave is bent and rotated considerably during its travel through the ionosphere. At the far end of the communications path the wave may be horizontal, vertical or somewhere in between at any given instant. For that reason, the main consideration for a good DX antenna is a low angle of radiation rather than the polarization.

Most HF-band antennas are either vertically or horizontally polarized. Although circular polarization is possible, just as it is at VHF and UHF, it is seldom used at HF. While most amateur antenna installations use the Earth's surface as their frame of reference, in cases such as satellite communication or EME the terms "vertical" and "horizontal" have no meaning with respect to polarization.

21.1.3 Current and Voltage Distribution

Using the dipole as an example, when power is fed to an antenna, the current and voltage vary along its length. The current is minimum at the ends, regardless of the antenna's length. The current does not actually reach zero at the current minima, because of capacitance at the antenna ends. Insulators, loops at the antenna ends, and support wires all contribute to this capacitance, which is also called the *end effect*. The opposite is true of the RF voltage. That is, there is a voltage maximum at each end.

In the case of a half-wave dipole at its resonant frequency there is a current maximum at the center and a voltage minimum at the center as illustrated in **Figure 21.1**. The graphs of current and voltage distribution along the wire represent the magnitude of the current and voltage waveforms similarly to the envelope of a modulated signal. The magnitude of the voltage and current distributions are 90° out of phase although the actual current and voltage waveforms are in phase, resulting in a purely resistive feed point impedance.

The pattern of alternating current and voltage maxima a quarter-wavelength apart repeats every half-wavelength along a resonant linear antenna as shown in Figure 21.1B. The phase of the current and voltage are inverted in each successive half-wavelength section. (If the antenna is non-resonant, there will still be a current minimum at an open end but the voltage and current patterns on the antenna will be different than shown here.)

Power is dissipated as heat or as signals by the resistance of the antenna, which consists of both the RF resistance of the wire (ohmic loss resistance) and the *radiation resistance*. The radiation resistance is the equivalent resistance that would dissipate the power the antenna radiates, with a current flowing in it equal to the antenna current at a current maximum. Radiation resistance represents the work done by creating current in the antenna that transfers the energy from the signal source to the radiated electromagnetic wave. The loss resistance of a half-wave antenna is ordinarily small, compared with the radiation resistance, and can usually be neglected for practical purposes except in electrically small antennas, such as mobile HF antennas.

21.1.4 Impedance

The *impedance* at a given point in the antenna is determined by the ratio of the voltage to the current at that point. For example, if there were 100 V and 1.4 A of RF cur-

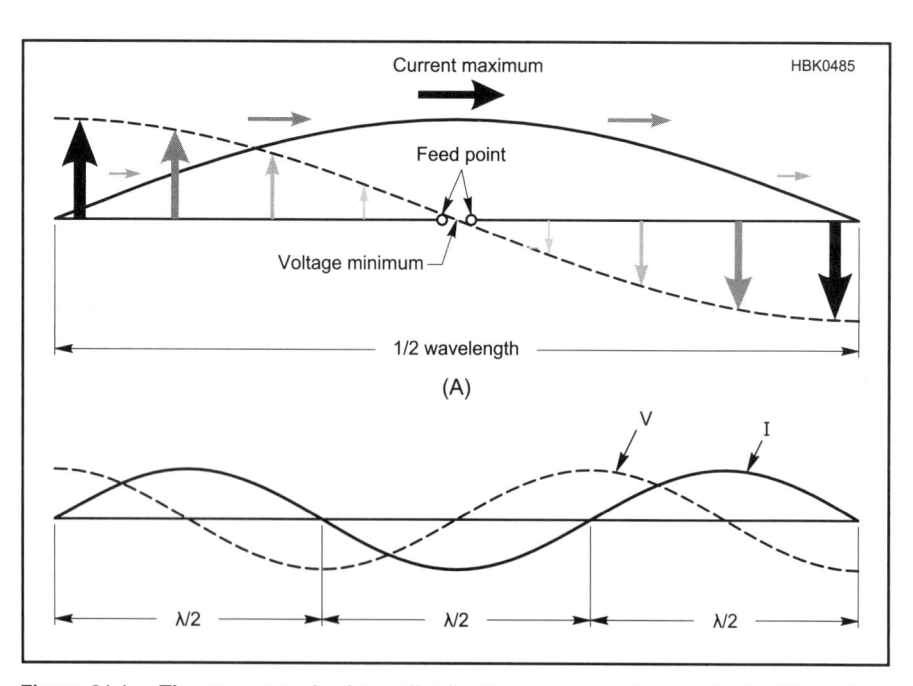

Figure 21.1 — The current and voltage distribution along a half-wave dipole (A) and for an antenna made from a series of half-wave dipoles (B). Both antennas are shown operating at a resonant frequency. Non-resonant antennas will exhibit a different pattern of voltage and current.

rent at a specified point in an antenna and if they were in phase, the impedance would be approximately 71 Ω. The antenna's *feed point impedance* is the impedance at the point where the feed line is attached. If the feed point location changes, so does the feed point impedance.

Antenna impedance may be either resistive or complex (that is, containing resistance and reactance). The impedance of a *resonant* antenna is purely resistive anywhere on the antenna, no matter what value that impedance may be. For example, the impedance of a resonant half-wave dipole may be low at the center of the antenna and high at the ends, but it is purely resistive in all cases, even though its magnitude changes.

The feed point impedance is important in determining the appropriate method of matching the impedance of the antenna and the transmission line. The effects of mismatched antenna and feed line impedances are described in detail in the **Transmission Lines** chapter of this book. Some mistakenly believe that a mismatch, however small, is a serious matter. This is not true. The significance of a perfect match becomes more pronounced only at VHF and higher, where feed line losses are a major factor. Minor mismatches at HF are rarely significant.

21.1.5 Impedance and Height Above Ground

The feed point impedance of an antenna varies with height above ground because of the effects of energy reflected from and absorbed by the ground. For example, a ½ λ (or half-wave) center-fed dipole will have a feed point impedance of approximately 75 Ω in free space far from ground, but **Figure 21.2** shows that only at certain electrical heights above ground will the feed point impedance be 75 Ω. The feed point impedance will vary from very low when the antenna is close to the ground to a maximum of nearly 100 Ω at 0.34 λ above ground, varying between ±5 Ω as the antenna is raised farther. The 75 Ω feed point impedance is most likely to be realized in a practical installation when the horizontal dipole is approximately ½, ¾ or 1 wavelength above ground. This is why few amateur λ/2 dipoles exhibit a center-fed feed point impedance of 75 Ω, even though they may be resonant.

Figure 21.2 compares the effects of perfect ground and typical soil at low antenna heights. The effect of height on the radiation resistance of a horizontal half-wave antenna is not drastic so long as the height of the antenna is greater than 0.2 λ. Below this height, while decreasing rapidly to zero over perfectly conducting ground, the resistance decreases less rapidly with height over actual lossy ground. At lower heights the resistance stops decreasing at around 0.15 λ, and thereafter increases as height decreases further. The reason for the increasing resistance is that more and more energy from the antenna is absorbed by the earth as the height drops below ¼ λ, seen as an increase in feed point impedance.

21.1.6 Antenna Bandwidth

The *bandwidth* of an antenna refers generally to the range of frequencies over which the antenna exhibits a specified level of performance. The bandwidth can be specified in units of frequency (MHz or kHz) or as a percentage of the antenna's design frequency.

Popular amateur usage of the term antenna bandwidth most often refers to the 2:1 *SWR bandwidth*, such as, "The 2:1 SWR bandwidth is 3.5 to 3.8 MHz" or "The antenna has a 10% SWR bandwidth" or "On 20 meters, the antenna has an SWR bandwidth of 200 kHz." Other specific bandwidth terms are also used, such as the *gain bandwidth* (the bandwidth over which gain is greater than a specified level) and the *front-to-back ratio bandwidth* (the bandwidth over which front-to-back ratio is greater than a specified level).

As operating frequency is lowered, an equivalent bandwidth in percentage becomes narrower in terms of frequency range in kHz or MHz. For example, a 5% bandwidth at 21 MHz is 1.05 MHz (more than wide enough to cover the whole band) but at 3.75 MHz only 187.5 kHz! Because of the wide percentage bandwidth of the lower frequency bands 160 meters is 10.5% wide, 80 meters is 3.4% wide) it is difficult to design an antenna with a bandwidth sufficient to include the whole band.

It is important to recognize that SWR bandwidth does not always relate directly to gain bandwidth. Depending on the amount of feed line loss, an 80 meter dipole with a relatively narrow 2:1 SWR bandwidth can still radiate a good signal at each end of the band, provided that an antenna tuner is used to allow the transmitter to load properly and feed line loss is not excessive. Broadbanding techniques, such as fanning the far ends of a dipole to simulate a conical type of dipole, can help broaden the SWR bandwidth.

21.1.7 Effects of Conductor Diameter

The impedance and resonant frequency of an antenna also depend on the diameter of the conductors that make up its elements in relation to the wavelength. As diameter of a conductor increases, its capacitance per unit length increases and inductance per unit length decreases. This has the net effect of lowering the frequency at which the antenna element is resonant, as illustrated in **Figure 21.3**. The larger the conductor diameter in

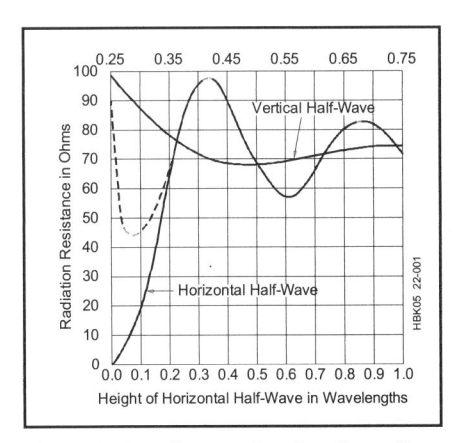

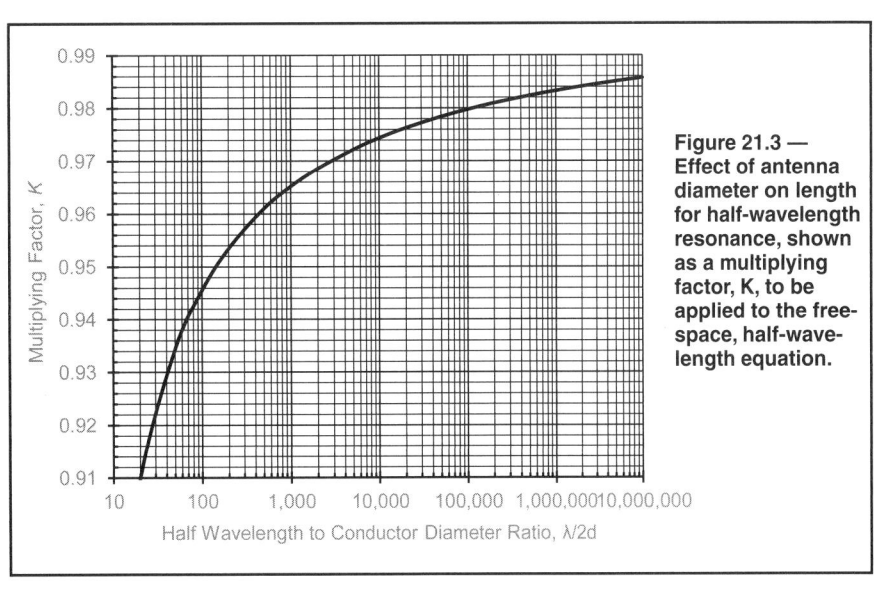

Figure 21.2 — Curves showing the radiation resistance of vertical and horizontal half-wavelength dipoles at various heights above ground. The broken-line portion of the curve for a horizontal dipole shows the resistance over *average* real earth, the solid line for perfectly conducting ground.

Figure 21.3 — Effect of antenna diameter on length for half-wavelength resonance, shown as a multiplying factor, K, to be applied to the free-space, half-wavelength equation.

terms of wavelength, the smaller its *length-to-diameter ratio (l/d)* and the lower the frequency at which a specific length of that conductor is ½ wavelength long electrically, in free space.

The speed of light, c, is exactly 299,792,458 meters per second, and a foot is exactly 0.3048 meters. Hence, a wave at a frequency f in MHz has a wavelength in feet given by:

$$\lambda(\text{in feet}) = \frac{983.571}{f(\text{in MHz})} \quad (1)$$

A dipole is a half wavelength long when its length is half of the length given by Eq. 1 or:

$$L_{\text{HalfWave}}(\text{in feet}) = \frac{491.786}{f(\text{in MHz})}$$

A dipole with a length of exactly one-half wavelength has a reactance of 42.5 Ω. The dipole can be shortened to achieve resonance. The resonant length is given by the product of the half-wave length times a multiplier K:

$$L_{\text{Resonant}}(\text{in feet}) = K \times \frac{491.786}{f(\text{in MHz})} \quad (2)$$

The multiplying factor K depends on wire diameter. The graph shown in Figure 21.3 was computed by Steve Stearns, K6OIK, who evaluated and compared theoretical and numerical methods for calculating dipole and monopole impedance (see References for Stearns, Tai and Long, and Schelkunoff).

The formulas above are for a dipole in free space. It should also be mentioned that K is not a velocity factor. Additional discussion will be published in the *ARRL Antenna Book*, 24th edition.

For example, a half-wavelength dipole for 7.2 MHz has an uncorrected length of 491.786 / 7.2 = 68.3 feet. If it is made from #12 AWG wire (0.081 inch dia) it has an l/d ratio of:

$$\frac{491.786}{7.2} (\text{ft}) \times \frac{12 \text{ in/ft}}{0.081 \text{ in}} = 10,119$$

The effect of l/d is accounted for by the factor K, which from Figure 21.3 is 0.975 for an l/d ratio of 10,119. Thus the resonant length of the half-wavelength dipole would be 0.975 × 68.3 = 66.6 feet. Most wire antennas at HF have l/d ratios in the range of 2500 to 25,000 with K = 0.97 to 0.98.

For single-wire HF antennas, the effects of ground and antenna construction make a precise accounting for K unnecessary in practice. At and above VHF, the effects of l/d ratio can be of some importance, since the wavelength is small.

Since the radiation resistance is affected relatively little by l/d ratio, the decreased L/C ratio causes the Q of the antenna to decrease. This means that the change in antenna impedance with frequency will be less, increasing the antenna's SWR bandwidth. This is often used to advantage on the lower HF bands by using multiple conductors in a cage or fan to decrease the l/d ratio.

21.1.8 Radiation Patterns

Radiation patterns are graphic representations of an antenna's directivity. Two examples are given in **Figures 21.4** and **21.5**. Shown in polar coordinates (see the **Radio Mathematics** downloadable supplemental content for information about polar coordinates), the angular scale shows direction and the scale from the center of the plot to the outer ring, calibrated in dB, shows the relative strength of the antenna's radiated signal (gain) at each angle. A line is plotted showing the antenna's relative gain (transmitting and receiving) at each angle. The antenna is located at the exact center of the plot with its orientation specified separately.

The pattern is composed of *nulls* (angles at which a gain minimum occurs) and *lobes* (a range of angles in which a gain maximum occurs). The *main lobe* is the lobe with the highest amplitude unless noted otherwise and unless several plots are being compared, the peak amplitude of the main lobe is placed at the outer ring as a 0 dB reference point. The peak of the main lobe can be located at any angle. All other lobes are *side lobes* which can be at any angle, including to the rear of the antenna.

Figure 21.4 is an *azimuthal* or *azimuth pattern* that shows the antenna's gain in all horizontal directions (azimuths) around the antenna. As with a map, 0° is at the top and bearing angle increases clockwise. (This is different from polar plots generated for mathematical functions in which 0° is at the right and angle increases counter-clockwise.)

Figure 21.5 is an *elevation pattern* that shows the antenna's gain at all vertical angles. In this case, the horizon at 0° is located to both sides of the antenna and the zenith (directly overhead) at 90°. The plot shown in Figure 21.5 assumes a ground plane (drawn from 0° to 0°) but in free-space, the plot would include the missing semicircle with –90° at the bottom. Without the ground reference, the term "elevation" has little meaning, however.

You'll also encounter E-plane and H-plane radiation patterns. These show the antenna's radiation pattern in the plane parallel to the E-field or H-field of the antenna. It's important

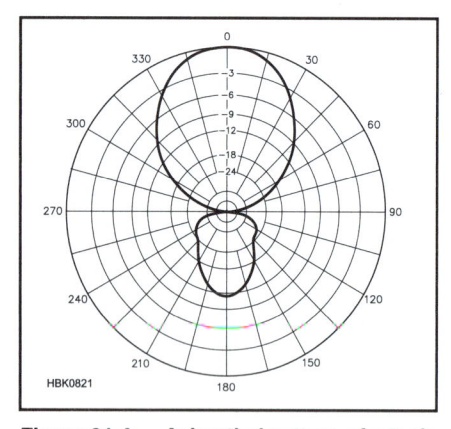

Figure 21.4 — Azimuthal pattern of a typical three-element Yagi beam antenna in free space. The Yagi's boom is along the 0° to 180° axis.

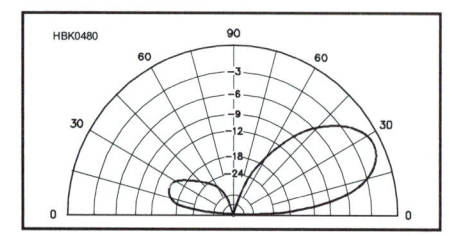

Figure 21.5 — Elevation pattern of a 3 element Yagi beam antenna placed ½ λ above perfect ground.

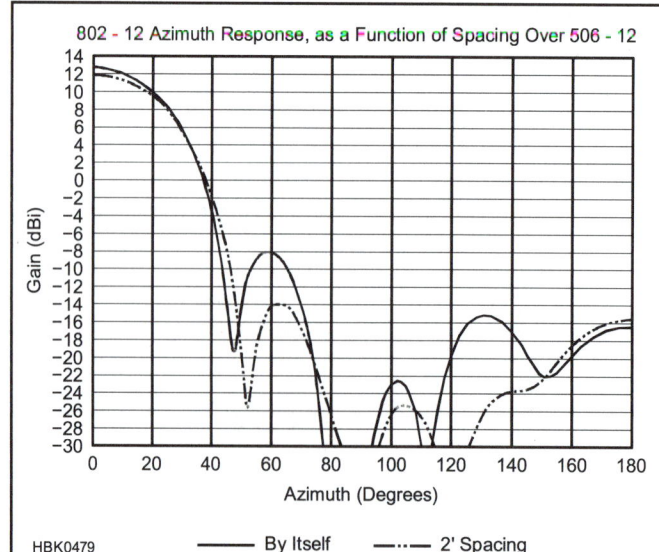

Figure 21.6 — Rectangular azimuthal pattern of an 8 element 2 meter Yagi beam antenna by itself and with another identical antenna stacked two feet above it. This example shows how a rectangular plot allows easier comparison of antenna patterns away from the main lobe.

to remember that the E-plane and H-plane do not have a fixed relationship to the Earth's surface. For example, the E-plane pattern from a horizontal dipole is an azimuthal pattern, but if the same dipole is oriented vertically, the E-plane pattern becomes an elevation pattern.

Antenna radiation patterns can also be plotted on rectangular coordinates with gain on the vertical axis in dB and angle on the horizontal axis as shown in **Figure 21.6**. This is particularly useful when several antennas are being compared. Multiple patterns in polar coordinates can be difficult to read, particularly close to the center of the plot.

The amplitude scale of antenna patterns is almost always in dB. The scale rings can be calibrated in several ways. The most common is for the outer ring to represent the peak amplitude of the antenna's strongest lobe as 0 dB. All other points on the pattern represent *relative gain* to the peak gain. The antenna's *absolute gain* with respect to an isotropic (dBi) antenna or dipole (dBd) is printed as a label somewhere near the pattern. If several antenna radiation patterns are shown on the same plot for comparison, the pattern with the largest gain value is usually assigned the role of 0 dB reference.

The gain amplitude scale is usually divided in one of two ways. One common division is to have rings at 0, –3, –6, –12, –18, and –24 dB. This makes it easy to see where the gain has fallen to one-half of the reference or peak value (–3 dB), one-quarter (–6 dB), one-sixteenth (–12 dB), and so on. Another popular division of the amplitude scale is 0, –10, –20, –30, and –40 dB with intermediate rings or tick marks to show the –2, –4, –6, and –8 dB levels. You will encounter a number of variations on these basic scales.

RADIATION PATTERN MEASUREMENTS

Given the basic radiation pattern and scales, it becomes easy to define several useful measurements or metrics by which antennas are compared, using their azimuthal patterns. Next to gain, the most commonly-used metric for directional antennas is the *front-to-back ratio (F/B)* or just "front-to-back." This is the difference in dB between the antenna's gain in the specified "forward" direction and in the opposite or "back" direction. The front-to-back ratio of the antenna in Figure 21.4 is about 11 dB. *Front-to-side ratio* is also used and is the difference between the antenna's "forward" gain and gain at right angles to the forward direction. This assumes the radiation pattern is symmetric and is of most use to antennas such as Yagis and quads that have elements arranged in parallel planes. The front-to-side ratio of the antenna in Figure 21.4 is more than 30 dB. Because the antenna's rear-ward pattern can have large amplitude variations, the *front-to-*

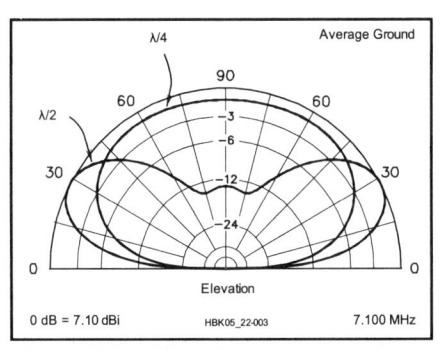

Figure 21.7 — Elevation patterns for two 40 meter dipoles over average ground (conductivity of 5 mS/m and dielectric constant of 13) at ¼ λ (33 foot) and ½ λ (66 foot) heights. The higher dipole has a peak gain of 7.1 dBi at an elevation angle of about 26°, while the lower dipole has more response at high elevation angles.

rear ratio is sometimes used. Front-to-rear uses the average of rear-ward gain over a specified angle, usually the 180° semicircle opposite the direction of the antenna's maximum gain, instead of a single gain figure at precisely 180° from the forward direction.

The antenna's *beamwidth* is the angle over which the antenna's main lobe gain is within 3 dB of the peak gain. Stated another way, the beamwidth is the angle between the directions at which the antenna's gain is –3 dB. In Figure 21.4, the antenna's main lobe beamwidth is about 54°, since the pattern crosses the –3 dB gain scale approximately 27° to either side of the peak direction. Antenna patterns with comparatively small beamwidths are referred to as "sharp" or "narrow."

An antenna with an azimuthal pattern that shows equal gain in all directions is called *omnidirectional*. This is not the same as an isotropic antenna that has equal gain in all directions, both vertical both horizontal.

21.1.9 Elevation Angle

For long-distance HF communication, the (vertical) *elevation angle* of maximum radiation, or *radiation angle*, is of considerable importance. You will want to erect your antenna so that its strongest radiation occurs at vertical angles resulting in the best performance at the distances over which you want to communicate. In general, the greater the height of a horizontally polarized antenna, the stronger its gain will be at lower vertical angles. **Figure 21.7** shows this effect at work in horizontal dipole antennas. (See the **Propagation** chapter and the *ARRL Antenna Book* for more information about how to determine the best elevation angles for communication.)

Since low radiation angles usually are most effective for long distance communications, this generally means that horizontal antennas should be high — higher is usually better. (The optimum angle for intercontinental contacts

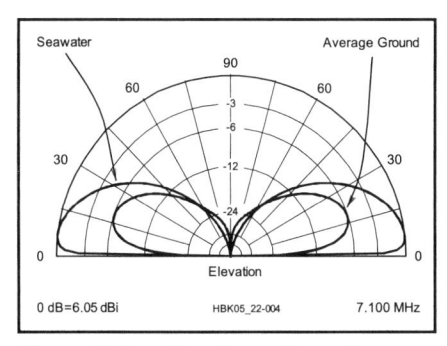

Figure 21.8 — Elevation patterns for a vertical dipole over sea water compared to average ground. In each case the center of the dipole is just over ¼ λ high. The low-angle response is greatly degraded over average ground compared to sea water, which is virtually a perfect ground.

on the HF bands is generally 15° or lower.) Experience shows that satisfactory results can be attained on the bands above 14 MHz with antenna heights between 40 and 70 feet.

Higher vertical angles can be useful for medium to short-range communications. For example, elevation angles between 20° and 65° are useful on the 40 and 80 meter bands over the roughly 550 mile path between Cleveland and Boston. Even higher angles may be useful on shorter paths when using these lower HF frequencies. A 75 meter dipole between 30 and 70 feet high works well for ranges out to several hundred miles.

For even shorter-range communications centered on your location, such as for emergency communications and regional nets, a very low antenna is used, generating its strongest radiation straight up. This is referred to as *Near-Vertical Incidence Skywave (NVIS)* communication. The antenna should be less than ¼ λ above ground and the frequency used should be below the ionosphere's critical frequency so that the signal is completely reflected back toward the ground over a wide area.

Azimuthal patterns must also specify at what elevation angle the antenna gain is measured or calculated. While an azimuthal pattern may be in the plane of the antenna (an elevation angle of 0°), for antennas located above ground, the gain will vary strongly with elevation angle.

21.1.10 Imperfect Ground

Earth conducts, but is far from being a perfect conductor. This influences the radiation pattern of the antennas that we use. The effect is most pronounced at high vertical angles (the ones most important for short-range communications and least important for long-distance communications) for horizontally polarized antennas. The consequences for vertical antennas are greatest at low angles, and are quite dramatic as can be clearly seen in **Figure 21.8**, where the elevation pattern

Antennas   21.5

for a 40 meter vertical half-wave dipole located over average ground is compared to one located over saltwater. At 10° elevation, the saltwater antenna has about 7 dB more gain than its landlocked counterpart.

An HF vertical antenna may work very well for a ham living in an area with rich soil. Ground of this type has very good conductivity. By contrast, a ham living where the soil is rocky or in a desert area may not be satisfied with the performance of a vertical HF antenna over such poorly conducting ground. Regardless of ground conductivity, the use of a ground screen of radial wires for HF verticals on land is necessary for good results.

When evaluating or comparing antennas, it is also important to include the effects of ground on antenna gain. Depending on height above ground and the qualities of the ground, reflections can increase apparent antenna gain by up to 6 dB. Because the actual installation of the antenna is unlikely to duplicate the environment in which the gain with reflections is claimed or measured, it is preferable to rely on free-space gain measurements or specifications that are independent of reflecting surfaces.

21.2 Dipoles and the Half-Wave Antenna

A fundamental form of antenna is a wire whose length is half the transmitting wavelength. It is the unit from which many more complex forms of antennas are constructed and is known as a *dipole antenna*. (The name di- meaning *two* and -pole meaning *electrical terminal* comes from the antenna having two distinct regions of electrical polarity as shown in Figure 21.1.) A dipole is resonant when it is electrically ½ λ long so that the current and voltage in the antenna are exactly 90° out of phase as shown in Figure 21.1. (Even though the magnitude of current and voltage along the antenna are 90° out of phase at resonance, the actual RF current and voltage are in-phase and the feed point impedance is entirely resistive at resonance.)

The actual length of a resonant ½ λ antenna will not be exactly equal to the half wavelength of the radio wave of that frequency in free space, but depends on the thickness of the conductor in relation to the wavelength as shown in Figure 21.3. An additional shortening effect occurs with wire antennas supported by insulators at the ends because of current flow through the capacitance at the wire ends due to the end effect. Interaction with the ground and any nearby conductors also affects the resonant length of the physical antenna.

The following formula is sufficiently accurate for dipoles below 10 MHz at heights of ⅛ to ¼ λ and made of common wire sizes. To calculate the length of a half-wave antenna in feet,

$$\text{Length (ft)} = \frac{492 \times 0.95}{f(\text{MHz})} = \frac{468}{f(\text{MHz})} \quad (2)$$

Example: A half-wave antenna for 7150 kHz (7.15 MHz) is 468/7.15 = 65.5 feet, or 65 feet 6 inches. This length is from end insulator to end insulator, including the loops of wire through the insulator and the length of wires that connect to the feed line. The loops and extra connections will add a small amount of electrical length to the antenna, so be prepared to make small adjustments in antenna length before making a final installation.

For antennas at higher frequencies and/or higher above ground, the best approach is to build the initial dipole using a numerator value of 485 to 490. Make temporary connections at the end insulators. Install the antenna and measure its SWR or impedance. Calculate the percentage difference between the desired and measured resonant frequencies. Adjust the antenna's length by the same amount. For example, for a high dipole at 14.150 MHz, start with an antenna that is 490 / 14.150 = 34.63 feet long. If the antenna's measured frequency of minimum SWR is 14.6 MHz, the antenna is 100 × 14.6 / 14.150 = 3.2 % too long and should be shortened by that amount, removing an equal amount of wire from each end of the antenna.

Above 30 MHz use the following formulas, particularly for antennas constructed from rod or tubing. K is taken from Figure 21.3.

$$\text{Length (ft)} = \frac{492 \times K}{f(\text{MHz})} \quad (3)$$

$$\text{Length (in)} = \frac{5904 \times K}{f(\text{MHz})} \quad (4)$$

Example: Find the length of a half-wave

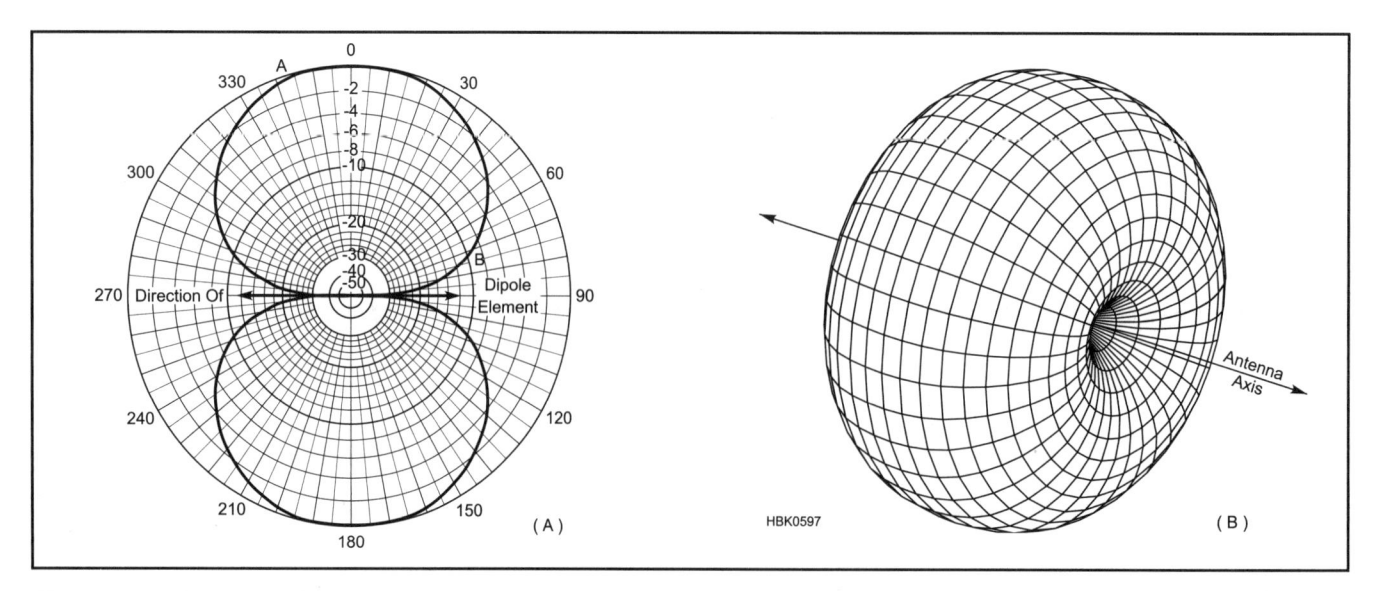

Figure 21.9 — Response of a dipole antenna in free space in the plane of the antenna with the antenna oriented along the 90° to 270° axis (A). The full three-dimensional pattern of the dipole is shown at (B). The pattern at A is a cross-section of the three-dimensional pattern taken perpendicularly to the axis of the antenna.

antenna at 50.1 MHz, if the antenna is made of ½ inch-diameter tubing. At 50.1 MHz, a half wavelength in space is

$$\frac{492}{50.1} = 9.82 \text{ ft}$$

The ratio of half wavelength to conductor diameter (changing wavelength to inches) is

$$\frac{(9.82 \text{ ft} \times 12 \text{ in./ft})}{0.5 \text{ in.}} = 235.7$$

From Figure 21.3, K = 0.945 for this ratio. The length of the antenna, from equation 3 is

$$\frac{492 \times 0.945}{50.1} = 9.28 \text{ ft}$$

or 9 feet 3-⅜ inches. The answer is obtained directly in inches by substitution in equation 4

$$\frac{5904 \times 0.945}{50.1} = 111.4 \text{ in}$$

Regardless of the formula used to calculate the length of the half-wave antenna, the effects of ground and conductive objects within a wavelength or so of the antenna usually make it necessary to adjust the installed length in order to obtain the lowest SWR at the desired frequency. Use of antenna modeling software may provide a more accurate initial length than a single formula.

The value of the SWR indicates the quality of the match between the impedance of the antenna and the feed line. If the lowest SWR obtainable is too high, an impedance-matching network may be used, as described in the **Transmission Lines** chapter. (High SWR may cause modern transmitters with solid-state power amplifiers to reduce power output as a protective measure for the output transistors.)

21.2.1 Radiation Characteristics

The radiation pattern of a dipole antenna in free space is strongest at right angles to the wire as shown in **Figure 21.9**. In an actual installation, the figure-8 pattern is less directive due to reflections from ground and other conducting surfaces. As the dipole is raised to ½ λ or greater above ground, nulls off the ends of the dipole become more pronounced. Sloping the antenna and coupling to the feed line tend to distort the pattern somewhat.

As a horizontal antenna is brought closer to ground, the elevation pattern peaks at a higher elevation angle as shown in Figure 21.7. **Figure 21.10** illustrates what happens to the directional pattern as antenna height changes. Figure 21.10C shows that there is significant radiation off the ends of a low horizontal dipole. For the ½ λ height (solid line), the radiation off the ends is only 7.6 dB lower than that in the broadside direction.

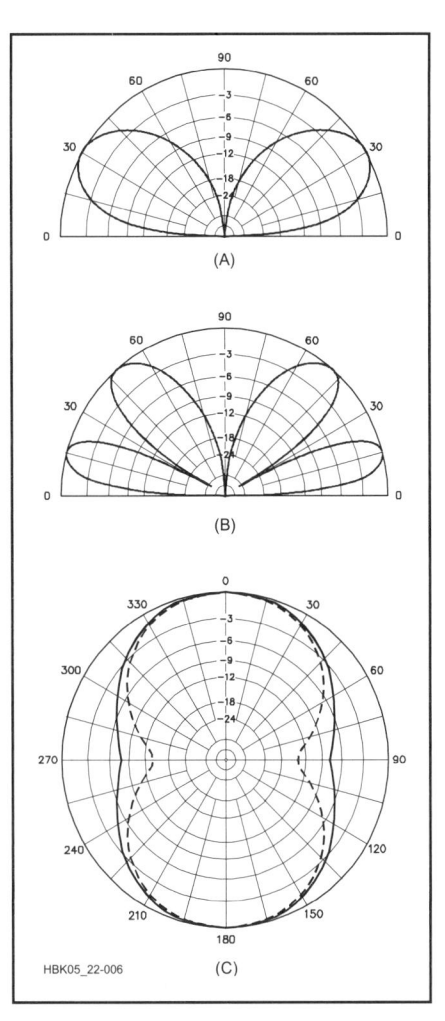

Figure 21.10 — At A, the elevation response pattern of a dipole antenna placed ½ λ above a perfectly conducting ground. At B, the pattern for the same antenna when raised to 1 λ. For both A and B, the conductor is coming out of the paper at a right angle. C shows the azimuth patterns of the dipole for the two heights at the most-favored elevation angle, the solid-line plot for the ½ λ height at an elevation angle of 30°, and the broken-line plot for the 1 λ height at an elevation angle of 15°. The conductor in C lies along the 90° to 270° axis.

Figure 21.10 also shows that for short-range communication that depends on high vertical angles of radiation (NVIS communications), a dipole can be too high. For these applications, the dipole should be installed at or below ¼ λ so that the antenna radiates strongly at high vertical angles and with little horizontal directivity.

21.2.2 Feed Methods

A feed line is attached directly to the dipole, generally at the center, where an insulator separates the antenna's conductor into two sections or "legs." This is the antenna's *feed point*. One conductor of the feed line is attached to each leg. **Figures 21.11A** and 21.11B show how the two types of feed lines are attached. There are numerous variations, of course

The low feed point impedance of the half-wave dipole at its resonant frequency, f_0, and odd harmonics results in a low SWR when fed with coaxial cable. The feed point impedance and resulting SWR with coaxial cable or "coax" will be high at even harmonics and other frequencies.

When fed with ladder line and a wide-range impedance-matching unit, a center-fed antenna can be used on nearly any frequency, including non-resonant frequencies. (An example of such an antenna system is presented as a project farther along in this section.) Another variation, shown in Figure 21.11B, is the *Zepp* (or *end-fed half wave, EFHW*) named for its original application as an antenna deployed from Zeppelin airships. The feed point impedance of a "Zepp" is quite high, requiring open-wire feed line and impedance matching techniques to deliver power effectively.

The EFHW has become popular for portable, low-power operation since it can be temporarily installed with only one support and a short coax feed line to an impedance-matching transformer at the feed point. The EFHW can also be used as variation of the *random-wire antenna* where it is attached directly to the output of the transmitter as described later in this chapter.

A dipole can be fed anywhere along its length, although the impedance of the antenna will vary as discussed earlier. One common variation is the *off-center-fed* (*OCF*) dipole (Figure 21.11C) where the feed point is offset from center by some amount and an impedance transformer matches the resulting moderately-high impedance to that of coaxial cable. The impedance transformer is usually paired with a choke balun to decouple the feed line. The OCF can also be fed with open-wire line.

21.2.3 Feed Point Baluns

Open-wire transmission lines and center-fed dipole antennas are *balanced*, that is, each conductor or section has the same impedance to earth ground. This is different from *unbalanced* coaxial cable, in which the shield is generally connected to an earth ground at some point, generally at the transmitter. To use balanced open-wire transmission lines with unbalanced equipment — most amateur equipment is unbalanced — a *balun* is required to make the transition between the balanced and unbalanced parts of the antenna system. "Balun" is an abbreviation of "balanced-to-unbalanced," the function of the device — it allows power to be transferred between the balanced and unbalanced por-

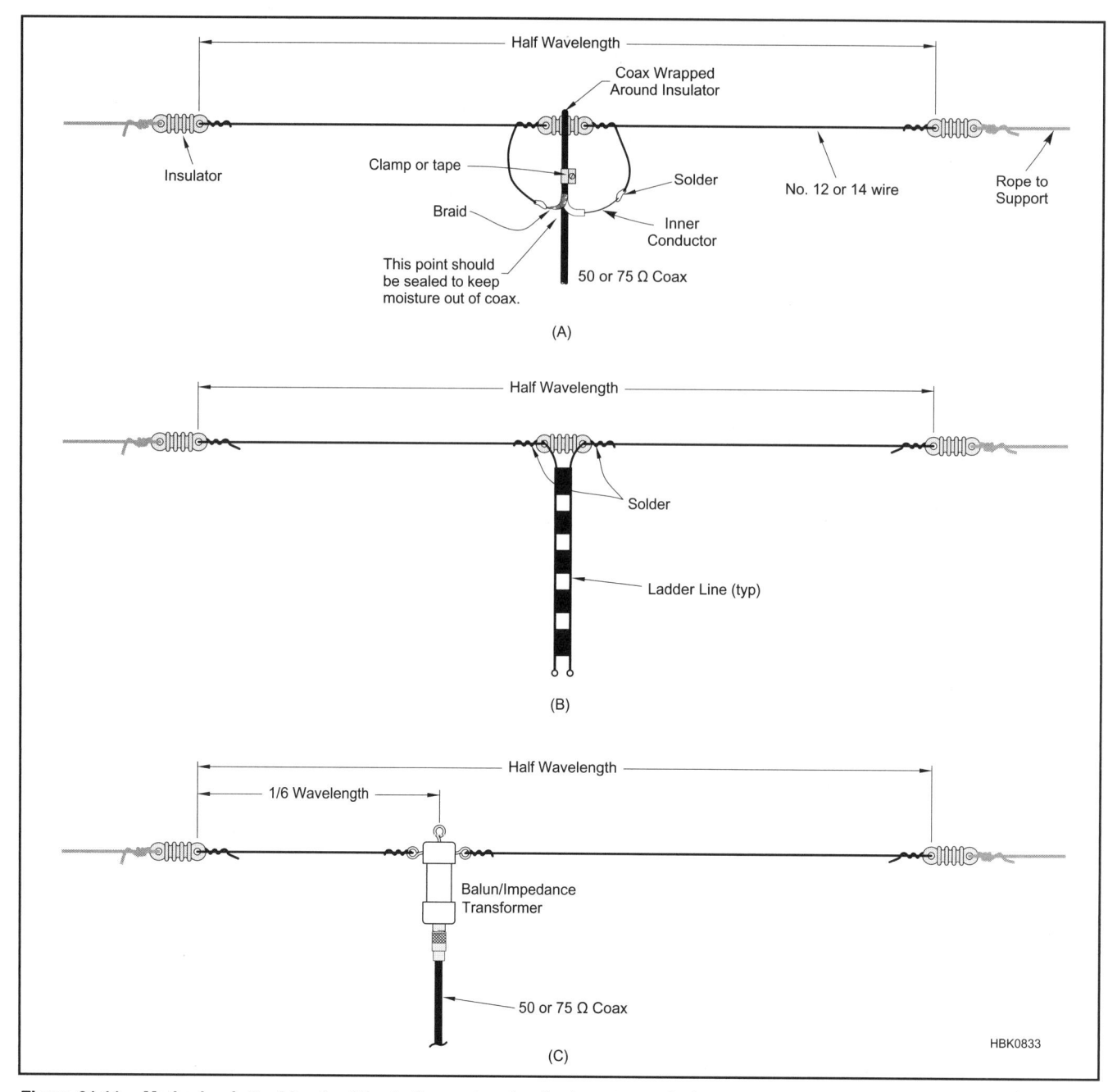

Figure 21.11— Methods of attaching feed line to the center of a dipole antenna. At A, a coaxial cable is attached to the dipole's center insulator. Ladder-line is attached to the feed point at B either at the center or at one end for a Zepp or end-fed half-wave (EFHW) antenna. The version in C is an off-center-fed (OCF) dipole with a combination balun and impedance matching transformer at the feed point.

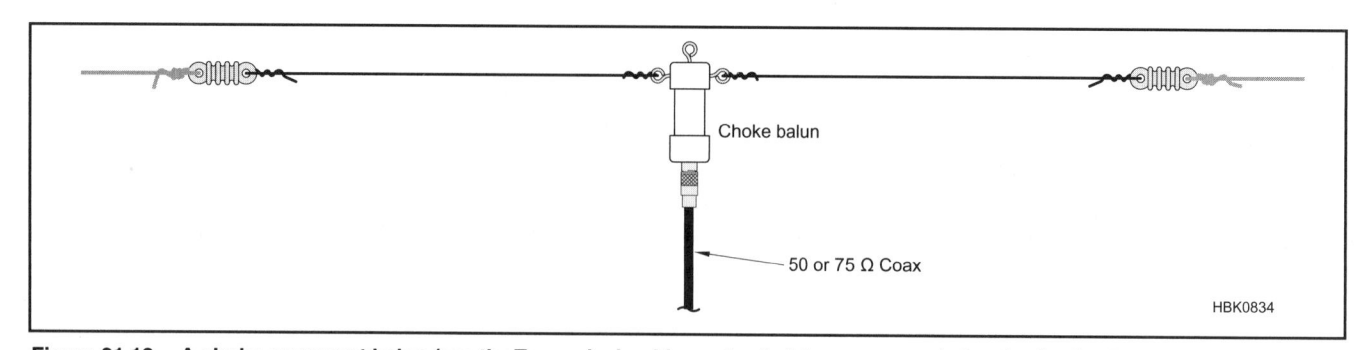

Figure 21.12— A choke or current balun (see the Transmission Lines chapter) is recommended at the feed point of a dipole fed by coaxial cable. The balun decouples the outer surface of the coax shield (see text). Baluns are not used with open-wire feed line.

tions of an antenna system in either direction. The most common application of baluns is to connect an unbalanced feed line to a balanced antenna. (Baluns and the related *ununs* are discussed in the **Transmission Lines** chapter.) Because dipoles are balanced, a balun is often used at the feed point when a dipole is fed with coax.

Due to the skin effect discussed in the **RF Techniques** chapter, the inside and outside of the coaxial cable shield act as separate conductors at RF. This "third conductor" of a coaxial cable unbalances the symmetry of the dipole antenna when the coax is connected directly to the dipole as shown in Figure 21.11A. As a result, RF current can flow on the outside of the cable shield to the enclosures of station equipment connected to the cable. This combination of the dipole and feed line shield is likely to have a different resonant frequency and feed point impedance than what was intended.

In order to *decouple* the coax shield from the antenna, a *choke* or *current balun* is recommended as shown in **Figure 21.12**. The choke balun creates a high impedance on the outside of the coax shield while leaving currents inside the coax unaffected. See the **Transmission Lines** chapter for choke balun designs.

Shield currents can also impair the function of instruments connected to the line (such as SWR meters and SWR-protection circuits in the transmitter). The shield current also produces some feed line radiation, which changes the antenna radiation pattern, and allows objects near the cable to affect the antenna-system performance.

The consequences may be negligible: A slight skewing of the antenna pattern usually goes unnoticed. Or, they may be significant: False SWR readings may cause the transmitter to reduce power unnecessarily; radiating coax near a TV feed line may cause strong local interference from overload. Therefore, it is better to eliminate feed line radiation whenever possible, and a choke balun should be used at any transition |between balanced and unbalanced systems. Even so, balanced or unbalanced systems without a balun often operate with no apparent problems. For temporary or emergency stations, do not let the lack of a balun deter you from operating.

21.2.4 Building Dipoles and Other Wire Antennas

The purpose of this section is to offer information on the actual physical construction of wire antennas. Because the dipole, in one of its configurations, is probably the most common amateur wire antenna, it is used in the following examples. The techniques described here, however, enhance the reliability and safety of all wire antennas.

WIRE

Choosing the right type of wire for the project at hand is the key to a successful antenna — the kind that works well and stays up through a winter ice storm or a gusty spring wind storm. What gauge of wire to use is the first question to settle; the answer depends on strength, ease of handling, cost, availability and visibility. Generally, antennas that are expected to support their own weight, plus the weight of the feed line should be made from #12 AWG or larger wire. (The National Electrical Code (NEC) specifies a minimum size of #10 AWG for external antennas.) Horizontal dipoles, Zepps, some long wires and the like fall into this category. Antennas supported in the center, such as inverted-V dipoles and delta loops, may be made from lighter material, such as #14 AWG wire.

The type of wire to be used is the next important decision. The wire specifications table in the **Component Data and References** chapter shows popular wire styles and sizes. The strongest wire suitable for antenna service is *copper-clad steel*, also known as *copperweld*. The copper coating is necessary for RF service because steel is a relatively poor conductor. Practically all of the RF current is confined to the copper coating because of skin effect. Copper-clad steel is outstanding for permanent installations, but it can be difficult to work with because of the stiffness of the steel core. Kinks, abrasion, or repeated flexing can crack the copper cladding, leading to rusting of the inner steel core. Damage to the cladding can result in increased resistance and loss. Rusting of the inner core will eventually weaken the antenna. Regularly inspecting the antenna visually or checking SWR for changes can help spot problems.

Solid-copper wire, either hard-drawn or soft-drawn, is another popular material. Easier to handle than copper-clad steel, solid copper is available in a wide range of sizes. It is generally more expensive however, because it is all copper. Soft-drawn stretches under tension, so periodic pruning of the antenna may be necessary in some cases. Enamel-coated *magnet-wire* is a suitable choice for experimental antennas because it is easy to manage, and the coating protects the wire from the weather. Although it stretches under tension, the wire may be pre-stretched before final installation and adjustment. A local electric motor rebuilder might be a good source for magnet wire.

Hook-up wire, speaker wire or even ac lamp cord are suitable for temporary installations. Almost any copper wire may be used, as long as it is strong enough for the demands of the installation.

Aluminum wire can be used for antennas, but is not as strong as copper or steel for the same diameter and soldering it to feed lines requires special techniques. Galvanized and steel wire, such as that used for electric fences, is inexpensive, but it is a much poorer conductor at RF than copper and should be avoided.

Kinking, which severely weakens wire, is a potential problem when handling any solid conductor. When uncoiling solid wire of any type — copper, steel, or aluminum — take care to unroll the wire or untangle it without pulling on a kink to straighten it. A kink is actually a very sharp twist in the wire and the wire will break at such a twist when flexed, such as from vibration in the wind.

Solid wire also tends to fail at connection or attachment points at which part of the wire is rigidly clamped. The repeated flexing from wind and other vibrations eventually causes metal fatigue and the wire breaks. Stranded wire is preferred for antennas that will be subjected to a lot of vibration and flexing. If stranded wire is not suitable, use a heavier gauge of solid wire to compensate.

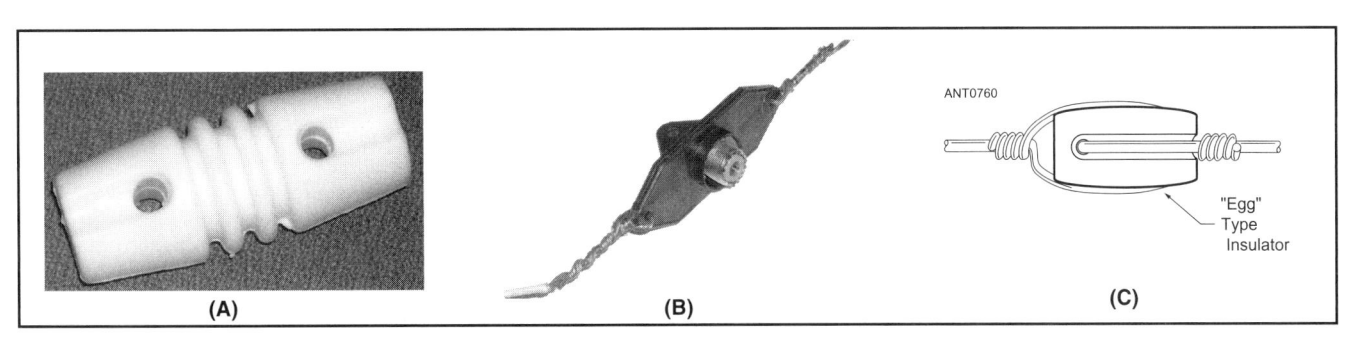

Figure 21.13 — (A) and (B) show examples of commercial center insulators: a dog-bone insulator and a Budwig HQ-1 insulator. (C) The correct way to attach a wire to a strain or "egg" insulator.

Insulated vs Bare Wire

Losses are the same (in the HF region at least) whether the antenna wire is insulated or bare. If insulated wire is used, a 3 to 5% shortening from the length calculated for a bare wire is required to obtain resonance at the desired frequency. This is caused by the increased distributed capacitance resulting from the higher dielectric constant of the plastic insulating material compared to air. The actual length for resonance must be determined experimentally by pruning and measuring because the dielectric constant of the insulating material varies from wire to wire. Wires that might come into contact with humans or animals should be insulated to reduce the chance of shock or burns.

INSULATORS

Wire antennas must be insulated at the ends and usually at the feed point. Commercially available insulators are made from ceramic, glass or plastic. Insulators are available from many Amateur Radio dealers. Local hardware and farm stores are other possible sources of insulators for electric fences. Ceramic or glass insulators will usually outlast the wire, so they are highly recommended for a safe, reliable, permanent installation. **Figure 21.13A** shows the proper way to attach a wire to a strain or "egg" insulator. Figures 21.13B and 21.13C show examples of center insulators. Figure 21.13B is popularly known as a "dog bone" insulator and is available in glass, ceramic, and plastic. The ridges are to prevent water or dust from forming a conductive path across the insulator. Figure 21.13C shows a Budwig HQ-1 insulator with a built-in SO-239 and wires for attaching to the antenna. Acceptable homemade insulators may be made from a variety of material including (but not limited to) polycarbonate sheet or rod, PVC tubing or plumbing fixtures, or fiberglass rod. Temporary or emergency antennas can even make use of stiff plastic from a discarded container or dry wood. **Figures 21.14A** and 21.14B show some homemade insulators. If you make your own insulators, be sure the material is sturdy enough to withstand the mechanical stress and UV-resistant to be suitable for prolonged outdoor use.

ATTACHING FEED LINES

Most wire antennas require an insulator at the feed point. Although there are many ways to connect the feed line, there are a few things to keep in mind. If you feed your antenna with coaxial cable, you have two choices. You can install an SO-239 connector on the center insulator and use a PL-259 on the end of your coax, or you can separate the center conductor from the braid, creating a pigtail connection, and attach the feed line directly to the antenna wire. Although it costs less to connect directly to the antenna, the use of connectors offers several advantages. (See the **Transmission Lines** chapter for more information about selecting and installing feed lines.)

Coaxial cable braid acts as a wick to soak up water. If you do not adequately seal the antenna end of the feed line, water will find its way into the braid. Water in the feed line will contaminate the braid, causing high losses and rendering the coax useless long before its normal lifetime is up. It is not uncommon for water to drip from the end of the coax inside the shack after a year or so of service if the antenna connection is not properly waterproofed. Use of a PL-259/SO-239 combination (or other connector of your choice) makes the task of waterproofing connections much easier. Another advantage to using the PL-259/SO-239 combination is that feed line replacement is much easier, should that become necessary or desirable.

Whether you use coaxial cable, ladder line, or twin lead to feed your antenna, an often-overlooked consideration is the mechanical strength of the connection. Wire antennas and feed lines tend to move a lot in the wind, and unless the feed line is attached securely, the connection will weaken with time. The resulting failure can range from a frustrating intermittent electrical connection to a complete separation of feed line and antenna. Figure 21.14B illustrates several different ways of attaching the feed line to the antenna. An idea for supporting ladder line is shown in **Figure 21.15**.

PUTTING IT TOGETHER

If made from the right materials and installed in the clear, the dipole should give years of maintenance-free service. As you build your antenna, keep in mind that if you get it right the first time, you won't have to do it again for a long time.

Figure 21.11 shows details of antenna construction. Although a dipole is used for the examples, the techniques illustrated here apply to any type of wire antenna. **Table 21.1** shows dipole lengths for the amateur HF bands. These lengths do not include the extra wire required to attach the wire to the insulator as shown in Figure 21.11. Determine the extra amount of wire required by experimenting with the insulator you intend to use. Add twice this amount of wire to the leg lengths in Table 21.1, one extra length for each insulator. (Four such attachments are required for each dipole — two on each leg.)

Most dipoles require a little pruning to reach the desired resonant frequency due to the effects of ground and nearby conducting objects and surfaces. (See the beginning of this section for an explanation.) Table 21.1 includes lengths based on the classic 468/f formula and on 490/f intended to be a starting length. Record the constructed length with all insulators attached. (The constructed length is measured between the ends of the loops at each

(A)

(B)

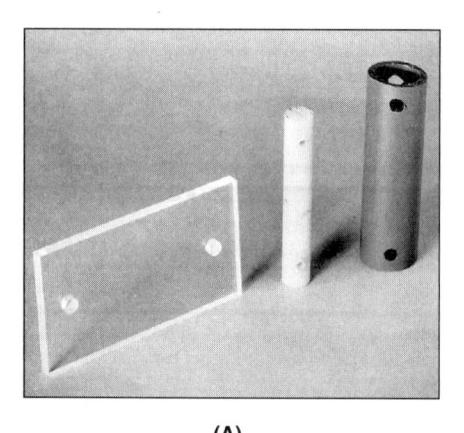

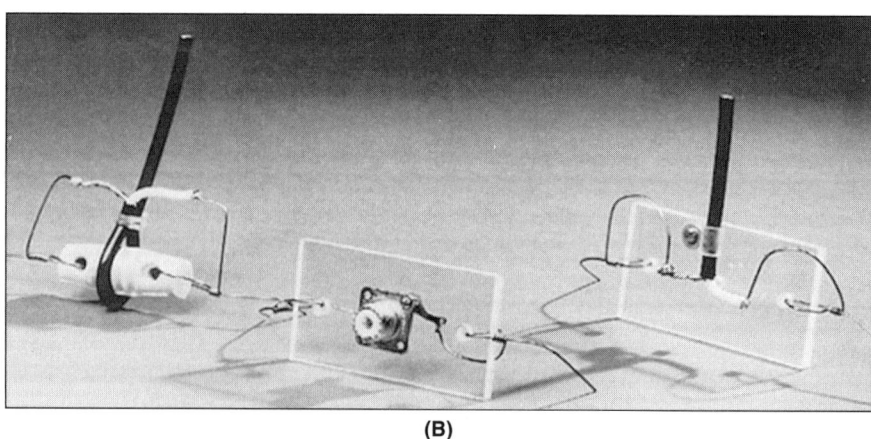

Figure 21.14 — (A) Some ideas for homemade antenna insulators. (B) Some homemade dipole center insulators. The one in the center includes a built-in SO-239 connector. Others are designed for direct connection to the feed line. Be sure to use UV-resistant plastic for insulators.

end of the wire and includes the length of any feed line-to-antenna connections.) Next, raise the dipole to the working height and find the frequency at which minimum SWR occurs. Multiply the frequency of the SWR minimum by the antenna length and divide the result by the desired f_0. The result is the finished length; trim both ends equally to reach that length and you're done. For example, if you want the SWR minimum to occur at 14.1 MHz and the first attempt with a constructed length of 33.8 feet results in an SWR minimum at 13.9 MHz, the final length for the antenna is

$$33.8 \times (13.9/14.1) = 33.3 \text{ ft}$$

In determining how well your antenna will work over the long term, how well you put the pieces together is second only to the ultimate strength of the materials used. Even the smallest details, such as how you connect the wire to the insulators, contribute significantly to antenna longevity. Where wires are soldered, use only enough heat to make a good connection. Excessive heat, such as from a propane torch, can anneal the wire, weakening it at the solder point.

By using plenty of wire at the end insulators and wrapping it tightly, you will decrease the possibility of the wire pulling loose in the wind. There is no need to solder the wire once it is wrapped. There is no electrical connection here, only mechanical.

Similarly, the feed line connection at the center insulator should be made to the antenna wires after they have been secured to the insulator. This way, you will be assured of a good electrical connection between the antenna and feed line without compromising the mechanical strength. Do a good job of soldering the antenna and feed line connections. Use a heavy iron or a soldering gun (200 W is a good size to use for this job), and be sure to clean the materials thoroughly before starting the job. If possible, solder the connections at a workbench, where the best possible joints may be made. Poorly soldered or unsoldered connections will become headaches as the wire oxidizes and the electrical integrity degrades with time. Besides degrading your antenna performance, poorly made joints can even be a cause of TVI because of rectification. Spray the connections with a UV-resistant acrylic coating or use a brush-on insulation coating for waterproofing.

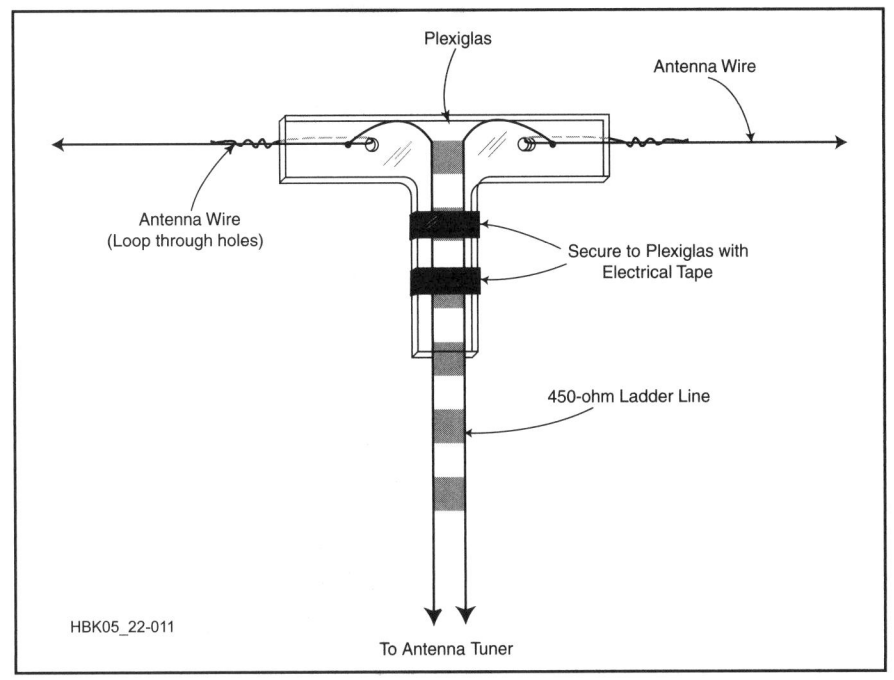

Figure 21.15 — A piece of cut polycarbonate can be used as a center insulator and to support a ladder-line feeder. The vertical section acts to reduce the flexing of the wires where they connect to the antenna. Tape or UV-resistant wire ties can be used to hold the line to the insulator.

Table 21.1
Dipole Dimensions for Amateur Bands

Table A – Dipole Lengths based on 468/f

Freq	Overall Length			Leg Length		
(MHz)	ft	in	m	ft	in	m
1.82	257	2	78.4	128	7	39.2
3.6	130	0	39.7	65	0	19.8
5.378	7	2	43.6	43	7	21.8
7.1	65	10	20.1	32	11	10.05
10.1	46	4	14.13	23	2	7.06
14.1	33	2	10.12	16	7	5.06
18.1	25	10	7.89	12	11	3.94
21.1	22	2	6.76	11	1	3.38
24.9	18	9 ½	5.73	9	4 ¾	2.87
28.4	16	6	5.03	8	3	2.51

Table B – Dipole Lengths based on 490/f

Freq	Overall Length			Leg Length		
(MHz)	ft	in	m	ft	in	m
1.82	269	3	82.1	134	7	41.1
3.6		136	1	41.5	66	1 20.8
5.37	91	3	27.8	45	7	13.9
7.1	69	0	21.0	34	6	10.5
10.1	48	6	14.8	24	3	7.4
14.1	34	9	10.6	17	5	5.3
18.1	27	1	8.26	13	6 ½	4.13
21.1	23	2 ½	7.08	11	7 ¼	3.54
24.9	19	8	6.00	9	10	3.00
28.4	17	3	5.26	8	7 ½	2.63

ATTACHING ANTENNA SUPPORTS

If towers, masts, or buildings are available, attaching the antenna support ropes or cables is fairly straightforward. Pulleys or guides such as stainless steel or aluminum carabiners or large screw eyes rated for the expected load should be used. Counterweights or springs can be used to allow the antenna to move in the wind.

Trees are a time-honored and very common solution to holding the antenna up in the air. They present some difficulties in attaching the support rope or cable, however. The most important consideration is safety. Any time a tree support is being considered, take care to ensure that there are no power lines at any voltage in or near the tree. The lines are not always easily visible. If a weight is propelled over or through the tree, it may fly well beyond the tree and cause the trailing line to contact power lines that way. In any case, don't become a statistic! Check the entire area around the tree for hazards.

If you can climb the tree and attach the support hardware, the main problem involves providing enough tension and flexibility to allow the supports to move with the tree during wind and storms. Climbing or hiring a tree climber can pay benefits over the long term with tree-supported antennas since a pulley and halyard can be securely attached to the tree. (More information on tree-mounting antennas can be found in the *ARRL Antenna Book*.)

If climbing is not an option, such as for a temporary or portable station or for trees not suitable for climbing, getting a line into the tree is a challenge. Hams have devised many different methods of getting a line over a branch, from the "Armstrong method" (throwing a weight such as an arborist's weight bag or a tennis ball throwing toy), to various fishing techniques, and even archery. Two very popular current methods are the slingshot and the compressed-air "spud gun." Both launch a small projectile attached to lightweight monofilament fishing through or over a tree. (Hint — paint the projectile a bright color so it's easy to find in brush or long grass.) That line is used to pull a length of twine or string over the branch and then the rope or cable that forms the final support. (The *QST* article "The W4SSY Spudgun" is available in this book's downloadable supplemental content and several vendors offer commercial versions of the compressed-air or slingshot launcher.)

Another option just being developed as this edition was being assembled is the use of an RPV (remotely-piloted vehicle) better known as a "drone." The lightest line is attached to the drone which is then piloted over the tree and back to the ground where the next line is attached as with the launcher or slingshot. Drones can rarely be flown *through* a tree, limiting line placement to the uppermost branches. This results in the highest possible support point but the branches are the smallest on the tree.

If you use a pulley, select a size that prevents the rope from slipping between the sheave and housing as the antenna and ropes move in the wind. So that the antenna stays up after installation, keep it away from tree branches and other objects that might rub or fall on the antenna. If the supports for the antenna move in the wind, such as trees, leave enough slack in the antenna that it is not pulled overly tight in normal winds. Other options are to use pulleys and counterweights to allow the antenna supports to flex without pulling on the antenna. (This and other installation topics are covered in the *ARRL Antenna Book*.)

ANTENNA SUPPORT ROPE

A good rope for holding up wire antennas with spans up to 150 or 200 feet is ¼-inch nylon rope, and UV-resistant 5/32- or 3/16-inch Dacron rope is also popular. After an installation with any new rope, it will be necessary to repeatedly take up the slack created by stretching. This process will continue over a period of several weeks, at which time most of the stretching will have taken place. Even a year after installation, however, some slack may still arise from stretching.

Make certain that the rope ends will not unravel. Most supply stores will cut the length with a hot knife; that will do the best job of sealing the ends. You can do it at home by simply melting the ends with a match or cigarette lighter. An alternative is to tightly wrap a few layers of electrical tape or heat shrink tubing around the ends. Be sure to tape the ends of all your ropes to protect them.

21.2.5 Dipole Configuration

Dipole antennas need not be installed horizontally and in a straight line. They are generally tolerant of bending, sloping or drooping. Bent dipoles may be used where antenna space is at a premium. **Figure 21.16** shows a couple of possibilities; there are many more. Bending distorts the radiation pattern somewhat and may affect the impedance as well, but compromises may be acceptable when the situation demands them. When an antenna bends back on itself (as in Figure 21.16B) some of the signal is canceled; avoid this if possible. Remember that dipole antennas are RF conductors. For safety's sake, mount all antennas away from conductors (especially power lines), combustibles and well beyond the reach of passersby.

21.2.6 Inverted-V Dipole

An *inverted-V* dipole is supported at the center with a single support, such as a tree or mast. While *V* describes the shape of this antenna, this antenna should not be confused with long-wire horizontal-V antennas, which are highly directive.

The inverted-V's radiation pattern and feed point impedance depend on the *apex angle* between the legs: As the apex angle decreases, so does feed point impedance, and the radiation pattern becomes less directive. At apex angles below 90°, the antenna efficiency begins to decrease, as well.

The proximity of ground to the antenna ends will lower the resonant frequency of the antenna so that a dipole may have to be shortened in the inverted-V configuration. Losses in the ground increase when the antenna ends are close to the ground. Keeping the ends eight feet or higher above ground reduces ground loss and also prevents humans and animals from coming in contact with the antenna.

Remember that antenna current produces the radiated signal, and current is maximum at the dipole center. Therefore, performance is best when the central area of the antenna is high and clear of nearby objects.

21.2.7 Sloping Dipole and End-Fed Half-Wave (EFHW)

A sloping dipole is shown in **Figure 21.17A**. This antenna is often used to favor one direction (the *forward direction* in the figure). With a non-conducting support and poor ground, signals off the back are somewhat weaker than those off the front. With a non-conducting mast and good ground, the response is omnidirectional.

A conductive support such as a tower can act as a parasitic element. (So does the coax shield, unless it is routed at 90° from the antenna or decoupled with a choke balun.) The parasitic effects vary with ground quality, support height and other conductors on the support (such as a beam at the top or other wire antennas). With such variables, performance is very difficult to predict although modeling may give some insight into how

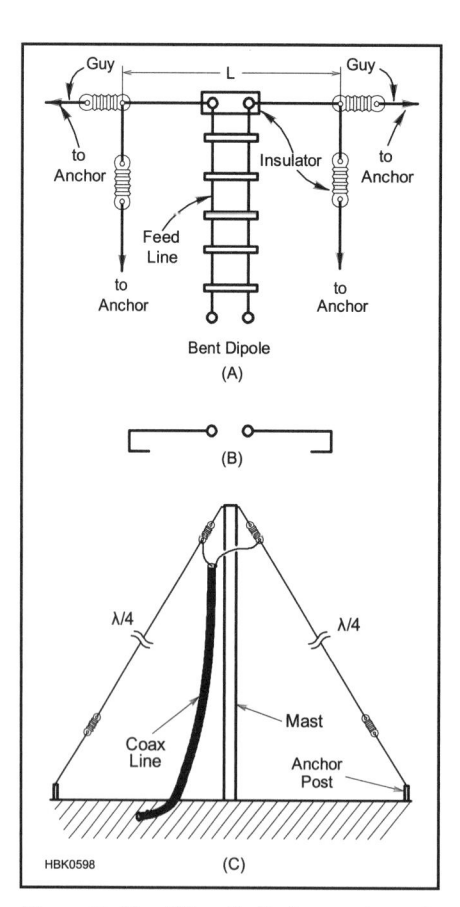

Figure 21.16 — When limited space is available for a dipole antenna, the ends can be bent downward as shown at A, or back on the radiator as shown at B. The inverted-V at C can be erected with the ends bent parallel with the ground when the available supporting structure is not high enough.

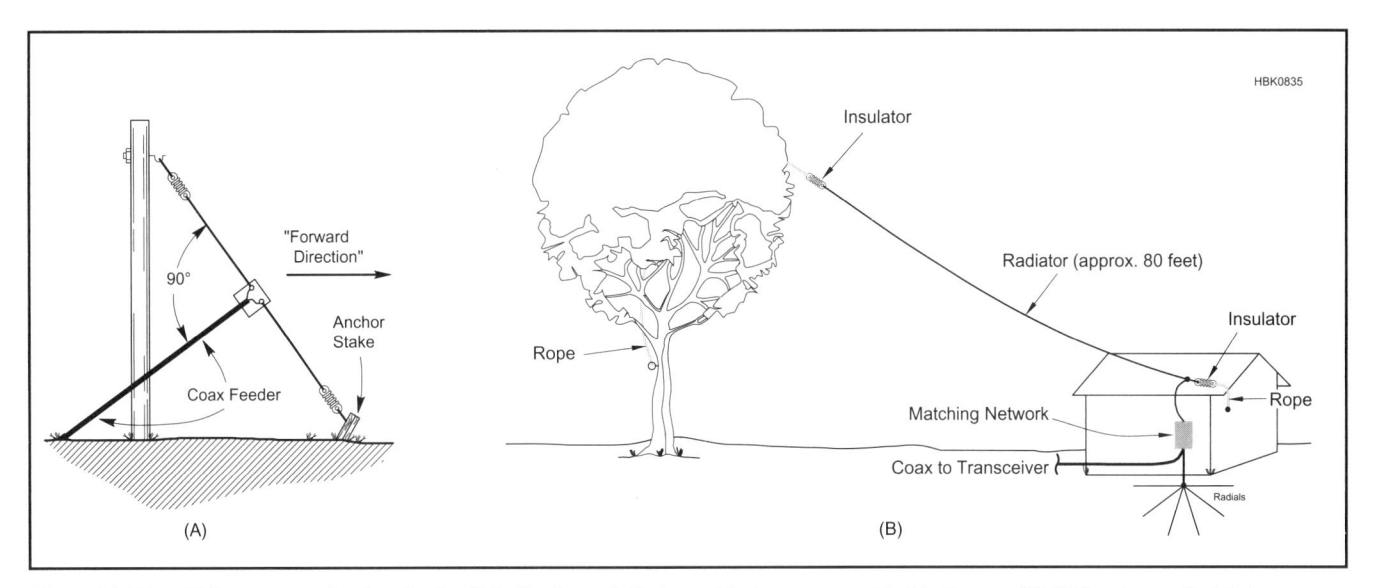

Figure 21.17 — At A, an example of a sloping ½ λ dipole, or *full sloper*. B shows an end-fed half-wave (EFHW) antenna that behaves similarly to the sloping dipole but is fed at one end through a matching network. Note the radials that form a counterpoise for the antenna. On the lower HF bands, maximum radiation for both antennas over poor to average earth is off the sides and in the forward direction as indicated, if a non-conductive support is used. A metal support will alter this pattern by acting as a parasitic element. How it alters the pattern is a complex issue depending on the electrical height of the mast, what other antennas are located on the mast and on the configuration of any guy wires.

the antenna will perform.

Losses increase as the antenna ends approach the support or the ground, so the same cautions about the height of the antenna ends applies as for the inverted-V antenna. To prevent feed line radiation, route the coax away from the feed point at 90° from the antenna as far as possible or use a choke balun.

Figure 21.17B shows a variation of the sloping dipole that has become popular for temporary and portable operation. The EFHW antenna is a sloping dipole, fed at one end. The open end is supported by a tree or mast or other convenient attachment point and the feed point is close to the ground. A 9:1 balun at the feed point allows a short piece of feed line to be attached, an automatic impedance-matching unit can be used, or the antenna can even be attached directly to the transmitting equipment. Some variations place the feed point a few feet from the end of the wire to lower the impedance and make it a little easier to match.

Regardless of whether a feed line is used or the antenna connected directly to the output of the transmitter, the EFHW requires a counterpoise or a few ground radials to work well. These conductors form part of the antenna system and will be "hot" with RF. For directly attached EFHW wires, the station equipment (and even the operator) will be part of the antenna system as well. A variation of the EFHW that avoids the need for a counterpoise connection is described in the article "An Off-Center End-Fed Dipole for Portable Operation on 40 to 6 Meters" by Kai Siwiak in the March 2015 issue *QST*. The article is included in the downloadable supplemental content for this book.

21.2.8 Shortened Dipoles

Inductive loading increases the electrical length of a conductor without increasing its physical length. Therefore, we can build physically-short dipole antennas by placing inductors in the antenna. These are called *loaded dipoles*, and *The ARRL Antenna Book* includes information on how to design them. There are some trade-offs involved: Inductively loaded antennas are less efficient and have narrower bandwidths than full-size antennas. Generally they should not be shortened more than 50%. David Birnbaum, K2LYV explains the process of designing loaded dipoles that work on two bands in an article contained in this book's downloadable supplemental information.

21.2.9 Half-Wave Vertical Dipole (HVD)

Unlike its horizontal counterpart, which has a figure-8 pattern, the azimuthal pattern of a vertical dipole is omnidirectional. In other words, it looks like a circle. Look again at Figures 21.7 and 21.8 and note the comparison between horizontal and vertical dipole elevation patterns. These two figures illustrate the fact that performance of a horizontal dipole depends to a great extent on its height above ground. By contrast, *half-wave vertical dipole* (*HVD*) performance is highly dependent on ground conductivity and dielectric constant.

Experiments by K8CH show that an HVD can compete favorably with horizontal dipole or inverted-V antennas at a similar height. The HVD only requires one main support (see the caution below on feed line orientation) which makes it a good choice for portable or temporary operation.

Figure 21.18 shows the elevation patterns for the vertical dipole and for the reference dipole at a pattern peak and at a null. The

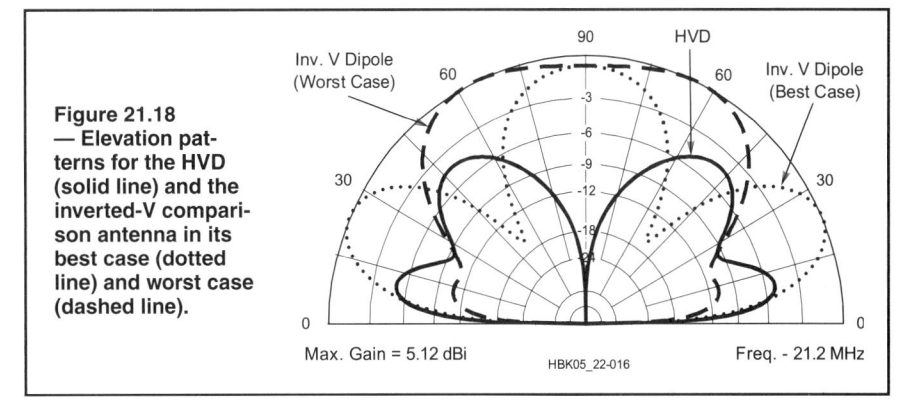

Figure 21.18 — Elevation patterns for the HVD (solid line) and the inverted-V comparison antenna in its best case (dotted line) and worst case (dashed line).

Max. Gain = 5.12 dBi   Freq. - 21.2 MHz

large lobe in the HVD pattern at 48° is caused by the antenna being elevated 14 feet above ground. This lobe will shrink at lower heights. The pattern of both antennas depend strongly on antenna height.

Another advantage of the HVD is its radiation resistance at low heights. Look back at Figure 21.2 at the curve for the vertical half-wave antenna. With its base just above ground, the HVD will have a radiation resistance of over 90 Ω. That can easily be turned to an advantage. Capacitive loading will lower the radiation resistance *and* shorten the antenna. It is possible to make a loaded vertical dipole that is half the height of an HVD and that has a good SWR when fed with 50 Ω coax.

One challenge to building the HVD is feed line decoupling. The feed line attached in the middle must be routed away from the antenna at right angles to prevent excessive shield current from distorting the antenna's pattern, even if a choke balun is used. This can be mechanically challenging.

21.2.10 Folded Dipoles

Figure 21.19 shows a *folded dipole* constructed from open-wire transmission line. The dipole is made from a ½ λ section of open-wire line with the two conductors connected together at each end of the antenna. The top conductor of the open-wire length is continuous from end to end. The lower conductor, however, is cut in the middle and the feed line attached at that point. Open-wire transmission line is then used to connect the transmitter.

A folded dipole has exactly the same gain and radiation pattern as a single-wire dipole. However, because of the mutual coupling between the upper and lower conductors that divides antenna current equally between the conductors, the feed point impedance of a single-wire dipole is multiplied by the square of the number of conductors in the antenna. In this case, there are two conductors in the antenna, so the feed point impedance is 2^2 = 4 times that of a single-wire dipole. (A three-wire folded dipole would have a nine times higher feed point impedance and so forth.)

A common use of the folded dipole is to raise the feed point impedance of the antenna to present a better impedance match to high impedance feed line. For example, if a very long feed line to a dipole is required, open-wire feed line would be used. By raising the dipole's feed point impedance, the SWR on the open-wire line is reduced from that of a single-wire dipole fed with open-wire feed line. Impedance matching to the usual 50 Ω can then be done at the transmitter.

A variation of the folded dipole called the *twin-folded terminated dipole* (*TFTD*) adds a resistor in the top conductor. Values of 300 to 600 Ω are used. The function of the resistor is to act as a *swamping* load, reducing the higher feed point impedances over a wide frequency range. A TFTD ½ λ long at 80 meters can be constructed to cover the entire 2 to 30 MHz range with SWR of 3:1 or less. The resistor dissipates some of the transmitter power (more than 50% at some frequencies!), but the improvement in SWR allows a coaxial feed line to be used without an impedance-matching unit. The increased convenience and installation outweigh the reduction in radiated signal. TFTD antennas are popular for emergency communications and where only a single HF antenna can be installed and high performance is not required, such as for regional coverage via NVIS as described below.

21.2.11 Multiband Dipole Systems

There are several ways to construct coax-fed multiband dipole systems. These techniques apply to dipoles of all orientations. Each method requires a little more work than a single dipole, but the materials don't cost much.

PARALLEL (FAN) DIPOLES

Parallel dipoles (also called *fan dipoles*) as shown in **Figure 21.20** are a simple and convenient answer. Center-fed dipoles have low feed point impedances near f_0 and its odd harmonics, and high impedances at other frequencies. This lets us construct simple multiband systems in which the antenna for the desired band is automatically active. Consider a 50 Ω resistor connected in parallel with a 5 kΩ resistor. A generator connected across the two resistors will see 49.5 Ω, and 99% of the current will flow through the 50 Ω resistor. When resonant and non-resonant antennas are connected in parallel, the same result occurs: The non-resonant antenna has a high impedance, so little current flows in it and it has little effect on the total feed point impedance. Thus, we can connect several dipoles together at the feed point, and power naturally flows to the resonant antenna.

There are some limits, however. Wires in

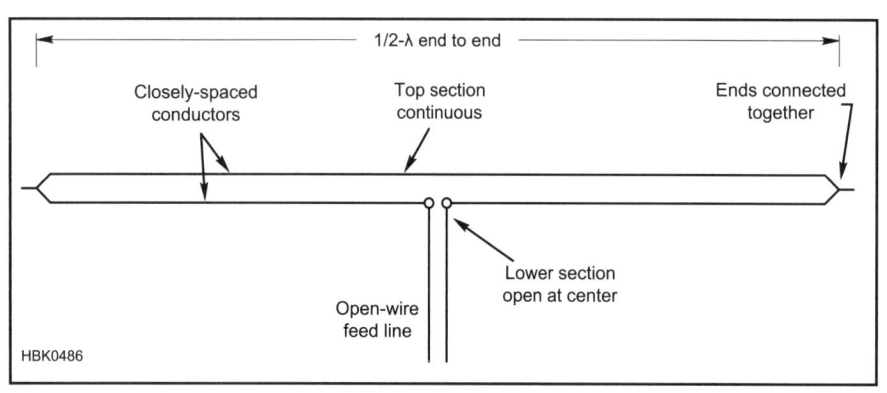

Figure 21.19 — The folded dipole is constructed from open-wire transmission line with the ends connected together. The close proximity of the two conductors and the resulting coupling act as an impedance transformer to raise the feed point impedance over that of a single-wire dipole by the square of the number of conductors used.

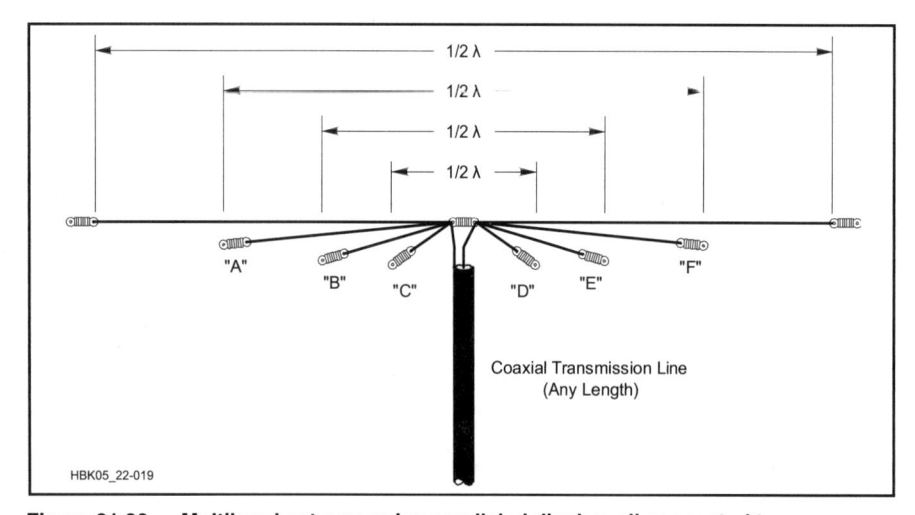

Figure 21.20 — Multiband antenna using paralleled dipoles, all connected to a common 50 or 75 Ω coax line. The ½ λ dimensions may be either for the centers of the various bands or selected for favorite frequencies in each band. Be prepared to adjust the length of the various elements — both longer and shorter — because of interaction among them. See text.

close proximity tend to be strongly coupled. In parallel dipoles, this coupling means that the resonant length of the shorter dipoles lengthens a few percent. Shorter antennas don't affect longer ones much, so adjust for resonance in order from longest to shortest. Coupling also reduces the bandwidth of shorter dipoles, so an impedance-matching unit may be needed to achieve an acceptable SWR across all bands covered. These effects can be reduced by spreading the ends of the dipoles apart. (This is where the name "fan dipole" comes from.)

Also, the power-distribution mechanism requires that only one of the parallel dipoles is near resonance on any amateur band. Separate dipoles for 80 and 30 meters should not be connected in parallel because the higher band is near an odd harmonic of the lower band (80/3=30) and center-fed dipoles have low impedance near odd harmonics. (The 40 and 15 meter bands have a similar relationship.) This means that you must either accept the performance of the low-band antenna operating on a harmonic or erect a separate antenna for those odd-harmonic bands. For example, four parallel-connected dipoles cut for 80, 40, 20 and 10 meters (fed by a single impedance-matching unit and coaxial cable) work reasonably on all HF bands from 80 through 10 meters.

TRAP DIPOLES

Trap dipoles (also called "trapped dipoles") provide multiband operation from a coax-fed single-wire dipole. **Figure 21.21** shows a two-band trap antenna. A trap consists of inductance and capacitance in parallel with a resonant frequency on the higher of the two bands of operation. The high impedance of the trap at its resonant frequency acts as a switch that effectively disconnects the wire beyond the trap. Thus, on the higher of the two bands of operation at which traps are resonant, only the portion of the antenna between the traps is active.

Above resonance, the trap presents a capacitive reactance. Below resonance, the trap is inductive. On the lower of the two bands of operation, then, the inductive reactance of the trap acts as a loading coil to create a shortened or loaded dipole with the wire beyond the trap.

Traps may be constructed from coiled sections of coax or from discrete inductors and capacitors. (Traps are also available commercially.) Choose capacitors (C1 in the figure) that are rated for high current and voltage. Mica transmitting capacitors are good. Ceramic "doorknob" transmitting capacitors will work but be sure to use NP0 temperature coefficient parts to minimize changes in capacitance with temperature. Use large wire for the inductors to reduce loss. Any reactance (X_L and X_C) above 100 Ω (at f_0) will work, but bandwidth increases with reactance (up to several thousand ohms). Check trap resonance before installation. This can be done with a grid-dip meter and a receiver or with an SWR analyzer or impedance bridge.

To construct a trap antenna, build a dipole for the higher band of operation and connect the pre-tuned traps to its ends. It is fairly complicated to calculate the additional wire needed for each band, so just add enough wire to make the antenna ½ λ long on the lower band of operation, pruning it as necessary. Because the inductance in each trap reduces the physical length needed for resonance, the finished antenna will be shorter than a simple ½ λ dipole on the lower band.

21.2.12 NVIS Antennas

The use of very low dipole antennas that radiate at very high elevation angles has become popular in emergency communications ("emcomm") systems. This works at low frequencies (3 to 10 MHz) that are lower than the ionosphere's critical frequency — the highest frequency for which a signal traveling vertically will be reflected. (See the **Propagation** chapter.) The most common band for NVIS communication is 75 meters because

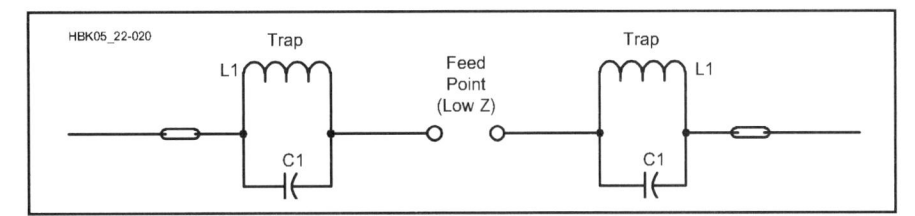

Figure 21.21 — Example of a trap dipole antenna. L1 and C1 can be tuned to the desired frequency by means of a grid-dip meter or SWR analyzer *before* they are installed in the antenna.

Turn a Horizontal Antenna Vertical

An option for adding at least one more band to a flat-top or inverted-V dipole is to turn it into a flat-top T vertical antenna. (See the T and Inverted-L Antennas section.) To do this, disconnect the feed line at the ground level, short the feed line conductors together, and connect them to the transmitter as a single wire. The remaining connection to the transmitter should be connected to a ground rod (as shown), counterpoise, or system of ground radials. (The antenna system's safety ground connection is still required.) A coaxial feed line is shown but the same technique works just as well for open-wire feed lines. An antenna tuner is required for either type of feed line.

This technique often allows a dipole to be used effectively at frequencies below those at which its horizontal section is resonant. For example, a 40 meter dipole can be used this way on 160 and 80 meters.

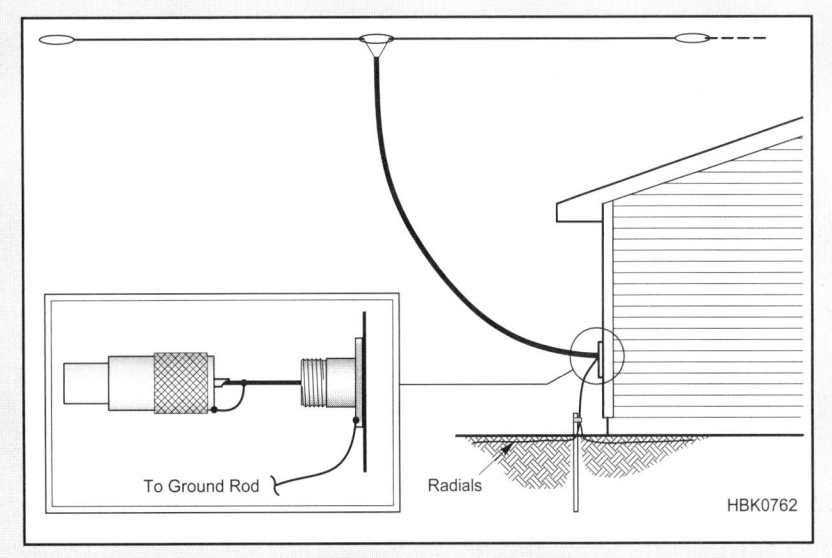

Figure 21.A1 – A dipole can be fed as a flat-top T vertical antenna by reconfiguring the feed line connections and exciting the antenna against ground.

Antennas 21.15

the critical frequency is almost always above 4 MHz. 60 meters is growing in popularity and 40 meters is often useful for NVIS communication through the day

No special antenna construction techniques are required for NVIS antennas — just build a ½ λ dipole and install it at a height of 0.10 – 0.25 λ. Good results can be obtained above and below this range but at heights below 0.05 λ ground losses may become significant and at increasing heights, a high-angle null develops in the antenna pattern, reducing NVIS effectiveness considerably. See the References entry for Witvliet for a recent paper on the subject.

At these low heights, the dipole's resonant frequency will be reduced because of the effects of ground. Shorten the antenna to achieve the desired resonant frequency, although feed point impedance will drop.

Project: Multiband Center-Fed Dipole

An 80 meter dipole fed with ladder line is a versatile antenna. If you add a wide-range matching network, you have a low-cost antenna system that works well across the entire HF spectrum, and even 6 meters. Countless hams have used one of these in single-antenna stations and for Field Day operations.

Figure 21.22 shows a typical installation for such an antenna. The inverted-V configuration is shown, lowering the total antenna length to 130 feet from the 135 feet used if the entire antenna is horizontal. Either configuration will work well. You can use a balanced impedance-matching unit with a balun between it and the transmitter. Many amateurs are successful in using unbalanced impedance-matching units with a balun at either the output or the input of the tuner. Don't be afraid to experiment!

This configuration is popular with other lengths for the antenna:
• 105 feet — 80 through 10 meters
• 88 feet — 80 through 10 meters
• The next lower band may also be covered if the impedance-matching unit has sufficient range, although the adjustment will be fairly sharp. Six meter coverage is possible, but depends on the station layout, length of feed line, and impedance-matching unit abilities. Again, don't be afraid to experiment!

For best results place the antenna as high as you can, and keep the antenna and ladder line clear of metal and other conductive objects. Despite significant SWR on some bands, the open-wire feed line keeps system losses low as described in the **Transmission Lines** chapter.

ARRL staff analyzed a 135 foot dipole at 50 feet above typical ground and compared that to an inverted-V with the center at 50 feet, and the ends at 10 feet. The results show that on the 80 meter band, it won't make much difference which configuration you choose. The inverted-V exhibits additional losses because of its proximity to ground. (Radiation patterns are available in the downloadable supplemental information.)

Installed horizontally, or as an inverted-V, the 135 foot center-fed dipole is a simple antenna that works well from 3.5 to 30 MHz (and on 1.8 MHz if the impedance-matching unit has sufficient range). The feed line impedance at the transmitter end may be out of range for the impedance-matching unit. In such a case, add ⅛ wavelength of feed line at that frequency. This may change the impedance to a value the impedance-matching unit can handle..

Project: 40 to 15 Meter Dual-Band Dipole

As mentioned earlier, dipoles have harmonic resonances at odd multiples of their fundamental resonances. Because 21 MHz is the third harmonic of 7 MHz, 7 MHz dipoles are harmonically resonant in the popular ham band at 21 MHz. This is attractive because it allows you to install a 40 meter dipole, feed it with coax, and use it without an antenna tuner on both 40 and 15 meters.

But there's a catch: The third harmonic resonance is actually higher than three times the fundamental resonant frequency. This is because there is no end effect in the center portion of the antenna where there are no insulators.

An easy fix for this, as shown in **Figure 21.23**, is to add capacitive loading to the antenna about ¼ λ wavelength (at 21.2 MHz) away from the feed point in both halves of the dipole. Known as *capacitance hats*, the simple loading wires shown lower the antenna's resonant frequency on 15 meters without substantially affecting resonance on 40 meters. This scheme can also be used to build a dipole that can be used on 80 and 30 meters and on 75 and 10 meters. (A project for a 75 and 10 meter dipole is included with the downloadable supplemental content.)

Measure, cut and adjust the dipole to resonance at the desired 40 meter frequency. Then, cut two 2-foot-long pieces of stiff wire (such as #12 or #14 AWG house wire) and solder the ends of each one together to form two loops. Twist the loops in the middle to form figure-8s, and strip and solder the wires where they cross. Install these capacitance hats on the dipole by stripping the antenna wire (if necessary) and soldering the hats to the dipole about a third of the way out from the feed point (placement isn't critical) on each wire. To resonate the antenna on 15 meters, use an antenna analyzer to adjust the loop shapes until the SWR is acceptable in the desired

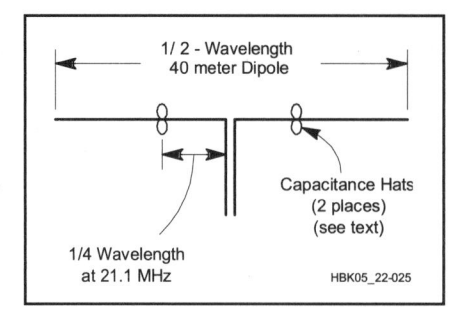

Figure 21.23 — Figure-8-shaped capacitance hats made and placed as described in the text, can make a 40 meter dipole resonate anywhere in the 15 meter band.

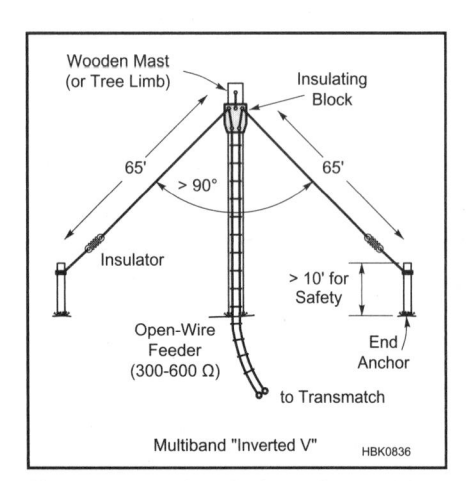

Figure 21.22 — Details for an inverted-V fed with open-wire line for multiband HF operation. The included angle between the two legs should be greater than 90° for best performance.

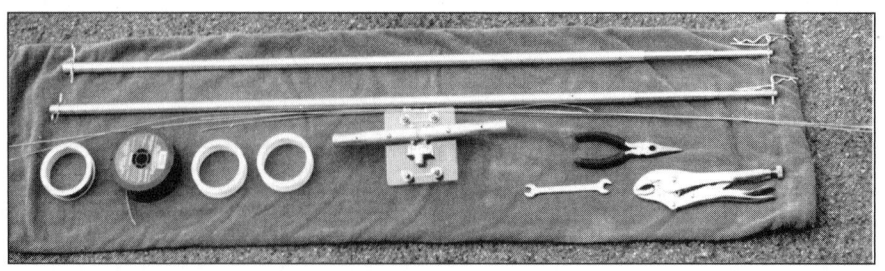

Figure 21.24 — The entire inverted-U antenna parts collection in semi-nested form, with its carrying bag. The tools stored with the antenna include a wrench to tighten the U-bolts for the mast-to-plate mount and a pair of pliers to help remove end wires from the tubing.

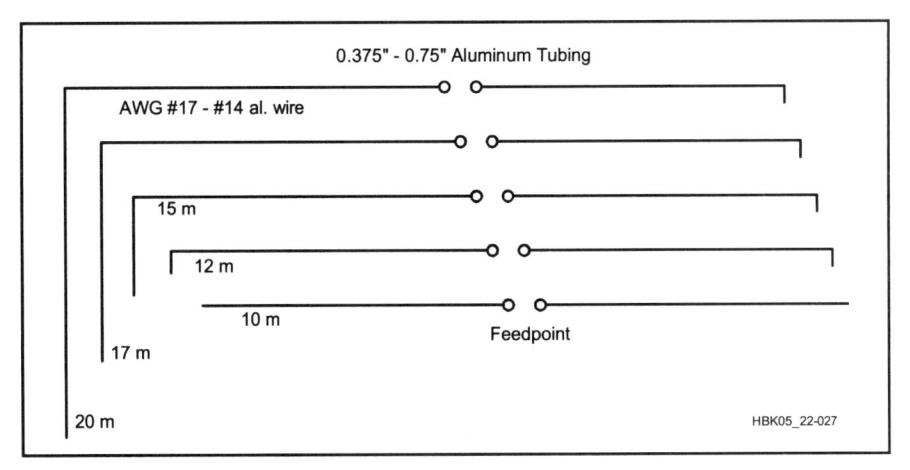

Figure 21.25 — The general outline of the inverted-U field dipole for 20 through 10 meters. Note that the vertical end extension wires apply to both ends of the main 10 meter dipole, which is constant for all bands.

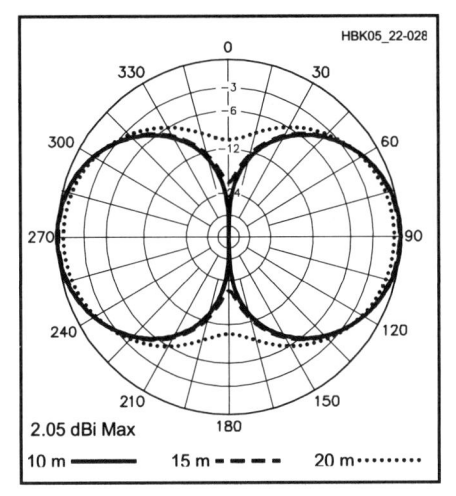

Figure 21.26 — Free-space E-plane (azimuth) patterns of the inverted-U for 10, 15, and 20 meters, showing the pattern changes with increasingly longer vertical end sections.

segment of the 15 meter band. Conversely, you can move the hats back and forth along the antenna until the desired SWR is achieved and then solder the hats to the antenna.

Project: W4RNL Rotatable Dipole Inverted-U Antenna

This simple rotatable dipole was designed and built by L.B. Cebik, W4RNL (SK), for use during the ARRL Field Day. For this and other portable operations we look for three antenna characteristics: simplicity, small size and light weight. Today, a number of lightweight collapsible masts are available. When properly guyed, some will support antennas in the 5 to 10 pound range. Most are suitable for 10 meter tubular dipoles and allow the user to hand-rotate the antenna. Extend the range of the antenna to cover 20 through 10 meters, and you put these 20 to 30 foot masts to even better use. The inverted-U meets this need. **Figure 21.24** shows the basic kit for the antenna. Complete construction details and more information about antenna performance are available with the downloadable supplemental content.

A dipole's highest current occurs within the first half of the distance from the feed point to the outer tips. Therefore, very little performance is lost if the outer end sections are bent. The W4RNL inverted-U starts with a 10 meter tubular dipole. You add wire extensions for 12, 15, 17 or 20 meters to cover those bands.

You only need enough space to erect a 10 meter rotatable dipole. The extensions hang down. **Figure 21.25** shows the relative proportions of the antenna on all bands from 10 to 20 meters. The 20 meter extensions are the length of half the 10 meter dipole.

Not much signal strength is lost by drooping up to half the overall element length straight down. What is lost in bidirectional gain shows up in decreased side nulls. **Figure 21.26** shows the free-space E-plane (azimuth) patterns of the inverted-U with a 10 meter horizontal section. There is an undetectable decrease in gain between the 10 meter and 15 meter versions. The 20 meter version shows a little over ½ dB gain decrease and a signal increase off the antenna ends.

The feed point impedance of the inverted-U remains well within acceptable limits for virtually all equipment, even at 20 feet above ground. Also, the SWR curves are very broad, so it's not as critical to find exact dimensions, even for special field conditions.

Changing bands is a simple matter. Remove the extensions for the band you are using and install the ends for the new band. An SWR check and possibly one more adjustment of the end lengths will put you back on the air.

With a dipole having drooping ends, safety is very important. At any power level, the ends of a dipole have high RF voltages, and we must keep them out of contact with human body parts. Do not use the antenna unless the wire ends for 20 meters are higher than any person can touch when the antenna is in use. Even with QRP power levels, the RF voltage on the wire ends can be dangerous. With the antenna at 20 feet at its center, the ends should be at least 10 feet above ground.

Project: Two W8NX Multiband, Coax-Trap Dipoles

Two different antennas are described here. The first covers the traditional 80, 40, 20, 15 and 10 meter bands, and the second covers 80, 40, 17 and 12 meters. (The complete article describing these antenna projects is available as part of this book's downloadable supplemental information package.) Each uses the same type of W8NX trap — connected for different modes of operation — and a pair of short capacitive stubs to enhance coverage. The W8NX coaxial-cable traps have two different modes: a high- and a low-impedance mode. The inner-conductor windings and shield windings of the traps are connected in series for both modes. However, either the low- or high-impedance point can be used as the trap's output terminal. For low-impedance trap operation, only the center conductor turns of the trap windings are used. For high-impedance operation, all turns are used, in the conventional manner for a trap. The short stubs on each antenna are strategically sized and located to permit more flexibility in adjusting the resonant frequencies of the antenna.

80, 40, 20, 15 AND 10 M DIPOLE

Figure 21.27 shows the configuration of the 80, 40, 20, 15 and 10 meter antenna. The

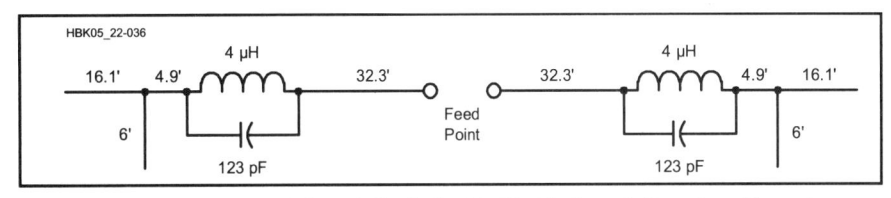

Figure 21.27 — A W8NX multiband dipole for 80, 40, 20, 15 and 10 meters. The values shown (123 pF and 4 μH) for the coaxial-cable traps are for parallel resonance at 7.15 MHz. The low-impedance output of each trap is used for this antenna.

Antennas 21.17

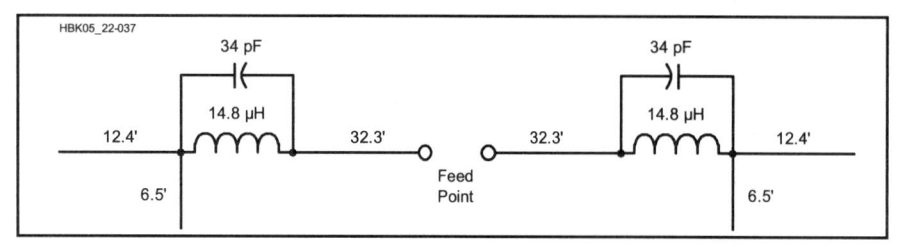

Figure 21.28 — A W8NX multiband dipole for 80, 40, 17 and 12 meters. For this antenna, the high-impedance output is used on each trap. The resonant frequency of the traps is 7.15 MHz.

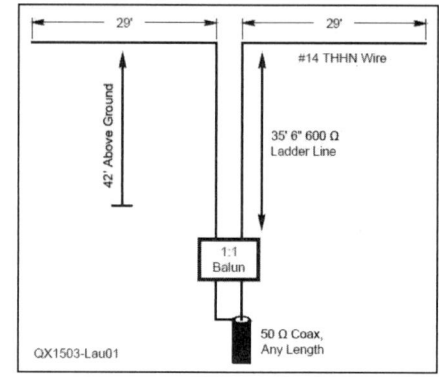

Figure 21.29 — Basic configuration of the triband dipole, consisting of a 58-foot doublet fed with 35.5 feet of 600 Ω open-wire feed line. SWR at the balun input is approximately 1.5:1 on 17 meters and 2.4:1 on 12 meters and 30 meters.

radiating elements are made of #14 AWG stranded copper wire. The element lengths are the wire span lengths in feet. These lengths do not include the lengths of the pigtails at the balun, traps and insulators. The 32.3-foot-long inner 40 meter segments are measured from the eyelet of the input balun to the tension-relief hole in the trap coil form. The 4.9 foot segment length is measured from the tension-relief hole in the trap to the 6 foot stub. The 16.1 foot outer-segment span is measured from the stub to the eyelet of the end insulator.

80, 40, 17 AND 12 METER DIPOLE

Figure 21.28 shows the configuration of the 80, 40, 17 and 12 meter antenna. Notice that the capacitive stubs are attached immediately outboard after the traps and are 6.5 feet long, ½ foot longer than those used in the other antenna. The traps are the same as those of the other antenna, but are connected for the high-impedance parallel-resonant output mode. Since only four bands are covered by this antenna, it is easier to fine tune it to precisely the desired frequency on all bands.

Project: Triband Dipole for 30, 17, and 12 Meters

(This antenna was originally described in the article "A Triband Dipole for 30, 17, and 12 Meters" by Zack Lau, W1VT in the Mar/Apr 2015 issue of *QEX*. A similar design by W1VT for 10, 20, and 40 meters described in the article "A Compact Multiband Dipole" from the March 2016 issue of *QST*. Both articles are available as PDF files with the downloadable supplemental content.)

The triband dipole in **Figure 21.29** is a 58 foot doublet made out of #14 THHN solid house wire fed with a 35.5 foot matching section of 600 Ω ladder line having a velocity factor of 0.91. It has modest gain over a dipole on all three of the design bands and SWR at the balun input is approximately 1.5:1 on 17 meters and 2.4:1 on 12 meters and 30 meters. These values of SWR are all easily matched to 1:1 with the auto-tuner built into many transceivers or with an external impedance matching unit.

If the antenna will be installed at a significantly different height, the length of the doublet and the open-wire feed line may have to be adjusted to obtain resonances in all three bands. The length of the 50 Ω cable feed line isn't critical.

The #14 THHN house wire has two layers of insulation: 15 mils of PVC and another 4 mils of nylon. While the nylon typically flakes off in less than a year, the antenna was modeled in *EZNEC* using an insulation thickness of 19 mils and a dielectric constant of 3.5. Changing the insulation thickness to 15 mils doesn't appreciably change the resonance points.

The somewhat low velocity factor of the open-wire line assumes it is constructed using the same insulated wire as the doublet. A spacing of 3 inches is recommended for constructing the 600 Ω open-wire line. If other wire types are used to construct the open-wire line, an accurate approximation for the impedance of air-insulated open-wire line is:

$$Z_0 = 276 \log_{10}(2S/d) \qquad (5)$$

where S is the center-to-center distance between the conductors and d is the diameter of the conductors in the same units as S.

(Z_0 for open-wire line is discussed in detail in the "Fundamentals" section of the Transmission Lines chapter.)

A 1:1 current or choke balun is required between the open wire feed line and the coax to prevent the outside of the coax shield from becoming a radiating antenna element and affecting feed point impedance. (See the section "Baluns and Transmission Line Transformers" in the **Transmission Lines** chapter.) The author recommends 11 turns of RG-58A/U on an FT-140-43 core as working well from 10 to 30 MHz. Steve Hunt, G3TXQ published an excellent balun design using 11 turns of RG-58 on a stacked pair of FT-240-52 toroids that provides a higher choking impedance which may be necessary if the antenna is to be used on other bands than 30, 17, or 12 meters where the open-wire line length does not result in a low impedance.

Assuming a height of 42 feet, on 17 meters the antenna has a clean, bidirectional pattern, with maximum gain of 8.9 dBi broadside to the wires, just like a dipole. (All antenna patterns are included in the full article.) On 30 meters, the antenna also has gain broadside to the wires of 6.9 dBi. On 12 meters the antenna has an azimuthal radiation pattern with four main lobes having 8.2 dBi gain, 50° off broadside. The broadside lobes are 3.5 dB weaker than the main lobes.

Antenna Modeling by Computer

Modern computer programs have made it a *lot* easier for a ham to evaluate antenna performance. The elevation plots for the 135 foot long center-fed dipole were generated using a sophisticated computer program known as *NEC*, short for "Numerical Electromagnetics Code." *NEC* is a general-purpose antenna modeling program, capable of modeling almost any antenna type, from the simplest dipole to extremely complex antenna designs. Various mainframe versions of *NEC* have been under continuous development by US government researchers for several decades.

But because it is a general-purpose program, *NEC* can be very slow when modeling some antennas — such as long-boom, multi-element Yagis. There are other, specialized programs that work on Yagis much faster than *NEC*. Indeed, *NEC* has developed a reputation for being accurate (if properly applied!), but decidedly difficult to learn and use. A number of commercial software developers have risen to the challenge and created more *user-friendly* versions such as *EZNEC* and *4nec2* which are advertised in *QST*.

NEC uses a *Method of Moments* algorithm. The mathematics behind this algorithm are pretty formidable to most hams, but the basic principle is simple. An antenna is broken down into a set of straight-line wire *segments*. The fields resulting from the current in each segment and from the mutual interaction between segments are vector-summed in the far field to create azimuth and elevation-plane patterns.

The most difficult part of using a *NEC*-type of modeling program is setting up the antenna's geometry — you must condition yourself to think in three-dimensional coordinates. Each end point of a wire is represented by three numbers: an x, y and z coordinate. An example should help sort things out. See **Figure 21.A2**, showing a *model* for a 135 foot center-fed dipole, made of #14 wire placed 50 feet above flat ground. This antenna is modeled as a single, straight wire.

For convenience, ground is located at the *origin* of the coordinate system, at (0, 0, 0) feet, directly under the center of the dipole. The dipole runs parallel to, and above, the y-axis. Above the origin, at a height of 50 feet, is the dipole's feed point. The *wingspread* of the dipole goes toward the left (that is, in the *negative y* direction) one-half the overall length, or –67.5 feet. Toward the right, it goes +67.5 feet. The *x* dimension of our dipole is zero. The dipole's ends are thus represented by two points, whose coordinates are: (0, –67.5, 50) and (0, 67.5, 50) feet. The thickness of the antenna is the diameter of the wire, #14 gauge.

To run the program you must specify the number of segments into which the dipole is divided for the method-of-moments analysis. The guideline for setting the number of segments is to use at least 10 segments per half-wavelength. In Figure 21.A2, our dipole has been divided into 11 segments for 80 meter operation. The use of 11 segments, an odd rather than an even number such as 10, places the dipole's feed point (the *source* in *NEC*-parlance) right at the antenna's center and at the center of segment number six.

Since we intend to use our 135 foot long dipole on all HF amateur bands, the number of segments used actually should vary with frequency. The penalty for using more segments in a program like *NEC* is that the program slows down roughly as the square of the segments — double the number and the speed drops to a fourth. However, using too few segments will introduce inaccuracies, particularly in computing the feed point impedance. The commercial versions of *NEC* handle such nitty-gritty details automatically.

Let's get a little more complicated and specify the 135 foot dipole, configured as an inverted-V. Here, as shown in **Figure 21.A3**, you must specify *two* wires. The two wires join at the top, (0, 0, 50) feet. Now the specification of the source becomes more complicated. The easiest way is to specify two sources, one on each end segment at the junction of the two wires. If you are using the *native* version of *NEC*, you may have to go back to your high-school trigonometry book to figure out how to specify the end points of our droopy dipole, with its 120° included angle. Figure 21.A3 shows the details, along with the trig equations needed.

So, you see that antenna modeling isn't entirely a cut-and-dried procedure. The commercial programs do their best to hide some of the more unwieldy parts of *NEC*, but there's still some art mixed in with the science. And as always, there are trade-offs to be made — segments versus speed, for example.

However, once you do figure out exactly how to use them, computer models are wonderful tools. They can help you while away a dreary winter's day, designing antennas on-screen — without having to risk life and limb climbing an ice-covered tower. And in a relatively short time a computer model can run hundreds, or even thousands, of simulations as you seek to optimize an antenna for a particular parameter. Doesn't that sound better than trying to optimally tweak an antenna by means of a thousand cut-and-try measurements, all the while hanging precariously from your tower by a climbing harness?! — *R. Dean Straw, N6BV*

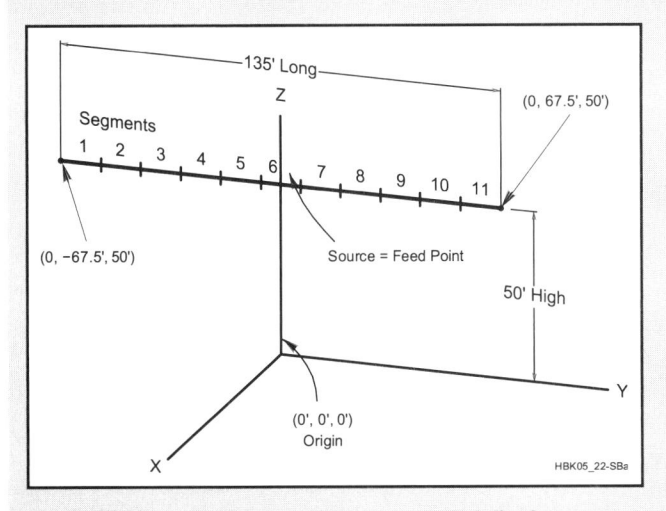

Figure 21.A2 — Model of a 135 foot center-fed dipole.

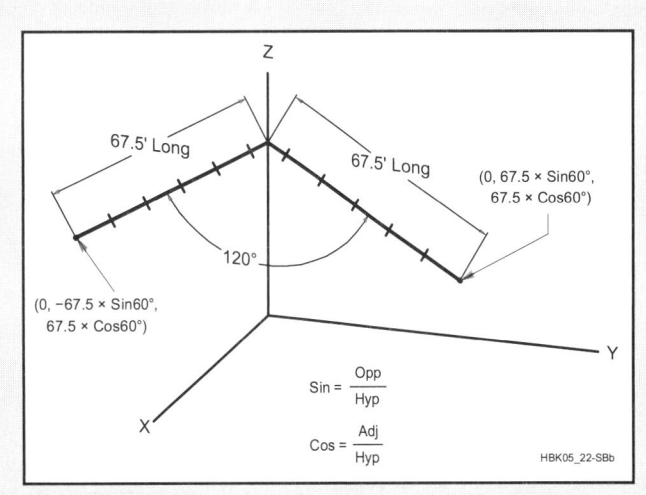

Figure 21.A3 — Model of the 135 foot dipole configured as an inverted V.

21.3 Vertical (Ground-Plane) Antennas

One of the more popular amateur HF antennas is the *vertical*. It usually refers to a single radiating element erected vertically over a *ground plane* of radial wires. A typical vertical is an electrical ¼ λ long and is constructed of wire or tubing. The vertical antenna is more accurately named the ground plane because the conductive surface (the ground plane) creates a path for return currents to the feed point, effectively creating the "missing half" of a ½ λ antenna. Another name for this type of antenna is the *monopole* (sometimes *unipole*).

The ground plane can be a solid, conducting surface, such as a vehicle body at VHF/UHF mobile antenna. At HF, this is impractical and systems of *ground radials* are used; wires laid out on the ground radially from the base of the antenna. One conductor of the feed line is attached to the vertical radiating element of the antenna and the remaining conductor is attached to the ground plane. The radial wires form a *ground screen* that gives the return currents a low-resistance path instead of flowing through lossy soil.

Single vertical antennas are omnidirectional radiators. This can be beneficial or detrimental, depending on the situation. On transmission there are no nulls in any direction, unlike most horizontal antennas. However, QRM on receive can't be nulled out from the directions that are not of interest unless multiple verticals are used in an array.

Ground-plane antennas need not be mounted vertically. A ground-plane antenna can operate in any orientation as long as the ground plane is perpendicular to the radiating element. Other considerations, such as minimizing cross-polarization between stations, may require a specific mounting orientation though. In addition, due to the size of HF antennas, mounting them vertically is usually the most practical solution.

A vertical antenna can be mounted at the Earth's surface, in which case it is a *ground-mounted vertical*. The ground plane is then constructed on the surface of the ground. A vertical antenna and the associated ground plane can also be installed above the ground. This often reduces ground losses, but it is more difficult to install the necessary number of radials. *Ground-independent* verticals are often mounted well above the ground because their operation does not rely on a ground plane.

21.3.1 Ground Systems

When compared to horizontal antennas, verticals also suffer more acutely from two main types of losses — *ground return losses* for currents in the near field, and *far-field ground losses*. Ground losses in the near field can be minimized by using many ground radials. This is covered in the sidebar, "Optimum Ground Systems for Vertical Antennas."

Far-field losses are highly dependent on the conductivity and dielectric constant of the soil around the antenna, extending out as far as 100 wavelengths from the base of the antenna. There is very little that someone can do to change the character of the ground that far away — other than moving to a small island surrounded by saltwater! Far-field losses greatly affect low-angle radiation, causing the radiation patterns of practical vertical antennas to fall far short of theoretical patterns over *perfect ground*, often seen in classical texts.

Figure 21.30 shows the elevation pattern

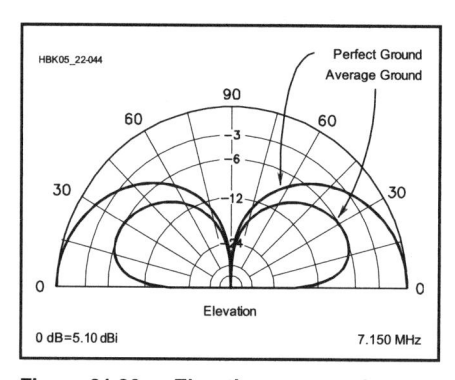

Figure 21.30 — Elevation patterns for two quarter-wave vertical antennas over different ground. One vertical is placed over perfect ground, and the other is placed over average ground. The far-field response at low elevation angles is greatly affected by the quality of the ground — as far as 100 λ away from the vertical antenna.

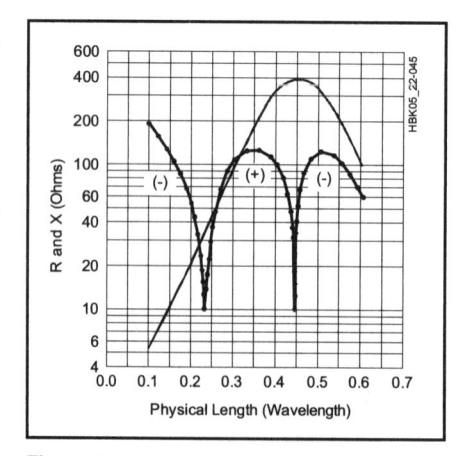

Figure 21.31 — Radiation resistance (solid curve) and reactance (dotted curve) of vertical antennas as a function of their electrical height.

response for two different 40 meter quarter-wave verticals. One is placed over a theoretical infinitely large, infinitely conducting ground. The second is placed over an extensive radial system over average soil, having a conductivity of 5 mS/m and a dielectric constant of 13. This sort of soil is typical of heavy clay found in pastoral regions of the US mid-Atlantic states. At a 10° elevation angle, the real antenna losses are almost 6 dB compared to the theoretical antenna; at 20° the difference is about 3 dB. See *The ARRL Antenna Book* chapter on the effects of ground for further details.

While real verticals over real ground are not a magic method to achieve low-angle radiation, cost versus performance and ease of installation are incentives that inspire many antenna builders. For use on the lower frequency amateur bands — notably 160 and 80 meters — it is not always practical to erect a full-size vertical. At 1.8 MHz, a full-sized quarter-wave vertical is 130 feet high. In such instances it is often necessary to accept a shorter radiating element and use some form of loading.

Figure 21.31 provides curves for the physical height of verticals in wavelength versus radiation resistance and reactance. Although the plots are based on perfectly conducting ground, they show general trends for installations where many radials have been laid out to make a ground screen. As the radiator is made shorter, the radiation resistance decreases — with 6 Ω being typical for a 0.1 λ high antenna. The lower the radiation resistance, the more the antenna efficiency depends on ground conductivity and the effectiveness of the ground screen. Also, the bandwidth decreases markedly as the length is reduced toward the left of the scale in Figure 21.31. It can be difficult to develop suitable matching networks when radiation resistance is very low.

Generally a large number of shorter radials results in a better ground system than a few longer ones. For example, eight ¼ λ radials are preferred over four ¼ λ radials. Optimum radial lengths are described in the sidebar.

The conductor size of the radials is not especially significant. Wire gauges from #4 to #20 AWG have been used successfully by amateurs. Copper wire is preferred, but where soil is low in acid (or alkali), aluminum wire can be used. The wires may be bare or insulated, and they can be laid on the earth's surface or buried a few inches below ground. Insulated wires will have greater longevity by virtue of reduced corrosion and dissolution from soil chemicals.

When property dimensions do not allow a classic installation of equally spaced radial wires, they can be placed on the ground as space permits. They may run away from the antenna in only one or two compass directions. They may be bent to fit on your property. Hardware cloth and chicken wire are also quite effective, although the galvanizing must be of high-quality to prevent rapid rusting.

A single ground rod, or group of them bonded together, is seldom as effective as a collection of random-length radial wires. (A ground rod at the vertical's base should be used for lightning protection.)

All radial wires should be connected together at the base of the vertical antenna. The electrical bond needs to be of low resistance. Best results will be obtained when the wires are soldered together at the junction point. When a grounded vertical is used, the ground wires should be affixed securely to the base of the driven element.

Ground return losses are lower when vertical antennas and their radials are elevated above ground, a point that is well-known by those using ground plane antennas on their roofs. Even on 160 or 80 meters, effective vertical antenna systems can be made with as few as four ¼ λ long radials elevated 10 to 20 feet off the ground.

21.3.2 Full-Size Vertical Antennas

When it is practical to erect a full-size ¼ λ vertical antenna, the forms shown in **Figure 21.32** are worthy of consideration. The example at A is the well-known *vertical ground plane*. The ground system consists of four above-ground radial wires. The length of the driven element and ¼ λ radials is derived from the standard equation

$$L(\text{ft}) = 234 / f(\text{MHz}) \quad (6)$$

With four equidistant radial wires drooped at approximately 30° (Figure 21.32A), the feed point impedance is roughly 50 Ω. When the radials are at right angles to the radiator (Figure 21.32B) the impedance approaches 36 Ω.

Besides minimizing ground return losses, another major advantage in this type of vertical antenna over a ground-mounted type is that the system can be elevated well above nearby conductive objects (power lines, trees, buildings and so on). When drooping radials are used, they can also serve as guy wires for the mast that supports the antenna. The coax shield braid is connected to the radials, and the center conductor to the driven element.

The *Marconi* vertical antenna shown in Figure 21.32C is the classic form taken by a ground-mounted vertical. It can be grounded at the base and *shunt fed*, or it can be isolated from ground, as shown, and *series fed*. As always, this vertical antenna depends on an effective ground system for efficient performance. If a perfect ground were located below the antenna, the feed impedance would be near 36 Ω. In a practical case, owing to imperfect ground, the impedance is more likely to be in the vicinity of 50 Ω.

Vertical antennas can be longer than ¼ λ, too; ⅜ λ, ½ λ, and ⅝ λ verticals can all be used with good results, although none will present a 50 Ω feed point impedance at the base. Non-resonant lengths have become popular for the same reasons as non-resonant horizontal antennas; when fed with low-loss feed line and a wide-range impedance matching unit, the antenna can be used on multiple bands. Various matching networks, described in the **Transmission Lines** chapter, can be employed. Antenna lengths above ½ λ are not recommended because the radiation pattern

---

Optimum Ground Systems for Vertical Antennas

A frequent question brought up by old-timers and newcomers alike is: "So, how many ground radials do I *really* need for my vertical antenna?" Most hams have heard the old standby tales about radials, such as "if a few are good, more must be better" or "lots of short radials are better than a few long ones."

John Stanley, K4ERO, eloquently summarized a study he did of the professional literature on this subject in his article "Optimum Ground Systems for Vertical Antennas" in December 1976 *QST*. His approach was to present the data in a sort of "cost-benefit" style in **Table 21.A**, reproduced here. John somewhat wryly created a new figure of merit — the total amount of wire needed for various radial configurations. This is expressed in terms of wavelengths of total radial wire.

Table 21.A
Optimum Ground-System Configurations

Configuration Designation	A	B	C	D	E	F
Number of radials	16	24	36	60	90	120
Length of each radial in wavelengths	0.1	0.125	0.15	0.2	0.25	0.4
Spacing of radials in degrees	22.5	15	10	6	4	3
Total length of radial wire installed, in wavelengths	1.6	3	5.4	12	22.5	48
Power loss in dB at low angles with a quarter-wave radiating element	3	2	1.5	1	0.5	0*
Feed point impedance in ohms with a quarter-wave radiating element	52	46	43	40	37	35

Note: Configuration designations are indicated only for text reference.
*Reference. The loss of this configuration is negligible compared to a perfectly conducting ground.

The results almost jumping out of this table are:
- If you can only install 16 radials (Case A), they needn't be very long — 0.1 λ is sufficient. You'll use 1.6 λ of radial wire in total, which is about 450 feet at 3.5 MHz.
- If you have the luxury of laying down 120 radials (Case F), they should be 0.4 λ long, and you'll gain about 3 dB over the 16 radial case. You'll also use 48 λ of total wire — For 80 meters, that would be about 13,500 feet!
- If you can't put out 120 radials, but can install 36 radials that are 0.15 λ long (Case C), you'll lose only 1.5 dB compared to the optimal Case F. You'll also use 5.4 λ of total wire, or 1,500 feet at 3.5 MHz.
- A 50 Ω SWR of 1:1 isn't necessarily a good thing — the worst-case ground system in Case A has the lowest SWR.

Table 21.A represents the case for "Average" quality soil, and it is valid for radial wires either laid on the ground or buried several inches in the ground. Note that such ground-mounted radials are detuned because of their proximity to that ground and hence don't have to be the classical quarter-wavelength that they need to be in "free space."

In his article John also made the point that ground-radial losses would only be significant on transmit, since the atmospheric noise on the amateur bands below 30 MHz is attenuated by ground losses, just as actual signals would be. This limits the ultimate signal-to-noise ratio in receiving.

So, there you have the tradeoffs — the loss in transmitted signal compared to the cost (and effort) needed to install more radial wires. You take your pick.

begins to break up into more than one lobe, developing a null at the horizon at 1 λ.

A gamma-match feed system for a grounded ¼ λ vertical is presented in Figure 21.32D. (The gamma match is also discussed in the **Transmission Lines** chapter.) Some rules of thumb for arriving at workable gamma-arm and capacitor dimensions are to make the rod length 0.04 to 0.05 λ, its diameter ⅓ to ½ that of the driven element and the center-to-center spacing between the gamma arm and the driven element roughly 0.007 λ. The capacitance of C1 at a 50 Ω matched condition will be about 7 pF per meter of wavelength. The absolute value of C1 will depend on whether the vertical is resonant and on the precise value of the radiation resistance. For best results, make the radiator approximately 3% shorter than the resonant length.

Amateur antenna towers lend themselves to use as shunt-fed verticals, even though an HF-band beam antenna is usually mounted on the tower. The overall system should be close to resonance at the desired operating frequency if a gamma feed is used. The HF-band beam will contribute somewhat to *top loading* of the tower. The natural resonance of such a system can be checked by dropping a #12 or #14 AWG wire from the top of the tower (connecting it to the tower top) to form a folded monopole (Figure 21.32E). A four- or five-turn link can be inserted between the lower end of the drop wire and the ground system. A dip meter is then inserted in the link or an antenna analyzer coupled to the link to determine the resonant frequency. Shunt feeding towers is discussed extensively in the *ARRL Antenna Book* and in ON4UN's *Low Band DXing*.

If the tower is equipped with guy wires, they should be broken up with strain insulators to prevent unwanted loading of the vertical. In such cases where the tower and beam antennas are not able to provide ¼ λ resonance, portions of the top guy wires can be used as top-loading capacitance. Experiment with the guy-wire lengths (using the dip-meter technique) while determining the proper dimensions. Modeling can save a lot of time in this part of the design.

A folded-monopole is depicted in Figure 21.32E. This system has the advantage of increased feed point impedance. Furthermore, an impedance-matching unit can be connected between the bottom of the drop wire and the ground system to permit operation on more than one band. For example, if the tower is resonant on 80 meters, it can be used as shown on 160 and 40 meters with reasonable results, even though it is not electrically long enough on 160 to act as a full-size antenna. The drop wire need not be a specific distance from the tower, but you might try spacings between 12 and 30 inches.

The method of feed shown at Figure

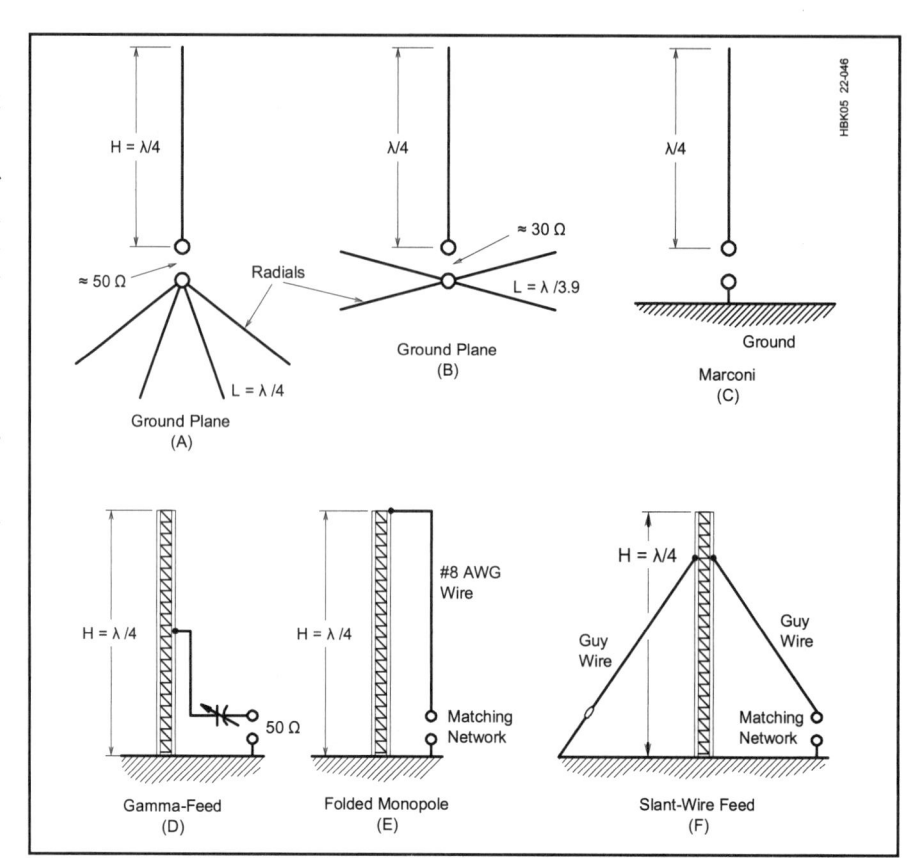

Figure 21.32 — Various types of vertical antennas.

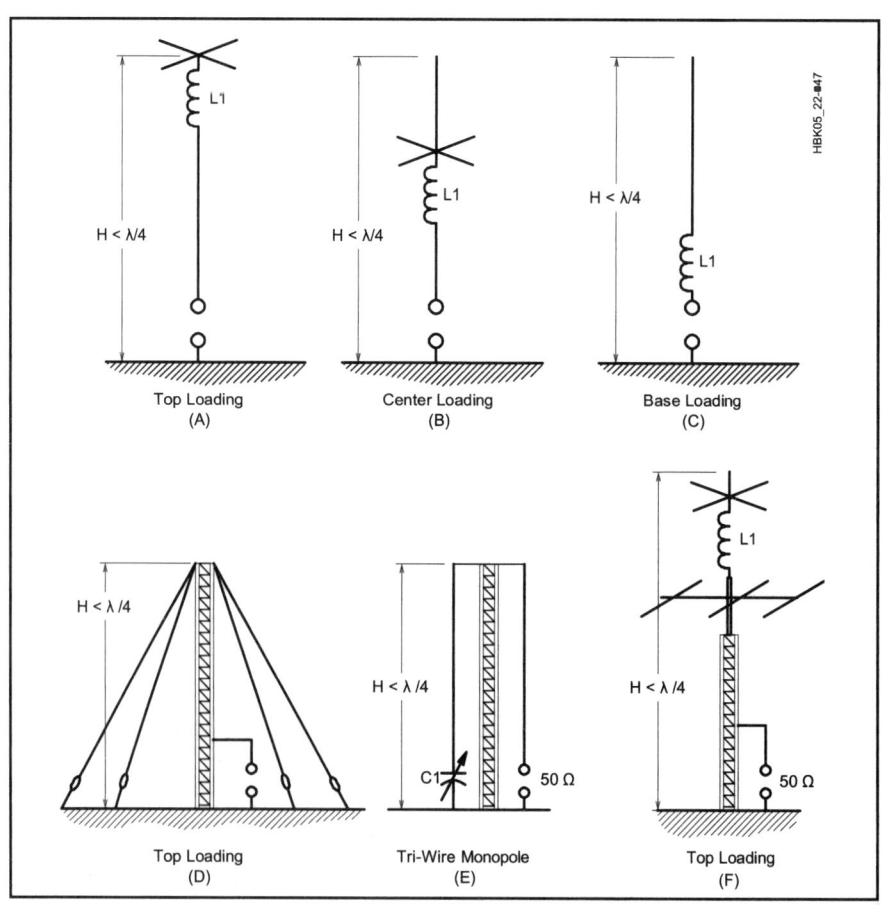

Figure 21.33 — Vertical antennas that are less than one-quarter wavelength in height.

21.32F is commonly referred to as *slant-wire feed*. The guy wires and the tower combine to provide quarter-wave resonance. A matching network is placed between the lower end of one guy wire and ground and adjusted for an SWR of 1:1. It does not matter at which level on the tower the guy wires are connected, assuming that the impedance-matching unit is capable of effecting a match to 50 Ω.

21.3.3 Physically Short Verticals

A group of short vertical radiators is presented in **Figure 21.33**. Illustrations A and B are for top and center loading. A capacitance hat is shown in each example. The hat should be as large as practical to increase the radiation resistance of the antenna and improve the bandwidth. The wire in the loading coil is chosen for the largest gauge consistent with ease of winding and coil-form size. The larger wire diameters will reduce the resistive (I^2R) losses in the system. The coil-form material should have a medium or high dielectric constant. Phenolic or fiberglass tubing is entirely adequate.

A base-loaded vertical is shown at C of Figure 21.33. The primary limitation is that the high current portion of the vertical exists in the coil rather than the driven element. With center loading, the portion of the antenna below the coil carries high current, and in the top-loaded version the entire vertical element carries high current. Since the high-current part of the antenna is responsible for most of the radiating, base loading is the least effective of the three methods. The radiation resistance of the coil-loaded antennas shown is usually less than 16 Ω.

A method for using guy wires to top load a short vertical is illustrated in Figure 21.33D. This system works well with gamma feed. The loading wires are trimmed to provide an electrical quarter wavelength for the overall system. This method of loading will result in a higher radiation resistance and greater bandwidth than the systems shown at A through C. If an HF or VHF array is at the top of the tower, it will simply contribute to the top loading.

A three-wire monopole is shown in Figure 21.33E. Two #8 AWG drop wires are connected to the top of the tower and brought to ground level. The wires can be spaced any convenient distance from the tower — normally 12 to 30 inches from the sides. C1 is adjusted for best SWR. This type of vertical has a fairly narrow bandwidth, but because C1 can be motor driven and controlled from the operating position, frequency changes can be accomplished easily. This technique will not be suitable for matching to 50 Ω line unless the tower is less than an electrical quarter wavelength high.

A different method for top loading is shown in Figure 21.33F. Barry Boothe, W9UCW, described this method in December 1974 *QST*. An extension is used at the top of the tower to create an electrical quarter-wavelength vertical. L1 is a loading coil with sufficient inductance to provide antenna resonance. This type of antenna lends itself to operation on 160 meters.

Project: Top-Loaded Low-Band Antenna

The short, top-loaded vertical antenna described here by Dick Stroud, W9SR, is of interest to hams with limited space or who are portable operators. It has been used on 40, 80 and 160 meters. The antenna uses a single 10 foot TV mast section for the vertical radiator, along with a capacitance hat, loading coil and short top mast. The overall height is less than 15 feet, as seen in **Figure 21.34**. The capacitance hat and loading coil assembly can be used with longer vertical radiators with changes to the coil inductance. A drawing showing complete dimensions and construction details is available with the downloadable supplemental content.

CAPACITANCE HAT

The capacitance hat consists of a hub that mounts to the top mast above the coil and six elements made from aluminum rod. The machining, drilling and tapping of the hub assembly can be done by nearly any machine shop if you don't have the facilities. Be sure to use stainless steel hardware throughout. (Thanks to Fred Gantzer, WØAWD, for building the original hub.)

The hub is made of two pieces of ½ inch thick aluminum as shown in **Figure 21.35**. The two pieces are bolted together to form the hub, which slides over the 1⅛ inch top mast. It is held in place with three 10-32 screws. The six elements of the capacitance hat are made from 3/16 inch aluminum rod, each 4.5 feet long. These are held in place with 6-32 screws.

LOADING COIL

The coil form is made from fiberglass tubing. A 6 inch length of 1.25 inch OD fiberglass tubing is centered over a 10 inch length of 1 inch OD tubing. The tubes telescope tightly and it may be necessary to lightly sand the smaller tube for a smooth fit.

The loading coil is wound on the 1.25 inch OD fiberglass tube. After the coil is optimized, it is covered with a length of shrink sleeving for weather protection. Coil winding information in the drawing in the downloadable supplemental content is for use with a 10 foot mast.

The bottom section of the coil assembly fits directly into the tapered upper section of the TV mast and the exposed upper fiberglass section of the coil assembly fits into a 2.5 foot long, 1.125 inch OD, aluminum upper mast. Stainless 8-32 screws join the pieces together and also provide a connection point for the loading coil wires. If you use a painted steel mast, be sure to remove paint from the connection point, and then weather-seal it after adjustment is complete.

The capacitance hat hub slides over the

Figure 21.34 — W9SR's short vertical uses top loading and a capacitance hat with a 10 foot TV mast to make a compact antenna for 160, 80 or 40 meters.

Figure 21.35 — The completed capacitance hat assembly is shown at A, and B shows a view of the upper mast assembly with the loading coil and capacitance hat.

Table 21.2
Shunt Inductor Winding Details

Frequency (MHz)	Turns
1.8	10 turns #16, spaced ⅛ inch
3.5	8.75 turns #16, spaced ⅛ inch
7	7.5 turns #16, spaced ⅛ inch

Note: All inductors are air wound, 1.75 inch ID. Dimensions shown are for use with 10 foot mast.

upper mast and is held in place with three screws. The hub is about 6 inches above the coil, but the location can be moved to change the resonance of the antenna slightly.

The completed capacitance hat and loading coil assembly are shown in Figure 21.35. A dab of Glyptal (exterior varnish or Loctite also works) locks the screws in place once adjustments have been made and the antenna is ready for installation.

The coaxial feed line attaches to the bottom of the TV mast. Again, use an 8-32 screw for attachment and clean any paint from the metal. To match the antenna to a 50 Ω transmission line, a small parallel (shunt) inductance is needed at the base. The inductor is air-wound with #16 AWG wire (see **Table 21.2**).

MOUNTING THE ANTENNA

A glass beverage bottle serves well as the base insulator, with the neck of the bottle fitting snugly into the TV mast. To support the base insulator, drill a hole large enough to accept the base of the bottle in the center of a 2 × 6 board about 14 inches long. Nail a piece of ¼ inch plywood over the bottom to keep the bottle from slipping through. To keep the base support board from moving around, drill a couple of holes and secure it to the ground with stakes.

The antenna is top-heavy and will need to be guyed. A simple insulated guy ring can be made from a 2 inch PVC coupling and placed on the mast just below the loading coil. The PVC is locked to the mast with three ¼-20 bolts. They are 1 inch long and have nuts on the inside and outside of the PVC. Three ¼ inch holes are drilled for the guy lines, made from lengths of ³⁄₁₆ inch nonabsorbent rope.

OPERATION

On-air results with a 10 foot mast have been very good, even with low power. The ground system for the early tests was nothing more than an 8 foot ground rod hammered into Hoosier soil. With this setup, and using about 90 W, many DX contacts were made over one week's time and stateside contacts were plentiful.

There is plenty of room to experiment however. Performance could be improved by using an extended radial system or raised and insulated radials. (Expect much better performance over average ground with a system of radials) Two, or even three, mast sections could be used with additional guys and proper loading coil inductance. If you use multiple masts, be sure to make a good electrical connection at the joints. The upper assembly is now permanently used to top load a 60 foot pole for transmitting on 160 meters.

21.3.4 Cables and Control Wires on Towers

Most vertical antennas of the type shown in Figure 21.32 and 21.33C-E consist of towers, usually with HF or VHF beam antennas at the top. The rotator control wires and the coaxial feeders to the top of the tower will not affect antenna performance adversely. In fact, they become a part of the composite antenna. To prevent unwanted RF currents from following the wires into the shack, simply dress them close to the tower legs and bring them to ground level. (Running the cables inside the tower works even better.) This decouples the wires at RF. The wires should then be routed along the earth surface (or buried underground) to the operating position. It is not necessary to use bypass capacitors or RF chokes in the rotator control leads if this is done, even when maximum legal power is employed.

21.3.5 Multiband Trap Verticals

The two-band trap vertical antenna of **Figure 21.36** operates in much the same manner as a trap dipole or trap Yagi. The notable difference is that the vertical is one-half of a dipole. The radial system (in-ground or above-ground) functions as a ground plane for the antenna, and provides an equivalent for the missing half of the dipole. Once again, the more effective the ground system, the better will be the antenna performance.

Trap verticals usually are designed to work as ¼ λ radiators. The portion of the antenna below the trap is adjusted as a ¼ λ radiator at the higher proposed operating frequency. That is, a 20/15 meter trap vertical would be a resonant quarter wavelength at 15 meter from the feed point to the bottom of the trap. The trap and that portion of the antenna above the trap (plus the 15 meter section below the trap) constitute the complete antenna during 20 meter operation. But because the trap is in the circuit, the overall physical length of the vertical antenna will be slightly less than that of a single-band, full-size 20 meter vertical.

"Ground-independent" multiband vertical antennas also have traps, but are designed to be electrically longer than ¼ λ. A common electrical length, is ⅜ λ, for example. The "traps" in these antennas are generally not parallel-LC circuits as described above. A variety of techniques are used with both parallel-LC traps and short resonant structures similar to stubs being used to change the antenna's electrical length at different frequencies.

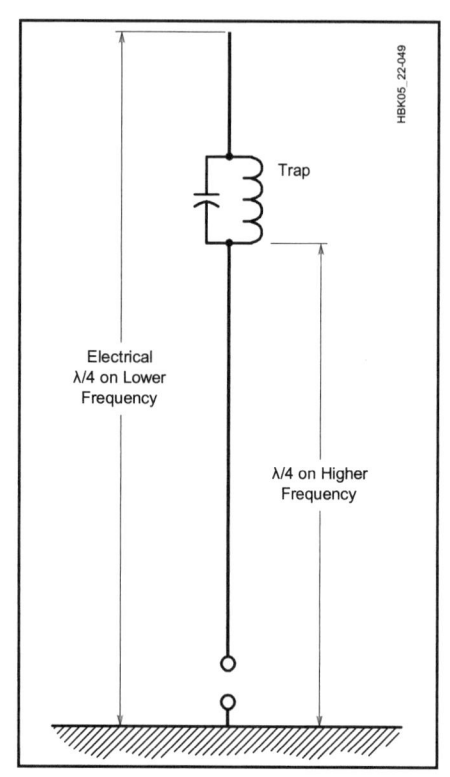

Figure 21.36 — A two-band trap vertical antenna. The trap should be resonated by itself as a parallel resonant circuit at the center of the operating range for the higher frequency band. The reactance of either the inductor or the capacitor range from 100 to 300 Ω. At the lower frequency the trap will act as a loading inductor, adding electrical length to the total antenna.

TRAPS

The trap functions as the name implies: the high impedance of the parallel resonant circuit "traps" the 15 meter energy and confines it to the part of the antenna below the trap. (See the **Electrical Fundamentals** chapter for more information on resonant LC circuits.) During 20 meter operation it allows the RF energy to reach all of the antenna. The trap in this example is tuned as a parallel resonant circuit to 21 MHz. At this frequency it electrically disconnects the top section of the vertical from the lower section because it presents a high impedance at 21 MHz, blocking 21 MHz current. Generally, the trap inductor and capacitor have a reactance of 100 to 300 Ω. Within that range it is not critical.

The trap is built and adjusted separately from the antenna. It should be resonated at the center of the portion of the band to be operated. Thus, if one's favorite part of the 15 meter band is between 21.0 and 21.1 MHz, the trap should be tuned to 21.05 MHz.

Resonance is checked by using a dip meter and detecting the signal in a calibrated receiver. An SWR analyzer can also be used.

Once the trap is adjusted it can be installed in the antenna, and no further adjustment will be required. It is easy, however, to be misled after the system is assembled: Attempts to check the trap resonance in the antenna will suggest that the trap has moved much lower in frequency (approximately 5 MHz lower in a 20/15 meter vertical). This is because the trap is now part of the overall antenna, and the resultant resonance is that of the total antenna. Measure the trap's resonant frequency separately from the rest of the antenna.

Multiband operation is quite practical by using the appropriate number of traps and tubing sections. The construction and adjustment procedure is the same, regardless of the number of bands covered. The highest frequency trap is always closest to the feed end of the antenna, and the lowest frequency trap is always the farthest from the feed point. As the operating frequency is progressively lowered, more traps and more tubing sections become a functional part of the antenna.

Traps should be weatherproofed to prevent moisture from detuning them. Several coatings of high dielectric compound are effective, such as polystyrene Q Dope or insulating varnish (see the article on weatherproofing by Dick Sander, K5QY, included with the downloadable supplemental content). Alternatively, a protective sleeve of heat-shrink tubing can be applied to the coil after completion. The coil form for the trap should be of high insulating quality and be rugged enough to sustain stress during periods of wind.

21.4 T and Inverted-L Antennas

The T and inverted L are variations on the vertical antenna. **Figure 21.37** shows a flat-top T vertical. The T is basically a shortened ¼ λ vertical with the flat-top T section acting as capacitive loading to length the antenna electrically. Dimension H should be as large as possible (up to ¼ λ) for best results. The horizontal section, L, is adjusted to a length that provides resonance. Maximum radiation is polarized vertically despite the horizontal top-loading wire because current in each horizontal half creates out-of-phase radiation that cancels.

A variation of the T antenna is depicted in **Figure 21.38**. This antenna is commonly referred to as an *inverted-L* and is basically a ⁵⁄₁₆ λ vertical bent in the middle so that the top section runs parallel to the ground. Similarly to the T antenna, the vertical section should be as long as possible. L is then added to provide an electrical ⁵⁄₁₆ λ overall.

Because the horizontal section does carry some current, there will be some horizontally-polarized radiation at high angles. This is often considered desirable because it provides local and regional coverage. The horizontal section need not be perfectly horizontal — sloping the wire at a shallow angle from horizontal does not greatly affect antenna performance. This allows the inverted-L to be constructed with a single vertical support.

A sidearm or a length of line attached to a tower can be used to support the vertical section of the T or inverted-L antenna. (Keep the vertical section of the antennas as far from the tower as is practical. Certain combinations of tower height and top loading can create a resonance that interacts severely with the antennas — a 70 foot tower and a 5-element Yagi, for example.)

Both the T and inverted-L antennas are ground-plane antennas and require a good ground system to be effective. If the T or inverted-L are used with a very good ground system, the feed-point impedance will approach 35 to 40 Ω so that the SWR approaches 1.4:1. The inverted-L or T can be constructed to be longer than needed for resonance as illustrated in Figure 21.38. This increases the feed point resistance increases to 50 Ω plus some inductive reactance due to the extra length. A series capacitor at the feed point then cancels the reactance, leaving a 50 Ω impedance suitable for direct connection by coaxial cable. **Table 21.3** provides values of capacitance for some combinations of vertical and horizontal height. A transmitting variable capacitor is recommended to allow the impedance match to be tuned.

Table 21.3
Inverted-L Dimensions for 50-Ω Feed Point Impedance at 1.82 MHz

Vertical Height (m)	Horizontal Length (m)	Inductive Reactance (Ω)	Capacitance Required (pF)
10	59.9	1238	71
20	39.7	517	169
30	21	235	372

Results modeled by *EZNEC 5.0* over real ground. Capacitance specified as series value to cancel inductive reactance.

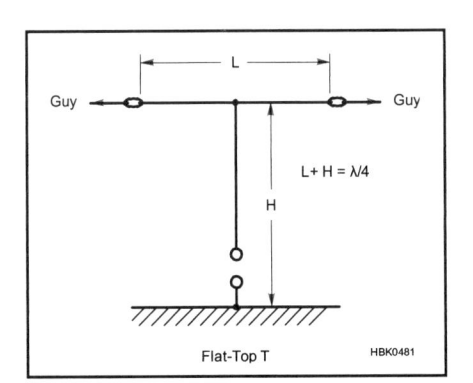

Figure 21.37 — The T antenna is basically a shortened ¼ λ vertical with the flat-top T section acting as capacitive loading to length the antenna electrically.

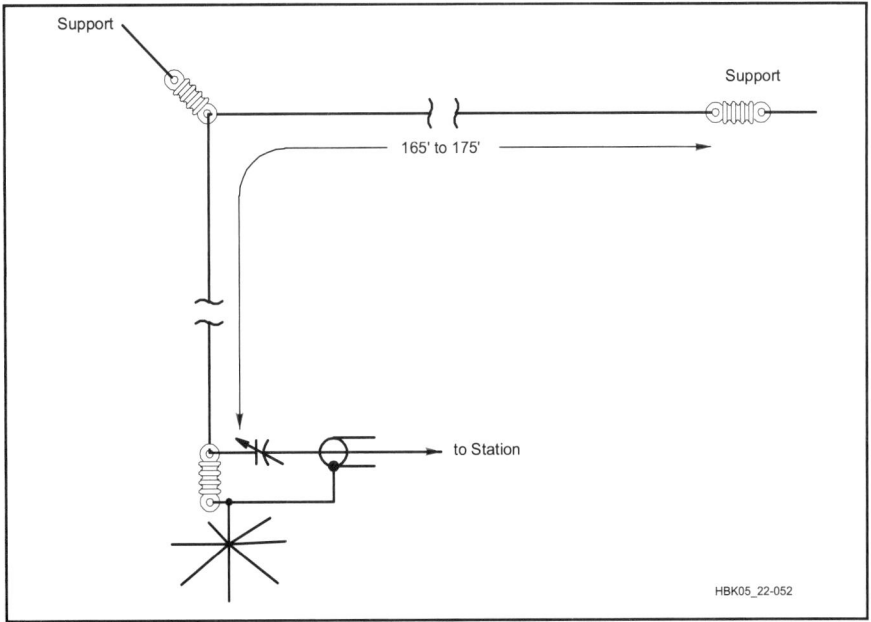

Figure 21.38 — The inverted-L antenna designed for the 1.8 MHz band. Overall wire length is 165 to 175 feet. The variable capacitor has a maximum capacitance of 500 to 800 pF.

21.5 Slopers and Vertical Dipoles

21.5.1 Half-Sloper Antenna

Many hams have had excellent results with *half-sloper* antennas, while others have not had such luck. Investigations by ARRL Technical Advisor John S. Belrose, VE2CV, have brought some insight to the situation through computer modeling and antenna-range tests. The following is taken from VE2CV's Technical Correspondence in Feb 1991 *QST*, pp 39 and 40. Essentially, the half-sloper is a top-fed vertical antenna that uses the structure at the top of the tower plane (such as a grounded Yagi antenna) as a ground plane and the tower acts as a reflector. See **Figure 21.39**.

For half-slopers, the input impedance, the resonant length of the sloping wire and the antenna pattern all depend on the tower height, the angle (between the sloper and tower) the type of Yagi and the Yagi orientation. Here are several configurations extracted from VE2CV's work:

At 160 meters — a 40 meter beam on top of a 95 foot tower with a 55° sloper apex angle. The radiation pattern varies little with Yagi type. The pattern is slightly cardioid with about 8 dB front-to-back ratio at a 25° takeoff angle (see Figure 21.39B and C). Input impedance is about 50 Ω.

At 80 meters — a 20 meter beam on top of a 50 foot tower with a 55° sloper apex angle. The radiation pattern and input impedance are similar to those of the 160 meter half-sloper.

At 40 meters — a 20 meter beam on top of a 50 foot tower with a 55° sloper apex angle. The radiation pattern and impedance depend strongly on the azimuth orientation of the Yagi. Impedance varies from 76 to 127 Ω depending on Yagi direction.

There are many configurations that will produce a reasonable feed point impedance and acceptable radiation pattern. Experimentation is usually required to find a design that works for a particular installation.

Project: Half-Wave Vertical Dipole (HVD)

Chuck Hutchinson, K8CH, describes a 15 meter vertical dipole (HVD) that he built for the ARRL book, *Simple and Fun Antennas for Hams*. The performance of this antenna, with its base at 14 feet, compares favorably with a horizontal dipole at 30 feet when making intercontinental QSOs.

CONSTRUCTION OF A 15 METER HVD

The 15 meter HVD consists of four 6 foot lengths of 0.875 inch aluminum tube with 0.058 wall thickness. In addition there are two 1 foot lengths of 0.75 inch tubing for splices, and two 1 foot lengths of 0.75 inch fiberglass rod for insulators. See **Table 21.4** for dimensions.

Start by cutting off 1 foot from a 6 foot length of 0.875 inch tubing. Next, insert six inches of one of the 1-foot-long 0.75 inch tubes into the machine-cut end of your tubing and fasten the tubes together. Now, slide an end of a 6 foot length of 0.875 tube over the

---

Table 21.4
HVD Dimensions
Length using 0.875-inch aluminum tubing

MHz	Feet	Inches
18.11	33	11
21.2	22	0
24.94	18	9
28.4	16	5

These lengths should divided by two to determine the length of the dipole legs

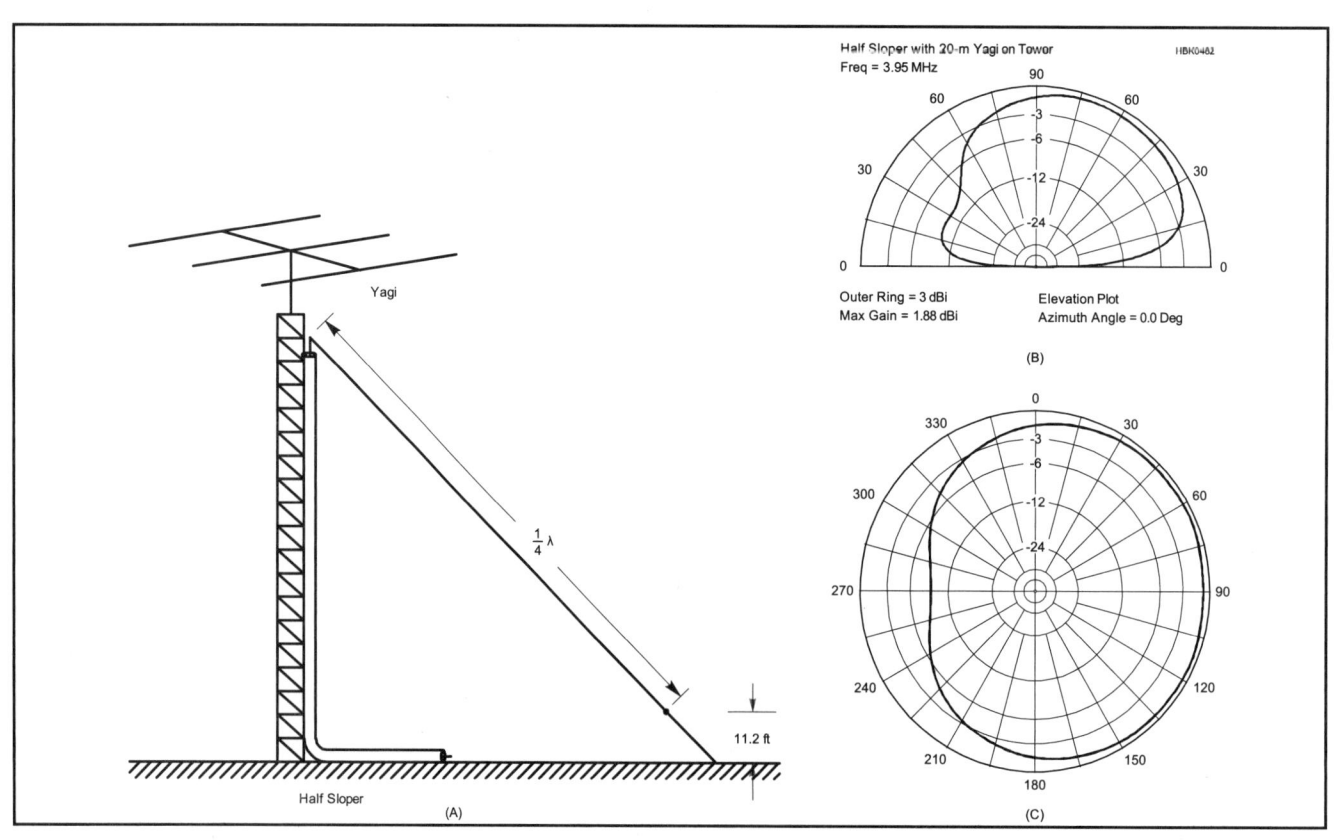

Figure 21.39 — The half-sloper antenna (A). B is the vertical radiation pattern in the plane of a half sloper, with the sloper to the right. C is the azimuthal pattern of the half sloper (90° azimuth is the direction of the sloping wire). Both patterns apply to 160 and 80 meter antennas described in the text.

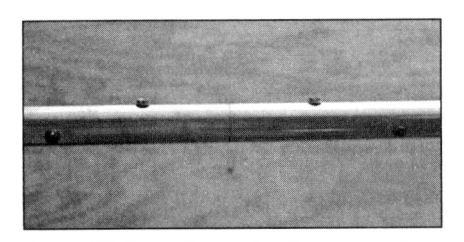

Figure 21.40 — Element splice uses a 1 foot length of 0.75 inch tubing inserted into the 0.875 inch sections to join them together. Self-tapping sheet-metal screws are used in this photo, but aluminum pop rivets or machine screws with washers and nuts can be used.

protruding end of the 0.75 tube and fasten them together. Repeat this procedure with the remaining 0.875 inch tubing.

You should now have two 11-foot-long elements. As you can see in **Figure 21.40**, K8CH was temporarily out of aluminum pop rivets, so he used sheet metal screws. Either will work fine, but pop rivets can easily be drilled out and the antenna disassembled if you ever want to make changes.

Because hand-made cuts are not perfectly square, put those element ends at the center of the antenna. Slip these cut ends over the ends of a 1 foot length of 0.75 inch fiberglass rod. This rod serves as the center insulator. Leave about a 1 inch gap at the center. Drill aluminum and fiberglass for #8 hardware as shown in **Figure 21.41**.

Now, slip half of the remaining 1 foot length of 0.75 inch fiberglass rod into one end of the dipole. (This end will be the bottom end or base.) Drill and secure with #8 hardware. See **Figure 21.42**.

The final step is to secure the guy wires to your vertical. You can see how K8CH did that in **Figure 21.43**. Start by drilling a pilot hole and then drive a sheet metal screw into the antenna about a foot above the center. The purpose of that screw is to prevent the clamp and guys from sliding down the antenna.

The guys are continuous lengths of 3/16 inch Dacron line. (The Dacron serves a dual purpose: it supports the antenna vertically, and it acts as an insulator.) Tie secure knots into the guy ends and secure these knotted ends to the antenna with a stainless-steel worm-screw-type hose clamp. Take care to not over tighten the clamps. You don't want the clamp to slip (the knots and the sheet-metal screw will help), but you especially don't want to cut your guy lines. Your antenna is ready for installation.

INSTALLATION

Installation requires two things. First, a place to sit or mount the base insulator. Second, you need anchors for the support guys.

K8CH used a piece of 2 × 6 lumber to make a socket to hold the HVD base securely in place. He drilled a ¾ inch-deep hole with a ¾ inch spade bit. A couple of pieces of 2 × 2 lumber at the ends of the base form a saddle which nicely straddles the ridge at the peak of his garage roof. You can see this in **Figure 21.44**. The dimensions are not critical. Paint your base to protect it from the weather.

BALUN

This antenna needs a common-mode choke balun to ensure that RF doesn't flow on the shield of the coax. (See the **Transmission Lines** chapter for more information on choke baluns.) Unlike a horizontal dipole, don't consider it an option to omit the common-mode choke when building and installing an HVD.

You can use 8 feet of the RG-213 feed line wound into 7 turns for a balun. Secure the turns together with electrical tape so that each turn lies parallel with the next turn, forming a solenoid coil. Secure the feed line and balun to one of the guy lines with UV-resistant cable ties.

Because the feed line slants away from the antenna, you'll want to do *all* that you can to eliminate common-mode currents from the feed line. For that reason, make another balun about 11.5 feet from the first one. This balun also consists of 8 feet of the RG-213 feed line wound into 7 turns. See **Figure 21.45** for a photo of the installed antenna.

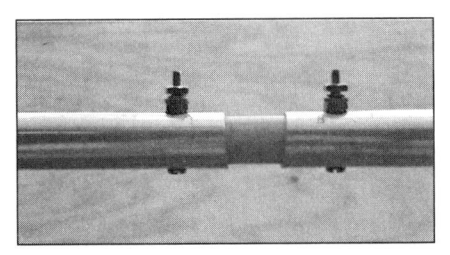

Figure 21.41 — The center insulator of the 15 meter HVD is a 1 foot length of 0.75 inch fiberglass rod. Insulator and elements have been drilled to accept #8 hardware.

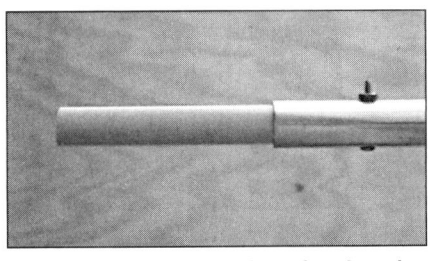

Figure 21.42 — The HVD base insulator is a 1 foot length of 0.75 inch fiberglass rod.

Figure 21.43 — Guys are made of Dacron line that is attached to the HVD by a stainless-steel worm-screw-type hose clamp. A self-tapping sheet-metal screw (not visible in the photo) prevents the clamp from sliding down the antenna.

Figure 21.44 — At K8CH, the HVD base insulator sits in this saddle-shaped wooden fixture. This was photo was taken before the fixture was painted — a necessary step to protect against the weather.

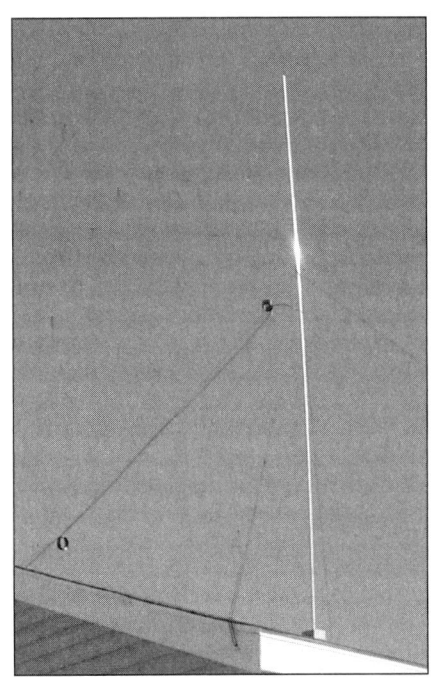

Figure 21.45 — The HVD installed at K8CH. An eye screw that is used for securing one of the guy lines is visible in the foreground. You can also see the two choke baluns that are used in the feed system (see text).

Project: Compact Vertical Dipole (CVD)

An HVD for 20 meters will be about 33 feet tall, and for 30 meters, it will be around 46 feet tall. Even the 20 meter version can prove to be a mechanical challenge. The compact vertical dipole (CVD), designed by Chuck Hutchinson, K8CH, uses capacitance loading to shorten the antenna. Starting with the 15 meter HVD described in the previous project, Chuck added capacitance loading wires to lower the resonance to 30 meters. Later, he shortened the wires to move resonance to the 20 meter band. This project describes those two CVDs.

PERFORMANCE ISSUES

Shortened antennas frequently suffer reduced performance caused by the shortening. A dipole that is less than ½ λ in length is a compromise antenna. The issue becomes how much is lost in the compromise. In this case there are two areas of primary interest, radiation efficiency and SWR bandwidth.

Radiation Efficiency

Capacitance loading at the dipole ends is the most efficient method of shortening the antenna. Current distribution in the high-current center of the antenna remains virtually unchanged. Since radiation is related directly to current, this is the most desirable form of loading. Computer modeling shows that radiation from a 30 meter CVD is only 0.66 dB less than that from a full-size 30 meter HVD when both have their bases 8 feet above ground. The angle of maximum radiation shifts up a bit for the CVD. Not a bad compromise when you consider that the CVD is 22 feet long compared to the approximately 46 foot length of the HVD.

SWR and SWR Bandwidth

Shortened antennas usually have lower radiation resistance and less SWR bandwidth than the full-size versions. The amount of change in the radiation resistance is related to the amount and type of loading (shortening), being lower with shorter the antennas. This can be a benefit in the case of a shortened vertical dipole. In Figure 21.2 you can see that vertical dipoles have a fairly high radiation resistance. With the dipole's lower end ⅛ λ above ground, the radiation resistance is roughly 80 Ω. In this case, a shorter antenna can have a better SWR when fed with 50 Ω coax.

SWR bandwidth tends to be wide for vertical dipoles in general. A properly designed CVD for 7 MHz or higher should give you good SWR (1.5:1 or better) across the entire band!

As you can see, in theory the CVD provides excellent performance in a compact package. Experience confirms the theory.

CONSTRUCTION

To convert the K8CH 15 meter HVD to 20 or 30 meters, you'll need to add four loading wires at the top and four more at the bottom of the HVD. The lengths are given in the table in **Figure 21.46**. The upper wires droop at a 45° angle and the lower wires run horizontally. The antenna is supported by four guy lines. You can connect the wires to the vertical portion with #8 hardware. Crimp and solder terminals on the wire ends to make connections easier. The technique is illustrated in **Figure 21.47**.

The upper loading wires can be extended with insulated line and used for additional guying. The lower wires are extended with insulated line and fasten to the guy lines so that the lower wires run horizontally.

Prune the lower wires for best SWR across the band of interest. The K8CH CVD has its base at 14 feet. This antenna has an SWR of less than 1.2:1 on 30 meters and less than 1.3:1 across the entire 20 meter band.

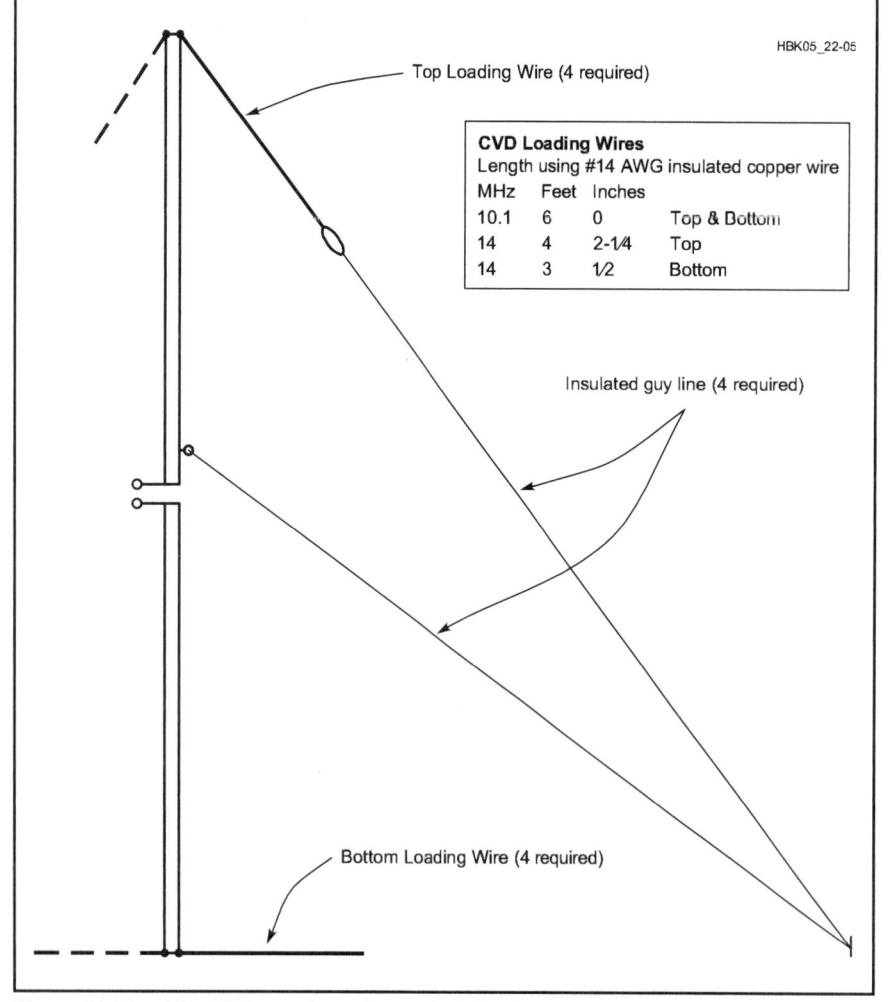

CVD Loading Wires
Length using #14 AWG insulated copper wire

MHz	Feet	Inches	
10.1	6	0	Top & Bottom
14	4	2-1/4	Top
14	3	1/2	Bottom

Figure 21.46 — The CVD consists of a vertical dipole and loading wires. Only one set of the four loading wires and only one guy line is shown in this drawing. See text for details.

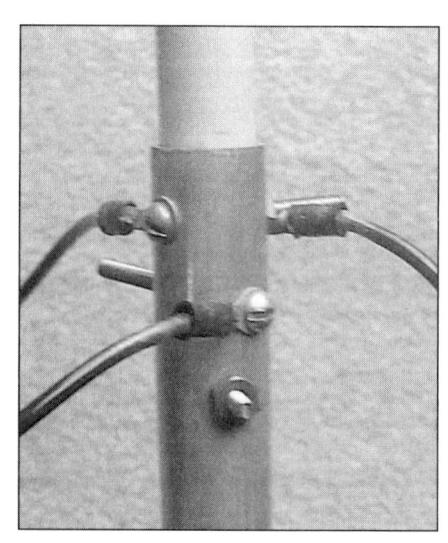

Figure 21.47 — CVD loading wires can be attached using #8 hardware. Crimp and solder terminals on the wire ends to make connections easier.

EXPERIENCE

The 30 meter CVD was compared to a ground-mounted quarter-wave vertical and a horizontal dipole at 30 feet. In tests, the CVD was always the superior antenna.

Later, the CVD loading wires were shortened for operation on 20 meters. Once again the results were very encouraging.

Project: All-Wire 30 Meter CVD

If you have a tree or other support that will support the upper end of a CVD at 32 feet above the ground, you might want to consider an all-wire version of the 30 meter CVD. The vertical is 24 feet long and it will have an SWR of less than 1.1:1 across the band. The four loading wires at top and bottom are each 5 feet, 2 inches long.

The configuration is shown in **Figure 21.48**. As with any vertical dipole, you'll need to use a balun between the feed line and the antenna.

Alternatively you can use two loading wires at the top and two at the bottom. In this case each of the loading wires is 8 feet, 7.5 inches long.

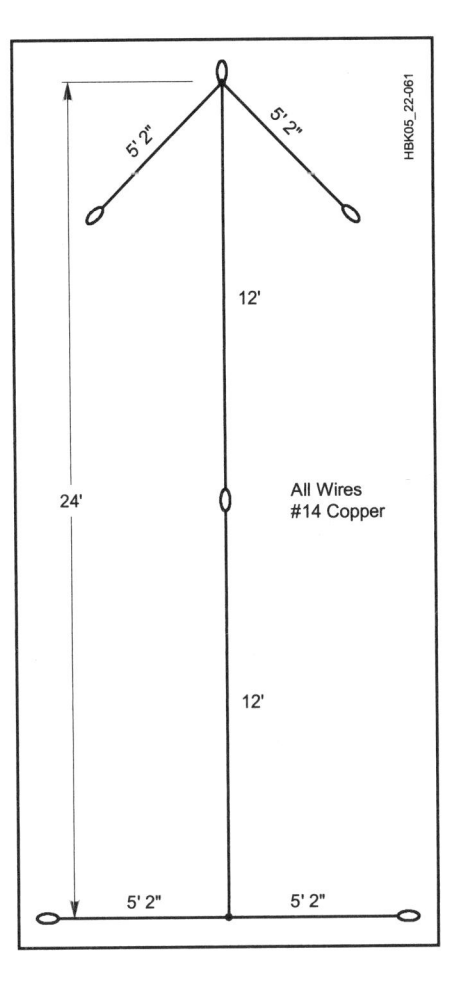

Figure 21.48 — The all-wire 30 meter CVD consists of a vertical dipole and loading wires. It can be made entirely with #14 AWG wire. Support lines have been omitted for simplicity. See text for details.

21.6 Yagi Antennas

Most antennas described earlier in this chapter have unity gain compared to a dipole, or just slightly more. For the purpose of obtaining gain and directivity it is convenient to use a Yagi-Uda *beam* antenna. The former is commonly called a *Yagi*. There are other forms of directive antennas, but the Yagi is by far the most popular used by amateurs. (For more information on phased arrays and other types of directive antennas, see the *ARRL Antenna Book*.)

Most operators prefer to erect these antennas for horizontal polarization, but they can be used as vertically polarized antennas merely by rotating the elements by 90°. In effect, the beam antenna is turned on its side for vertical polarization. The number of elements used will depend on the gain desired and the limits of the supporting structure. At HF, many amateurs obtain satisfactory results with only two elements in a beam antenna, while others have four or five elements operating on a single amateur band, called a *monoband beam*. On VHF and above, Yagis with many elements are common, particularly for simplex communication without repeaters. For fixed point-to-point communications, such as repeater links, Yagis with three or four elements are more common.

Regardless of the number of elements used, the height-above-ground considerations discussed earlier for dipole antennas remain valid with respect to the angle of radiation. This is demonstrated in **Figure 21.49** at A and B where a comparison of radiation characteristics is given for a 3 element Yagi at one-half and one wavelength above average ground. It can be seen that the higher antenna (Figure 21.49B) has a main lobe that is more favorable for DX work (roughly 15°) than the lobe of the lower antenna in Figure 21.49A (approximately 30°). The pattern at B shows that some useful high-angle radiation exists also, and the higher lobe is suitable for short-skip contacts when propagation conditions dictate the need.

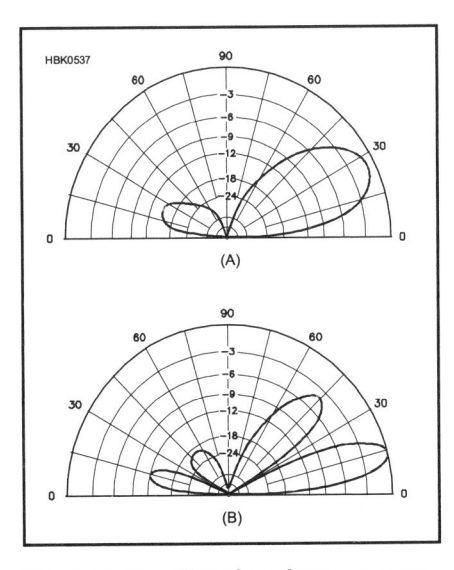

Figure 21.49 — Elevation-plane response of a 3 element Yagi placed ½ λ above perfect ground at A and the same antenna spaced 1 λ above ground at B.

Antennas 21.29

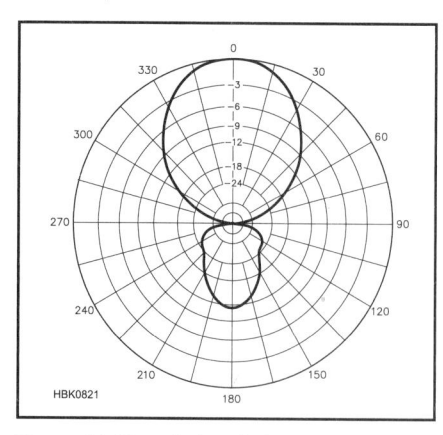

Figure 21.50 — Azimuthal pattern of a typical three-element Yagi in free space. The Yagi's boom is along the 0° to 180° axis.

The azimuth pattern for the same antenna is provided in **Figure 21.50**. (This is a free-space pattern, so the pattern is taken in the plane of the antenna. Remember that azimuth patterns taken over a reflecting surface must also specify the elevation angle at which the pattern was measured or calculated.) Most of the power is concentrated in the main lobe at 0° azimuth. The lobe directly behind the main lobe at 180° is often called the *back lobe* or *rear lobe*. The front-to-back ratio (F/B) of this antenna is just less than 12 dB — the peak power difference, in decibels, between the main lobe at 0° and the rearward lobe at 180°. It is infrequent that two 3 element Yagis with different element spacing and tuning will yield the same lobe patterns. The patterns also change with frequency of operation. The pattern of Figure 21.50 is shown only for illustrative purposes.

21.6.1 Parasitic Excitation

In a Yagi antenna only one element (the *driven element*) is connected to the feed line. The additional elements are *coupled* to the driven element because they are so close. (Element-to-element spacing in a Yagi antenna is generally on the order of 1/10 to 1/8 wavelength.) This *mutual coupling* results in currents being induced in the non-driven elements from the radiated field of the driven element. These elements are called *parasitic elements* and the Yagi antenna is therefore a *parasitic array*. (An antenna in which multiple elements all receive power from the transmitter is called a *driven array*.) The currents induced in the parasitic elements also result in radiated fields, just as if the current were the result of power from a feed line. This is called *re-radiation*, and it has a 180° phase shift from the current-inducing field. The combination of the field radiated by the driven element, the fields from the parasitic elements, and the physical spacing of the elements results in the fields having the proper phase relationship so as to focus the radiated energy in the desired direction and reject it in other directions.

The parasitic element is called a *director* when it reinforces radiation along a line pointing to it from the driven element, and a *reflector* in the opposite case. Whether the parasitic element is a director or reflector depends on the parasitic element tuning, which is usually adjusted by changing its length. The structure on which the elements are mounted is called the *boom* of the antenna.

21.6.2 Yagi Gain, Front-to-Back Ratio and SWR

The gain of a Yagi antenna with parasitic elements varies with the spacing and tuning of the elements. Element tuning is a function of length, diameter and *taper schedule* (the steps in length and diameter) if the element is constructed with telescoping tubing. For any given number of elements and the spacing between them, there is a tuning condition that will result in maximum gain. However, the maximum front-to-back ratio seldom, if ever, occurs at the same condition that gives maximum forward gain. The impedance of the driven element in a parasitic array, and thus the SWR, also varies with the tuning and spacing.

It is important to remember that all these parameters change as the operating frequency is varied. For example, if you operate both the CW and phone portions of the 20 meter band with a Yagi antenna, you probably will want an antenna with consistent performance over most of the band. Such designs typically must sacrifice a little gain in order to achieve good F/B and SWR performance across the band.

Gain and F/B performance generally improve with the number of elements. In Yagi antennas with more than three elements (a driven element and one director and reflector), the additional elements are added as directors, since little additional benefit is obtained from multiple reflectors. Wider spacing also improves gain and F/B up to a certain point, depending on a number of factors, beyond which performance begins to fall. Optimizing element spacing is a complex problem and no single spacing satisfies all design requirements. For the lower HF bands, the size of the antenna quickly becomes impractical for truly *optimal* designs, and compromise is necessary.

21.6.3 Two-Element Beams

A two-element beam is useful — especially where space or other considerations prevent the use of a three-element, or larger, beam. The general practice is to tune the parasitic element as a reflector and space it about 0.15 λ from the driven element, although some successful antennas have been built with 0.1-λ spacing and director tuning.

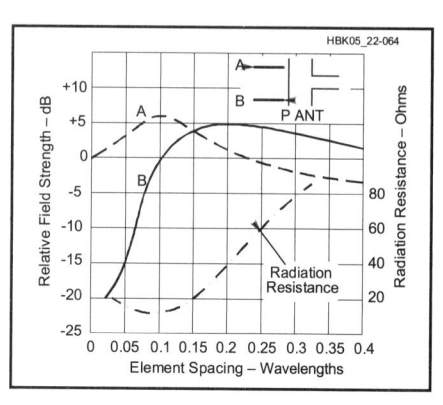

Figure 21.51 — Gain vs element spacing for a two-element Yagi, having one driven and one parasitic element. The reference point, 0 dB, is the field strength from a half-wave antenna alone.

Gain vs element spacing for a two-element antenna is given in **Figure 21.51** for the special case where the parasitic element is resonant. It is indicative of the performance to be expected under maximum-gain tuning conditions. Changing the tuning of the driven element in a Yagi or quad will not materially affect the gain or F/R. Thus, only the spacing and the tuning of the single parasitic element have any effect on the performance of a 2 element Yagi.

In Figure 21.51, the greatest gain is in the direction A (in which the parasitic element is acting as a director) at spacings of less than 0.14 λ, and in direction B (in which the parasitic element is a reflector) at greater spacings. The front-to-back ratio is the difference in decibels between curves A and B along the boom of the antenna. The figure also shows variation in radiation resistance of the driven element.

These curves are for the special case of a self-resonant parasitic element, but are representative of how a two-element Yagi works. At most spacings the gain as a reflector can be increased by slight lengthening of the parasitic element; the gain as a director can be increased by shortening. This also improves the front-to-rear ratio.

Most two-element Yagi designs achieve a compromise F/R of about 10 dB, together with an acceptable SWR and gain across a frequency band with a percentage bandwidth less than about 4%.

21.6.4 Three-Element Beams

A theoretical investigation of the three-element case (director, driven element and reflector) has indicated a maximum gain of about 9.7 dBi (7.6 dBd). A number of experimental investigations have shown that

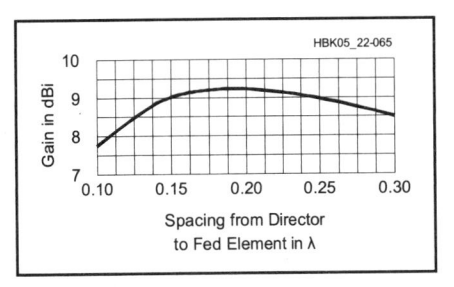

Figure 21.52 — General relationship of gain of three-element Yagi vs director spacing, the reflector being fixed at 0.2 λ. This antenna is tuned for maximum forward gain.

the spacing between the driven element and reflector for maximum gain is in the region of 0.15 to 0.25 λ. With 0.2 λ reflector spacing, **Figure 21.52** shows that the gain variation with director spacing is not especially critical. Also, the overall length of the array (boom length in the case of a rotatable antenna) can be anywhere between 0.35 and 0.45 λ with no appreciable difference in the maximum gain obtainable.

If maximum gain is desired, wide spacing of both elements is beneficial because adjustment of tuning or element length is less critical and the input resistance of the driven element is generally higher than with close spacing. A higher input resistance improves the efficiency of the antenna and makes a greater bandwidth possible. However, a total antenna length, director to reflector, of more than 0.3 λ at frequencies of the order of 14 MHz introduces difficulty from a construction standpoint. Lengths of 0.25 to 0.3 λ are therefore used frequently for this band, even though they are less than optimum from the viewpoint of maximum gain.

In general, Yagi antenna gain drops off less rapidly when the reflector length is increased beyond the optimum value than it does for a corresponding decrease below the optimum value. The opposite is true of a director. It is

Table 21.5
Standard Sizes of Aluminum Tubing
6061-T6 (61S-T6) Round Aluminum Tube in 12-ft Lengths

OD (in)	Wall Thickness (in)	stubs ga	ID (in)	Approx Weight (lb) per ft	per length
3/16	0.035	no. 20	0.117	0.019	0.228
	0.049	no. 18	0.089	0.025	0.330
1/4	0.035	no. 20	0.180	0.027	0.324
	0.049	no. 18	0.152	0.036	0.432
	0.058	no. 17	0.134	0.041	0.492
5/16	0.035	no. 20	0.242	0.036	0.432
	0.049	no. 18	0.214	0.047	0.564
	0.058	no. 17	0.196	0.055	0.660
3/8	0.035	no. 20	0.305	0.043	0.516
	0.049	no. 18	0.277	0.060	0.720
	0.058	no. 17	0.259	0.068	0.816
	0.065	no. 16	0.245	0.074	0.888
7/16	0.035	no. 20	0.367	0.051	0.612
	0.049	no. 18	0.339	0.070	0.840
	0.065	no. 16	0.307	0.089	1.068
1/2	0.028	no. 22	0.444	0.049	0.588
	0.035	no. 20	0.430	0.059	0.708
	0.049	no. 18	0.402	0.082	0.948
	0.058	no. 17	0.384	0.095	1.040
	0.065	no. 16	0.370	0.107	1.284
5/8	0.028	no. 22	0.569	0.061	0.732
	0.035	no. 20	0.555	0.075	0.900
	0.049	no. 18	0.527	0.106	1.272
	0.058	no. 17	0.509	0.121	1.452
	0.065	no. 16	0.495	0.137	1.644
3/4	0.035	no. 20	0.680	0.091	1.092
	0.049	no. 18	0.652	0.125	1.500
	0.058	no. 17	0.634	0.148	1.776
	0.065	no. 16	0.620	0.160	1.920
	0.083	no. 14	0.584	0.204	2.448
7/8	0.035	no. 20	0.805	0.108	1.308
	0.049	no. 18	0.777	0.151	1.810
	0.058	no. 17	0.759	0.175	2.100
	0.065	no. 16	0.745	0.199	2.399
1	0.035	no. 20	0.930	0.123	1.467
	0.049	no. 18	0.902	0.170	2.040
	0.058	no. 17	0.884	0.202	2.424
	0.065	no. 16	0.870	0.220	2.640
	0.083	no. 14	0.834	0.281	3.372
1 1/8	0.035	no. 20	1.055	0.139	1.668
	0.058	no. 17	1.009	0.228	2.736
1 1/4	0.035	no. 20	1.180	0.155	1.860
	0.049	no. 18	1.152	0.210	2.520
	0.058	no. 17	1.134	0.256	3.072
	0.065	no. 16	1.120	0.284	3.408
	0.083	no. 14	1.084	0.357	4.284
1 3/8	0.035	no. 20	1.305	0.173	2.076
	0.058	no. 17	1.259	0.282	3.384
1 1/2	0.035	no. 20	1.430	0.180	2.160
	0.049	no. 18	1.402	0.260	3.120
	0.058	no. 17	1.384	0.309	3.708
	0.065	no. 16	1.370	0.344	4.128
	0.083	no. 14	1.334	0.434	5.208
	*0.125	1/8"	1.250	0.630	7.416
	*0.250	1/4"	1.000	1.150	14.823
1 5/8	0.035	no. 20	1.555	0.206	2.472
	0.058	no. 17	1.509	0.336	4.032
1 3/4	0.058	no. 17	1.634	0.363	4.356
	0.083	no. 14	1.584	0.510	6.120
1 7/8	0.508	no. 17	1.759	0.389	4.668
2	0.049	no. 18	1.902	0.350	4.200
	0.065	no. 16	1.870	0.450	5.400
	0.083	no. 14	1.834	0.590	7.080
	*0.125	1/8"	1.750	0.870	9.960
	*0.250	1/4"	1.500	1.620	19.920
2 1/4	0.049	no. 18	2.152	0.398	4.776
	0.065	no. 16	2.120	0.520	6.240
	0.083	no. 14	2.084	0.660	7.920
2 1/2	0.065	no. 16	2.370	0.587	7.044
	0.083	no. 14	2.334	0.740	8.880
	*0.125	1/8"	2.250	1.100	12.720
	*0.250	1/4"	2.000	2.080	25.440
3	0.065	no. 16	2.870	0.710	8.520
	*0.125	1/8"	2.700	1.330	15.600
	*0.250	1/4"	2.500	2.540	31.200

*These sizes are extruded; all other sizes are drawn tubes. Shown here are standard sizes of aluminum tubing that are stocked by most aluminum suppliers or distributors in the United States and Canada. Don Daso, K4ZA, explains the different aluminum alloy types in this books's downloadable supplemental article "Workshop Chronicles: Alloy Designations."

Antennas 21.31

therefore advisable to err, if necessary, on the long side for a reflector and on the short side for a director. This also tends to make the antenna performance less dependent on the exact frequency at which it is operated. An increase above the design frequency has the same effect as increasing the length of both parasitic elements, while a decrease in frequency has the same effect as shortening both elements. By making the director slightly short and the reflector slightly long, there will be a greater spread between the upper and lower frequencies at which the gain starts to show a rapid decrease.

21.6.5 Construction of Yagi Antennas

Most beams and verticals are made from sections of aluminum tubing. Compromise beams have been fashioned from less-expensive materials such as electrical conduit (steel) or bamboo poles wrapped with conductive tape or aluminum foil. The steel conduit is heavy, is a poor conductor and is subject to rust. Similarly, bamboo with conducting material attached to it may deteriorate rapidly in the weather. Given the drawbacks of alternative materials, aluminum tubing (or rod for VHF and UHF Yagis) is far and away the best choice for antenna construction.

For reference, **Table 21.5** details the standard sizes of aluminum tubing, available in many metropolitan areas. Metal distributors, local and online, usually stock popular sizes of aluminum tubing. Several *QST* advertisers stock an extensive line of tubing specifically for antenna construction and cut to shippable lengths. Tubing usually comes in 12 foot lengths, although 20 foot lengths are available in some sizes. Your aluminum dealer will probably also sell aluminum plate in various thicknesses needed for boom-to-mast and boom-to-element connections.

Aluminum is rated according to its hardness. The most common material used in antenna construction is grade 6061-T6. This material is relatively strong and has good workability. In addition, it will bend without taking a *set*, an advantage in antenna applications where the pieces are constantly flexing in the wind. The softer grades (5051, 3003 and so on) will bend much more easily, while harder grades (7075 and so on) are more brittle.

Wall thickness is of primary concern when selecting tubing. It is of utmost importance that the tubing fits snugly where the element sections join. Sloppy joints will make a mechanically unstable antenna. The magic wall thickness is 0.058 inch. For example (from Table 21.5), 1 inch outside diameter (OD) tubing with a 0.058 inch wall has an inside diameter (ID) of 0.884 inch. The next smaller size of tubing, 7⁄8 inch, has an OD of 0.875 inch. The 0.009 inch difference provides just the right amount of clearance for a snug fit.

Figure 21.53 shows several methods of fastening antenna element sections together. The slot and hose clamp method shown at the upper left is probably the best for joints where adjustments are needed. Generally, one adjustable joint on each side of the element is sufficient to tune the antenna — usually the tips at each end of an element are made adjustable. Stainless steel hose clamps (beware — some "stainless steel" models do not have a stainless screw and will rust) are recommended for longest antenna life.

The remaining photos show possible fastening methods for joints that are not adjustable. At the upper right, machine screws and nuts hold the elements in place. At the lower left, sheet metal screws are used. At the lower right, rivets secure the tubing. If the antenna is to be assembled permanently, rivets are the best choice. Once in place, they are permanent. Properly installed, they rarely work free, regardless of vibration or wind. If aluminum rivets with aluminum mandrels are employed, they will never rust. Also, being aluminum, there is no danger of corrosion from interaction between dissimilar metals. If the antenna is to be disassembled and moved periodically, either machine or sheet metal screws will work. If machine screws are used, however, take precautions to keep the nuts from vibrating free. Use of lock washers, lock nuts and flexible adhesive such as silicone bathtub sealant or a thread-locking compound will keep the hardware in place. For portable or temporary use, such as Field Day, rivets may be held in place with electrical tape and removed when the operation is finished.

Use of a conductive grease at the element joints is essential for long life. Left untreated, the aluminum surfaces will oxidize in the weather, resulting in a poor connection. Some trade names for this conductive grease are Penetrox, OxGard, and Noalox. Many electrical supply houses and hardware stores carry these products.

DRIVEN ELEMENT

The ARRL recommends *plumbers delight* construction, in which all elements are mounted directly on, and grounded to, the boom. This puts the entire array at dc ground potential, affording better lightning protection. A gamma- or T-match section can be used for matching the feed line to the array.

An alternative method is to insulate the driven element from the boom, but use a *hairpin* or *beta match*, the center point of which is electrically neutral and can be attached directly to the boom, restoring the dc ground for the driven element.

Direct feed designs in which the feed point impedance of the driven element is close to 50 Ω, require no impedance matching structure. Like hairpin-matched designs, the driven element must be insulated from the boom, requiring some additional mechanical complexity.

Regardless of the design, a current or choke balun should be used (see the **Transmission Lines** chapter) to prevent the outer surface of the feed line shield from interacting with the antenna directly or by picking up the radiated signal. Such interaction can degrade the antenna's radiation pattern, especially by compromising signal rejection to the side and rear.

BOOM MATERIAL

The boom size for a rotatable Yagi or quad should be selected to provide stability to the entire system. The best diameter for the boom depends on several factors, but mostly the element weight, number of elements and overall length. Two-inch-diameter booms should not be made any longer than 24 feet

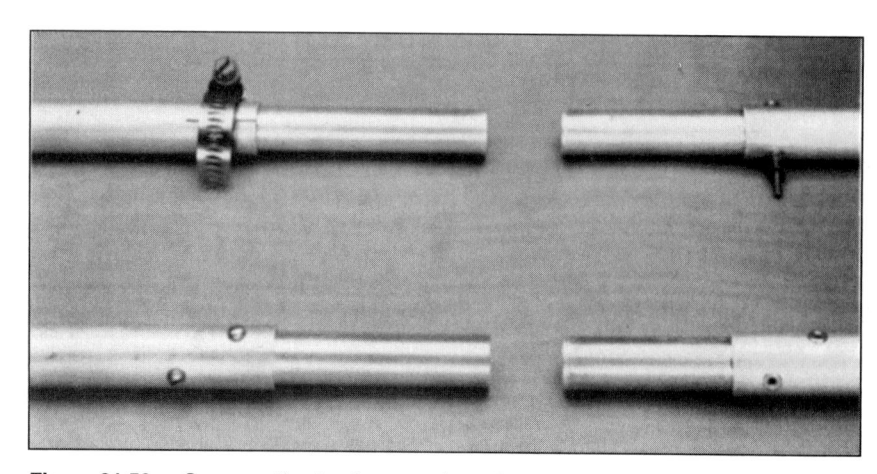

Figure 21.53 — Some methods of connecting telescoping tubing sections to build beam elements. See text for a discussion of each method.

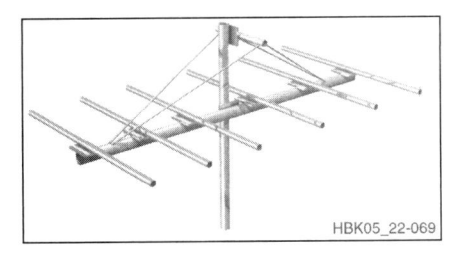

Figure 21.54 — A long boom needs both vertical and horizontal support. The crossbar mounted above the boom can support a double truss, which will help keep the antenna in position.

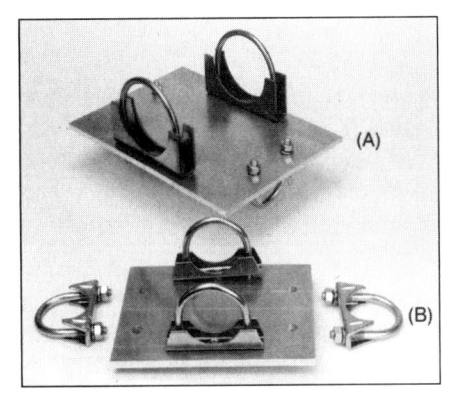

Figure 21.55 — The boom-to-element plate at A uses muffler-clamp-type U-bolts and saddles to secure the round tubing to the flat plate. The boom-to-mast plate at B is similar to the boom-to-element plate. The main difference is the size of materials used.

Table 21.6
10 Meter Optimized Yagi Designs

	Spacing Between Elements (in)	Seg 1 Length (in)	Seg 2 Length (in)	Seg 3 Length (in)	Midband Gain F/R
310-08					
Refl	0	24	18	66.750	7.2 dBi
DE	36	24	18	57.625	22.9 dB
Dir 1	54	24	18	53.125	
410-14					
Refl	0	24	18	64.875	8.4 dBi
DE	36	24	18	58.625	30.9 dB
Dir 1	36	24	18	57.000	
Dir 2	90	24	18	47.750	
510-24					
Refl	0	24	18	65.625	10.3 dBi
DE	36	24	18	58.000	25.9 dB
Dir 1	36	24	18	57.125	
Dir 2	99	24	18	55.000	
Dir 3	111	24	18	50.750	

Note: For all antennas, the tube diameters are: Seg 1=0.750 inch, Seg 2=0.625 inch, Seg 3=0.500 inch.

Table 21.7
12 Meter Optimized Yagi Designs

	Spacing Between Elements (in)	Seg 1 Length (in)	Seg 2 Length (in)	Seg 3 Length (in)	Midband Gain F/R
312-10					
Refl	0	36	18	69.000	7.5 dBi
DE	40	36	18	59.125	24.8 dB
Dir 1	74	36	18	54.000	
412-15					
Refl	0	36	18	66.875	8.5 dBi
DE	46	36	18	60.625	27.8 dB
Dir 1	46	36	18	58.625	
Dir 2	82	36	18	50.875	
512-20					
Refl	0	36	18	69.750	9.5 dBi
DE	46	36	18	61.750	24.9 dB
Dir 1	46	36	18	60.500	
Dir 2	48	36	18	55.500	
Dir 3	94	36	18	54.625	

Note: For all antennas, the tube diameters are: Seg 1 = 0.750 inch, Seg 2 = 0.625 inch, Seg 3 = 0.500 inch.

unless additional support is given to reduce both vertical and horizontal bending forces. Suitable reinforcement for a long 2 inch boom can consist of a truss or a truss and lateral support, as shown in **Figure 21.54**.

A boom length of 24 feet is about the point where a 3 inch diameter begins to be very worthwhile. This dimension provides a considerable amount of improvement in overall mechanical stability as well as increased clamping surface area for element hardware. The latter is extremely important to prevent rotation of elements around the boom if heavy icing is commonplace. Pinning an element to the boom with a large bolt helps in this regard. On smaller diameter booms, however, the elements sometimes work loose and tend to elongate the pinning holes in both the element and the boom. After some time the elements shift their positions slightly (sometimes from day to day) and give a ragged appearance to the system, even though this may not harm the electrical performance.

A 3 inch diameter boom with a wall thickness of 0.065 inch is very satisfactory for antennas up to about a five-element, 20 meter array that is spaced on a 40 foot boom. A truss is recommended for any boom longer than 24 feet. One possible source for large boom material is irrigation tubing sold at farm supply houses.

PUTTING IT TOGETHER

Once you assemble the boom and elements, the next step is to fasten the elements to the boom securely and then fasten the boom to the mast or supporting structure using mounting plates as shown in **Figure 21.55**. Be sure to leave plenty of material on either side of the U-bolt holes on the element-to-boom mounting plates. The U-bolts selected should be a snug fit for the tubing. If possible, buy muffler-clamp U-bolts that come with saddles.

The *boom-to-mast* plate shown in Figure 21.55B is similar to the *boom-to-element* plate in 21.55A. The size of the plate and number of U-bolts used will depend on the size of the antenna. Generally, antennas for the bands up through 20 meters require only two U-bolts each for the mast and boom. Longer antennas for 15 and 20 meters

Antennas 21.33

Table 21.8
15 Meter Optimized Yagi Designs

	Spacing Between Elements (in)	Seg 1 Length (in)	Seg 2 Length (in)	Seg 3 Length (in)	Seg 4 Length (in)	Midband Gain F/R
315-12						
Refl	0	30	36	18	61.375	7.6 dBi
DE	48	30	36	18	49.625	25.5 dB
Dir 1	92	30	36	18	43.500	
415-18						
Refl	0	30	36	18	59.750	8.3 dBi
DE	56	30	36	18	50.875	31.2 dB
Dir 1	56	30	36	18	48.000	
Dir 2	98	30	36	18	36.625	
515-24						
Refl	0	30	36	18	62.000	9.4 dBi
DE	48	30	36	18	52.375	25.8 dB
Dir 1	48	30	36	18	47.875	
Dir 2	52	30	36	18	47.000	
Dir 3	134	30	36	18	41.000	

Note: For all antennas, the tube diameters (in inches) are: Seg 1 = 0.875, Seg 2 = 0.750, Seg 3 = 0.625, Seg 4 = 0.500.

Table 21.9
17 Meter Optimized Yagi Designs

	Spacing Between Elements (in)	Seg 1 Length (in)	Seg 2 Length (in)	Seg 3 Length (in)	Seg 4 Length (in)	Seg 5 Length (in)	Midband Gain F/R
317-14							
Refl	0	24	24	36	24	60.125	8.1 dBi
DE	65	24	24	36	24	52.625	24.3 dB
Dir 1	97	24	24	36	24	48.500	
417-20							
Refl	0	24	24	36	24	61.500	8.5 dBi
DE	48	24	24	36	24	54.250	27.7 dB
Dir 1	48	24	24	36	24	52.625	
Dir 2	138	24	24	36	24	40.500	

Note: For all antennas, tube diameters (inches) are: Seg 1=1.000, Seg 2=0.875, Seg 3=0.750, Seg 4=0.625, Seg 5=0.500.

Table 21.10
20 Meter Optimized Yagi Designs

	Spacing Between Elements (in.)	Seg 1 Length (in.)	Seg 2 Length (in.)	Seg 3 Length (in.)	Seg 4 Length (in.)	Seg 5 Length (in.)	Seg 6 Length (in.)	Midband Gain F/R
320-16								
Refl	0	48	24	20	42	20	69.625	7.3 dBi
DE	80	48	24	20	42	20	51.250	23.4 dB
Dir 1	106	48	24	20	42	20	42.625	
420-26								
Refl	0	48	24	20	42	20	65.625	8.6 dBi
DE	72	48	24	20	42	20	53.375	23.4 dB
Dir 1	60	48	24	20	42	20	51.750	
Dir 2	174	48	24	20	42	20	38.625	

Note: For all antennas, tube diameters (inches) are: Seg 1=1.000, Seg 2=0.875, Seg 3=0.750, Seg 4=0.625, Seg 5=0.500. Seg 6=0.375.

(35 foot booms and up) and most 40 meter beams should have four U-bolts each for the boom and mast because of the torque that the long booms and elements exert as the antennas move in the wind. When tightening the U-bolts, be careful not to crush the tubing. Once the wall begins to collapse, the connection begins to weaken. Many aluminum suppliers sell ¼ inch or ⅜ inch thick plates just right for this application. Often they will shear pieces to the correct size on request. As with tubing, the relatively hard 6061-T6 grade is a good choice for mounting plates.

The antenna should be put together with good-quality hardware. Stainless steel or galvanized hardware is best for long life and is available from several Amateur Radio dealers. Stainless steel hardware can develop surface defects called *galling* that can cause threads on nuts and bolts to seize. On hardware ¼ inch and larger, the use of an anti-seize compound is recommended. Anti-seize compound is available from auto parts stores or a small amount of grease or anti-oxidation compound can help lubricate the threads.

Rust will attack plated steel hardware after a short time, making nuts difficult, if not impossible, to remove. If you use plated hardware, paint it with a good zinc-chromate primer and a finish coat or two.

Good-quality hardware is more expensive initially, but if you do it right the first time, you won't have to take the antenna down after a few years and replace the hardware. Also, when repairing or modifying an installation, nothing is more frustrating than fighting rusty hardware at the top of a tower.

Project: Family of Computer-Optimized HF Yagis

Yagi designers are now able to take advantage of powerful personal computers and software to optimize their designs for the parameters of gain, F/R and SWR across frequency bands. Dean Straw, N6BV, has designed a family of Yagis for HF bands. These can be found in **Tables 21.6** to **21.10**, for the 10, 12, 15, 17 and 20 meter amateur bands, respectively.

For 12 through 20 meters, each design has been optimized for better than 20 dB F/R, and an SWR of less than 2:1 across the entire amateur frequency band. For the 10 meter band, the designs were optimized for the lower 800 kHz of the band, from 28.0 to 28.8 MHz. Each Yagi element is made of telescoping 6061-T6 aluminum tubing, with 0.058 inch thick walls. This type of element can be telescoped easily, using techniques shown in Figure 21.53. Measuring each element to an accuracy of ⅛ inch results in performance remarkably consistent with the computations, without any need for tweaking or fine-tuning when the Yagi is on the tower.

The dimensions shown are designed for specific telescoping aluminum elements, but the elements may be scaled to different sizes by using the information about tapering and scaling in The ARRL Antenna Book, although with a likelihood of deterioration in performance over the whole frequency band.

Each element is mounted above the boom with a heavy rectangular aluminum boom-to-element plate, by means of galvanized U-bolts with saddles, as shown in Figure 21.55. This method of element mounting is rugged and stable, and because the element is mounted away from the boom, the amount of element detuning due to the presence of the boom is minimal. The element dimensions given in each table already take into account any element detuning due to the mounting plate. The element mounting plate for all the 10 meter Yagis is a 0.250 inch thick flat aluminum plate, 4 inches wide by 4 inches long. For the 12 and 15 meter Yagis, a 0.375 inch thick flat aluminum plate, 5 inches wide by 6 inches long is used, and for the 17 and 20 meter Yagis, a 0.375 inch thick flat aluminum plate, 6 inches wide by 8 inches long is used. Where the plate is rectangular, the long dimension is in line with the element.

Each design table shows the dimensions for *one-half* of each element, mounted on one side of the boom. The other half of each element is the same, mounted on the other side of the boom. Use a tubing sleeve inside the center portion of the element so that the element is not crushed by the mounting U-bolts. Each telescoping section is inserted 3 inches into the next size of tubing. For example, in the 310-08 design for 10 meters (3 elements on an 8 foot boom), the reflector tip, made out of ½ inch OD tubing, sticks out 66.75 inches from the ⅝ inch OD tubing. For each 10 meter element, the overall length of each ⅝ inch OD piece of tubing is 21 inches, before insertion into the ¾ inch piece. Since the ¾ inch OD tubing is 24 inches long on each side of the boom, the center portion of each element is actually 48 inches of uncut ¾ inch OD tubing.

The boom for all these antennas should be constructed with at least 2 inch OD tubing, with 0.065 inch wall thickness. Because each boom has three inches of extra length at each end, the reflector is actually placed three inches from one end of the boom. For the 310-08 design, the driven element is placed 36 inches ahead of the reflector, and the director is placed 54 inches ahead of the driven element. The antenna is attached to the mast with the *boom-to-mast* mounting plate shown in Figure 21.55.

Each antenna is designed with a driven element length appropriate for a gamma or T matching network, as shown in **Figure 21.56**. The variable gamma or T capacitors can be housed in small plastic enclosures for weatherproofing; receiving-type variable capacitors with close plate spacing can be used at powers up to a few hundred watts. Maximum capacitance required is usually 140 pF at 14 MHz and proportionally less at the higher frequencies.

The driven-element's length may require slight readjustment for best match, particularly if a different matching network is used. *Do not change either the lengths or the telescoping tubing schedule of the parasitic elements* — they have been optimized for best performance and will not be affected by tuning of the driven element.

TUNING ADJUSTMENTS

To tune the gamma match, adjust the gamma capacitor for best SWR, then adjust the position of the shorting strap or bar that connects the gamma rod to the driven element. Repeat this alternating sequence of adjustments until a satisfactory SWR is reached.

To tune the T-match, the position of the shorting straps and C1 and C2 are adjusted alternately for a best SWR. To maintain balance of the antenna, the position of the straps and capacitor settings should be the same for each side and adjusted together. A coaxial 4:1 balun transformer is shown at Figure 21.56C. A toroidal balun can be used in place of the coax model shown. The toroidal version has a broader frequency range than the coaxial one. The T match is adjusted for 200 Ω and the balun steps this balanced value down to 50 Ω, unbalanced. Or the T match can be set for 300 Ω, and the balun used to step this down to 75 Ω unbalanced.

Dimensions for the gamma and T match rods will depend on the tubing size used, and the spacing of the parasitic elements of the beam. Capacitors C1 and C2 can be 140 pF for 14 MHz beams. Somewhat less capacitance will be needed at 21 and 28 MHz.

Preliminary matching adjustments can be done on the ground. The beam should be aligned vertically so that the reflector element is closest to and a few feet off the ground, with the beam pointing upward. The matching system is then adjusted for best SWR. When the antenna is raised to its operating height, only slight touch-up of the matching network may be required.

A *choke balun* (see the **Transmission Lines** chapter) should be used to isolate the coaxial feed line shield from the antenna. Secure the feed line to the boom of the antenna between the feed point and the supporting mast.

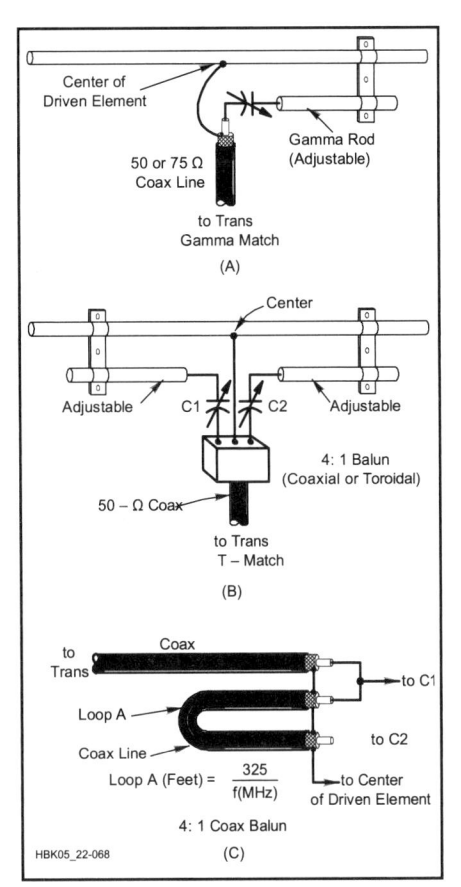

Figure 21.56 — Illustrations of gamma and T matching systems. At A, the gamma rod is adjusted along with the capacitor until the lowest SWR is obtained. A T match is shown at B. It is the same as two gamma-match rods. A 4:1 coaxial balun transformer for use with the T match is shown at C.

Loop A (Feet) = $\dfrac{325}{f(\text{MHz})}$

21.7 Quad and Loop Antennas

One of the more effective DX antennas is the *quad*. It consists of two or more loops of wire, each supported by a bamboo or fiberglass cross-arm assembly. The loops are ¼ λ per side (one full wavelength overall). One loop is driven and the other serves as a parasitic element — usually a reflector. The design of the quad is similar to that of the Yagi, except that the elements are loops instead of dipoles. A two-element quad can achieve better F/R, gain and SWR across a band, at the expense of greater mechanical complexity compared to a two-element Yagi and very nearly the same performance as a three-element Yagi.

A variation of the quad is called the *delta loop*. The electrical properties of both antennas are the same. Both antennas are shown in **Figure 21.57**. They differ mainly in their physical properties, one being of plumber's delight construction, while the other uses insulating support members. One or more directors can be added to either antenna if additional gain and directivity are desired, though most operators use the two-element arrangement.

It is possible to interlace quads or deltas for two or more bands, but if this is done the lengths calculated using the formulas given in Figure 21.57 may have to be changed slightly to compensate for the proximity effect of the second antenna. Using a tuning capacitor as shown in the following project allows the antenna to be adjusted for peak performance without cumbersome adjustment of wire lengths.

If multiple arrays are used, each antenna should be tuned separately for maximum forward gain, or best front-to-rear ratio, as observed on a field-strength meter. The reflector stub on the quad should be adjusted for this condition. The resonance of the antenna can be found by checking the frequency at which the lowest SWR occurs. By lengthening or shortening it, the driven element length can be adjusted for resonance in the most-used portion of the band.

A gamma match can be used at the feed point of the driven element to match the impedance to that of coaxial cable. Because the loop's feed point impedance is *higher* than that of 50 Ω coaxial cable, a *synchronous transmission line transformer* or *Q-section* (see the **Transmission Lines** chapter) with an impedance intermediate to that of the loop and the coaxial cable can be used.

Project: Five-Band, Two-Element HF Quad

Two multi-band quad designs covering 20 through 10 meters are described in this project. One was constructed by William A. Stein, KC6T, from scratch, and the other was built by Al Doig, W6NBH, using modified commercial triband quad hardware. The principles of construction and adjustment are the same for both models, and the performance results are also essentially identical. One of the main advantages of this design is the ease of (relatively) independent performance adjustments for each of the five bands. These quads were described by William A. Stein, KC6T, in *QST* for April 1992. Both models use 8-foot-long, 2 inch diameter booms, and conventional X-shaped spreaders (with two sides of each quad loop parallel to the ground).

Each driven element is fed separately, but running five separate feed lines to the shack would be unwieldy. A remote coax switch on the boom is used to select the feed line for each element. A gamma match or quarter-wave synchronous transmission line transformer is used to match the feed point impedance of the element to 50 Ω.

These designs can also be simplified to monoband quads by using the formulas in Figure 21.57 for loop dimensions and spacing. It is recommended to the antenna builder unfamiliar with quads that a monoband quad be attempted first in order to become acquainted with the techniques of building a quad. Once comfortable with constructing and erecting the quad, success with a multi-band design is much easier to achieve.

Complete construction details and more information about the performance of these designs are available with the downloadable supplemental content.

21.7.1 Loop Antennas

The loop antennas described in this section are continuous loops at least one wavelength in circumference and formed into open shapes with sides that are approximately equal, such as triangles, diamonds, squares, or circles. Smaller loops used for receiving purposes are discussed in the *ARRL Antenna Book*. Loops with ratios of side lengths greater than 2 or 3:1 begin to have special characteristics beyond the scope of this chapter.

A 1 λ loop can be thought of as two ½ λ dipoles with their ends connected together and pulled apart into an open shape as described above. The feed point of one dipole is replaced with a short circuit so that there is only one feed point on the antenna. As such, the current and voltage distribution around the loop is an extension of Figure 21.1. Three typical loop shapes and the current distributions on them are shown in **Figure 21.58**. Note that the current flow reverses at points ¼ λ to either side of the feed point. That means the current direction opposite the feed point is the same as at the feed point.

The maximum radiation strength of a 1 λ loop is perpendicular to the plane of the loop and minimum in the plane of the loop. If the

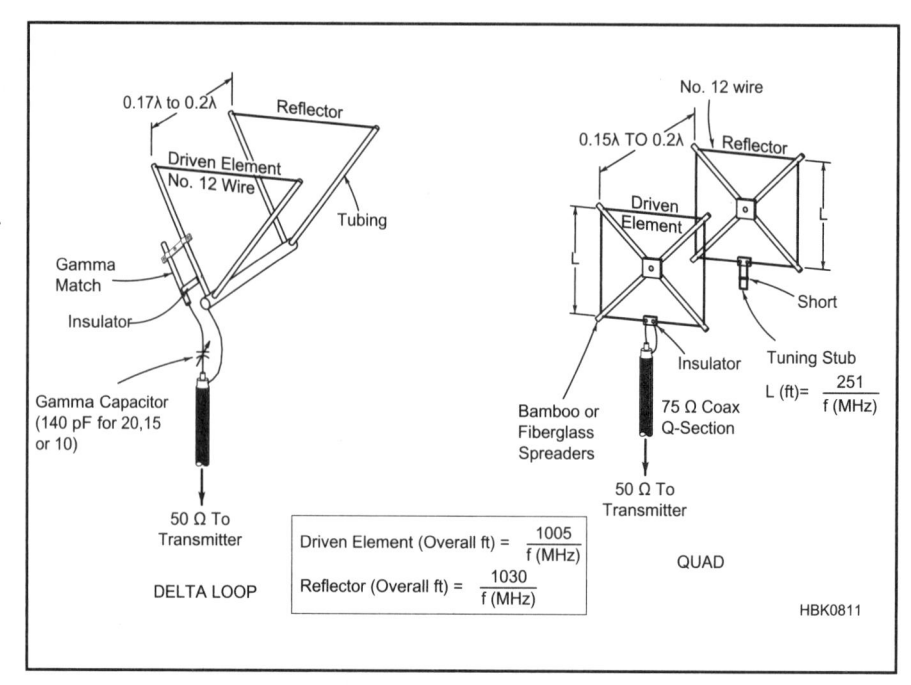

Figure 21.57 — Information on building a quad or a delta-loop antenna. The antennas are electrically similar, but the delta-loop uses plumber's delight construction. The λ/4 length of 75 Ω coax or Q-section acts as a synchronous transmission-line transformer from the approximate 100 Ω feed point impedance of the quad to the 50 Ω feed line.

$$\text{Driven Element (Overall ft)} = \frac{1005}{f \text{ (MHz)}}$$

$$\text{Reflector (Overall ft)} = \frac{1030}{f \text{ (MHz)}}$$

$$L \text{ (ft)} = \frac{251}{f \text{ (MHz)}}$$

loop is horizontal, the antenna radiates best straight up and straight down and poorly to the sides. The gain of a 1 λ loop in the direction of maximum radiation is approximately 1 dBd.

If the plane of the three loops shown in Figure 21.58 is vertical, the radiation is horizontally polarized because the fields radiated by the vertical components of current are symmetrical and opposing, so they cancel, leaving only the horizontally polarized fields that reinforce each other perpendicular to the loop plane. If the feed point of the antenna is moved to a vertical side or the antenna is rotated 90°, it is the horizontally polarized fields that will cancel, leaving a vertically polarized field, still maximum perpendicular to the plane of the loop. Feeding the loop at some other location, rotating the loop by some intermediate value, or constructing the loop in an asymmetrical shape will result in polarization somewhere between vertical and horizontal, but the maximum radiation will still occur perpendicular to the plane of the loop.

In contrast to straight-wire antennas, the electrical length of the circumference of a 1 λ loop is shorter than the actual length. For a loop made of bare #18 AWG wire and operating at a frequency of 14 MHz, so that the length-to-diameter ratio is very large, the loop will be close to resonance in free space when:

Length (feet) = 1032/f (MHz)   (7)

The radiation resistance of a resonant 1 λ loop is approximately 120 Ω under these conditions. Since the loop dimensions are larger than those of a ½ λ dipole, the radiation efficiency is high and the SWR bandwidth of the antenna significantly larger than for the dipole.

The loop antenna is resonant on all frequencies at which it is an integral number of wavelengths in circumference; f_0, $2f_0$, $3f_0$, etc. That means an 80 meter 1 λ loop will also have a relatively low feed point impedance on 40, 30, 20, 15, 12, and 10 meters. As each side of the loop becomes longer electrically, the radiation pattern of the loop begins to develop nulls perpendicular to the plane of the loop and lobes that are closer to the plane of the loop. A horizontal diamond-shaped loop with legs more than a wavelength long is a *rhombic* antenna and can develop significant gain along the long axis of the antenna. (The diamond-shaped rhombic is the origin of the symbol of the ARRL and many other radio organizations.)

Project: Low-Band Quad and Delta Loops

(The following material is summarized from Chapter 10 of *ON4UN's Low-Band DXing, Fifth Edition.*) Dimensions for these designs assume an operating frequency of 3.75 MHz. The dimensions for the loops in this section may be scaled to frequencies in the 160, 60, 40 or 30 meter bands. The performance of the loops will vary with height above ground and ground conductivity.

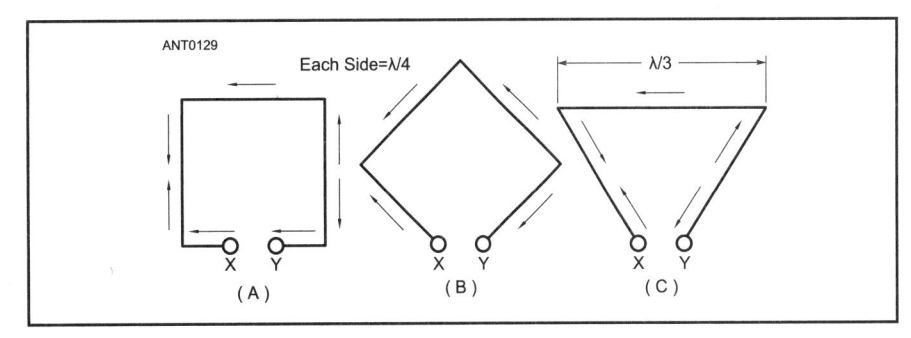

Figure 21.58 — At A and B, loops have sides ¼ λ long, and at C having sides ⅓ λ long for a total conductor length of 1 λ. The polarization depends on the orientation of the loop and on the position of the feed point (terminals X-Y) around the perimeter of the loop.

SQUARE LOOP

Figure 21.59 shows the vertical-plane radiation patterns for a quad loop over very poor ground and over very good ground on the same dB scale for both horizontal and vertical polarization. Polarization of the loop

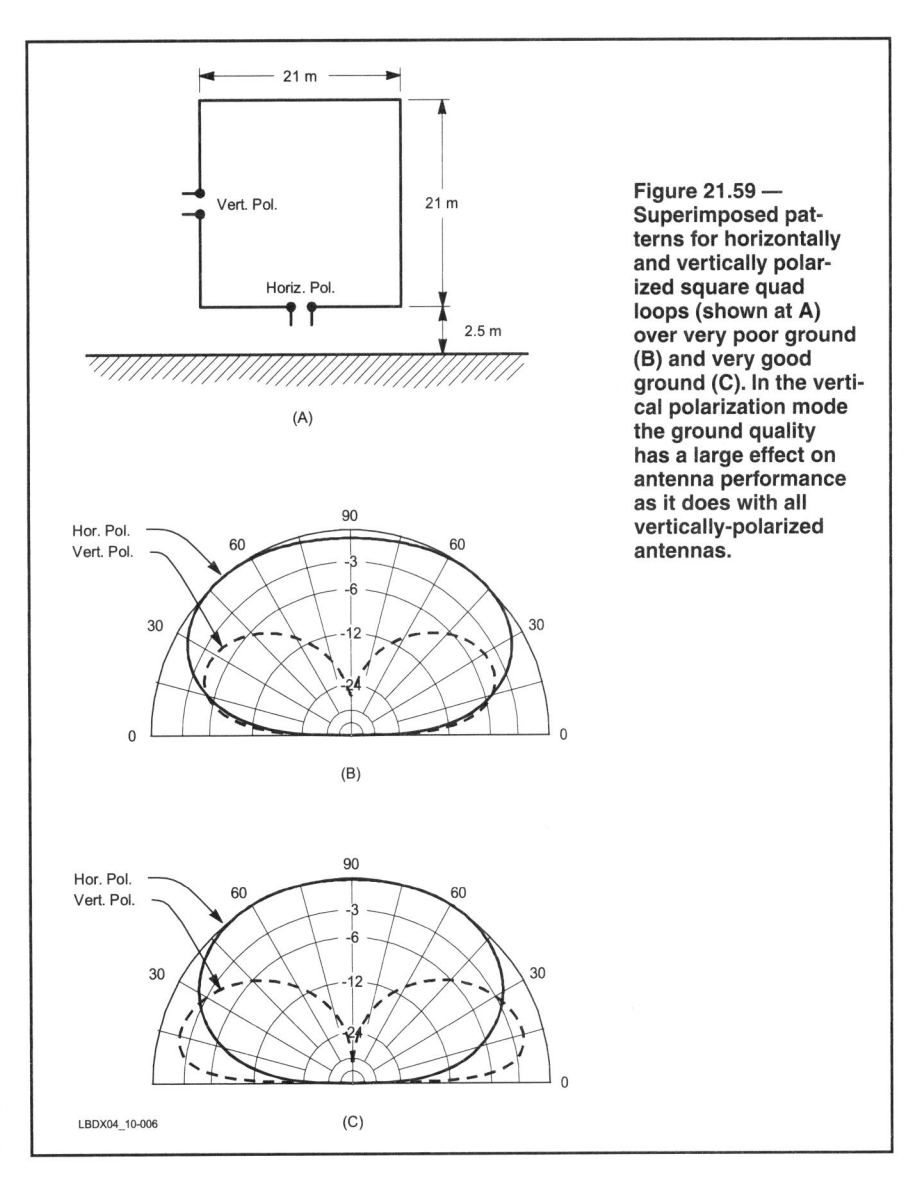

Figure 21.59 — Superimposed patterns for horizontally and vertically polarized square quad loops (shown at A) over very poor ground (B) and very good ground (C). In the vertical polarization mode the ground quality has a large effect on antenna performance as it does with all vertically-polarized antennas.

depends on the location of the feed point as shown in the figure.

The vertically polarized quad loop can be considered as two shortened top-loaded vertical dipoles, spaced ¼ λ apart. Broadside radiation from the horizontal elements of the quad is very low because the currents in the horizontal legs are approximately equal but in opposite directions in each half of the leg. The radiation angle in the broadside direction will be essentially the same as for either of the vertical members.

The resulting radiation angle will depend on the quality of the ground up to several wavelengths away from the antenna, as is the case with all vertically polarized antennas. The quality of the ground is as important as it is for any other vertical antenna, meaning that vertically polarized loops close to the ground will not work well over poor soil. In a typical situation on 80 meters, a vertically-polarized quad loop will radiate an excellent low-angle signal (lobe peak at approximately 21°) when operated over average ground. Over poorer ground, the peak elevation angle would be closer to 30°. The horizontal directivity is rather poor and amounts to approximately 3.3 dB of side rejection at any elevation angle.

A horizontally polarized quad-loop antenna can be thought of as two stacked short dipoles with a peak elevation angle dependent on the height of the loop. The low horizontally polarized quad (top at 0.3 λ) radiates most of its energy right at or near zenith angle (straight up). At low wave angles (20° to 45°) the horizontally polarized loop shows more front-to-side ratio (5 to 10 dB) than the vertically polarized rectangular loop.

With a horizontally polarized quad loop the angle of peak radiation is very dependent on the antenna height but not so much on the quality of the ground. At very low heights, the angle of peak radiation varies between 50° and 60° (but is rather constant all the way up to 90°). This is very good for NVIS and regional communication but not very good for DX. As far as gain is concerned, there is a 2.5-dB gain difference between very good and very poor ground, which is only half the difference found with the vertically polarized loop.

Comparing the gains of the horizontally and vertically polarized loops, Figure 21.59 shows that at very low antenna heights the gain is about 3 dB better for the horizontally polarized loop. But this gain exists at a high wave angle (50° to 90°) while the vertically polarized loop at very low heights radiates at 17° to 25°.

At heights from 3 to 6 meters for the bottom leg, feed point resistance for the horizontally polarized loop is approximately 100 to 120 Ω over average ground. For vertical polarization, feed point resistance varies from 200 to 170 Ω.

The quad loop feed point should be symmetrical, whether you feed the quad in the middle of the vertical or the horizontal wire. At the feed point, use a common-mode choke balun (see the **Transmission Lines** chapter) as current flowing on the outside of the coaxial feed line could upset the radiation pattern.

DELTA LOOP

Figure 21.60 shows the configuration as well as the superimposed elevation patterns for vertically and horizontally polarized low-height equilateral triangle delta loops over two different types of ground (same dB scale). The model was constructed for a frequency of 3.75 MHz. The base is 2.5 meters above ground, which puts the apex at 26.8 meters. Over good ground, the vertically polarized delta loop shows nearly 3 dB front-to-side ratio at the peak radiation angle of 22°. With average ground the gain is 1.3 dBi.

Over very poor ground, the horizontally polarized delta loop is better than the vertically polarized loop for all wave angles above 35°. Below 35° the vertically polarized loop takes over, but quite marginally. The maximum gain of the vertically and the horizontally polarized loops differs by only 2 dB but the big difference is that for the horizontally polarized loop, the gain occurs at almost 90°, while for the vertically polarized loop it occurs at 25°. The vertically polarized antenna also gives good high-angle rejection (rejection of local signals), while the horizontally polarized loop will not.

Over very good ground, the performance at low angles is greatly improved for both polarizations. The vertically polarized loop is still better at any elevation angle under 30° than when horizontally polarized. At a 10° radiation angle the difference is as high as 10 dB. This makes the vertically polarized delta over good ground far superior for DX operating.

Most practical delta loops show a feed point impedance between 50 and 100 Ω, depending on the exact geometry and coupling to other antennas. The antenna can be fed directly with a 50 or 70 Ω coaxial cable, or via a 70 Ω quarter-wave transformer (see the **Transmission Lines** chapter) if the feed point impedance is near 100 Ω. At the feed point, use a common-mode choke balun (see the **Transmission Lines** chapter) as current flowing on the outside of the coaxial feed line could upset the radiation pattern.

THE BOTTOM-CORNER-FED DELTA LOOP

Figure 21.61 shows the layout of the delta loop being fed at one of the two bottom corners. The antenna is slightly compressed from the previous section with a slightly lower apex and longer base than the loop described in the previous section. Because of the "incorrect" location of the feed point, cancellation of radiation from the base wire is incomplete, resulting in a significant horizontally polarized radiation component. The total field has a very uniform gain coverage (within 1 dB) from 25° to 90°. This may be a disadvantage for the rejection of high-angle signals when working DX at low angles.

Due to the feed point location, the end-fire radiation (radiation in line with the loop) has become asymmetrical with a side null of nearly 12 dB at the peak radiation angle of 29°. The loop actually radiates its maximum signal about 18° off the broadside direction. This feed point configuration greatly affects the pattern of the loop so use bottom-corner-feed with care.

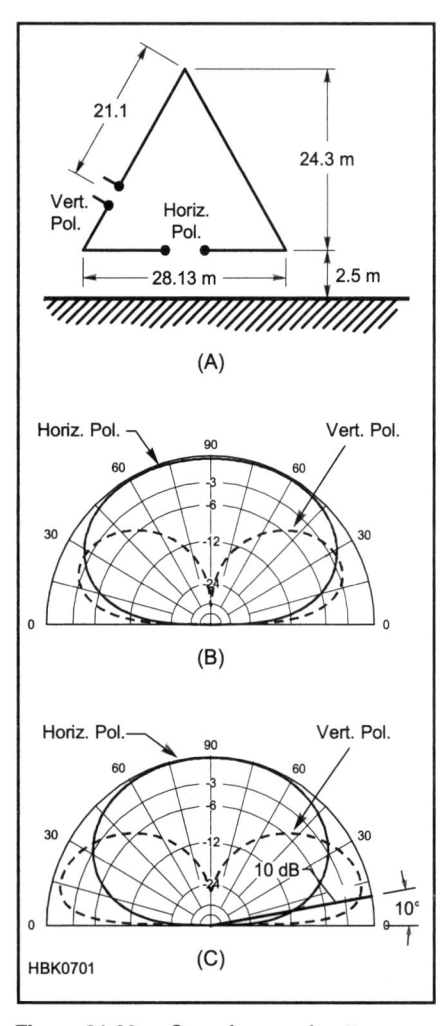

Figure 21.60 — Superimposed patterns for horizontally and vertically polarized delta quad loops (shown at A) over very poor ground (B) and very good ground (C). Over better ground, the vertically polarized loop performs much better at low radiation angles, while over both good and poor ground the vertically polarized loop gives good discrimination against high-angle local signals.

Project: Two-Band Loop for 30 and 40 Meters

The following antenna design is from a *QST* Hints and Kinks entry by James Brenner, NT4B, in the May 1989 issue. The version shown in **Figure 21.62** is fed at the apex of a delta loop but can be adapted to a square or quad loop shape.

The original design was derived from "The Mini X-Q Loop" in *All About Cubical Quad Antennas* by Bill Orr, W6SAI (now out of print) which is 1½ λ in circumference, with an open circuit opposite the feed point. That antenna has approximately 1 dB of additional gain over a 1 λ loop. Since 30 and 40 meters are close to the same 1:1½ λ ratio, one loop can be converted between 1 λ on 40 meters and 1½ λ on 30 meters with a switch.

A large, ceramic SPST knife switch is installed in the center of the delta loop's bottom leg as shown in Figure 21.62. With the switch open, the loop acts a 1½ λ loop at 10.5 MHz, so 18 inch wires were added to the loop on either side of the switch to lengthen the antenna and lower the resonant frequency to 10.1 MHz. Closing the switch shorts out the wires and the loop becomes a regular 1 λ continuous loop for 40 meters.

Note that there is fairly high voltage present at the switch when transmitting on 30 meters. If a relay is used, be sure the contact spacing is sufficient to avoid arcing or use additional pairs of contacts to increase the overall spacing.

The antenna is fed through a quarter-wave transformer (see the **Transmission Lines** chapter) of 75 Ω RG-11 coax, approximately 23 feet long. According to the author, when configured for 40 meters, the loop has a satisfactory SWR of less than 2:1 on 15 meters. In addition, the 30 meter configuration can be used successfully on 80 meters with the use of an antenna tuner.

Figure 21.61 — Configuration and radiation patterns for the delta loop when fed in one of the bottom corners at a frequency of 3.75 MHz. Incomplete cancellation of radiation from the horizontal wire produces a strong high-angle horizontally polarized component. The antenna also shows horizontal directivity that varies strongly with vertical radiation angle.

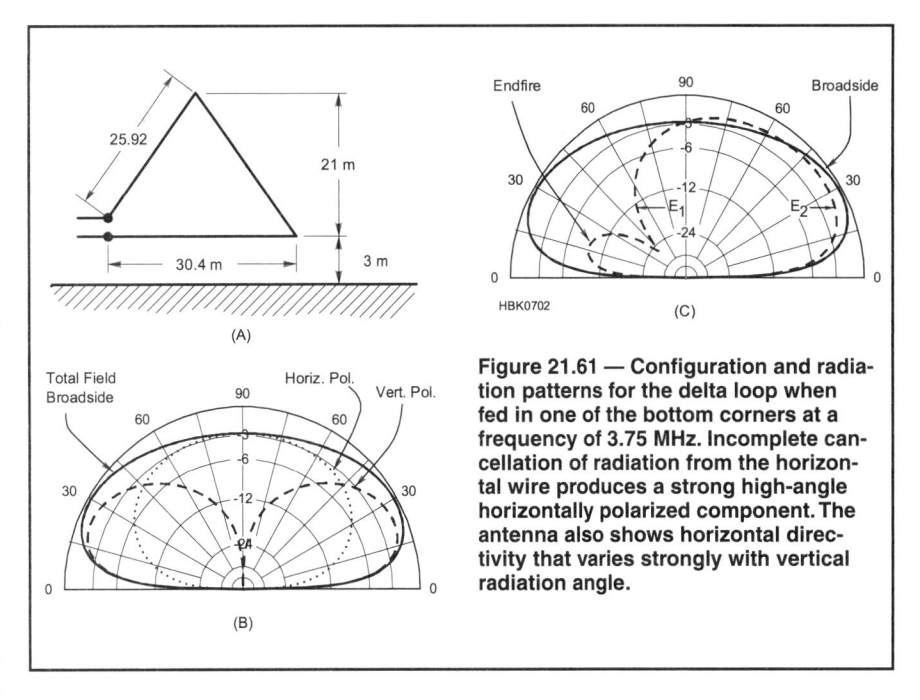

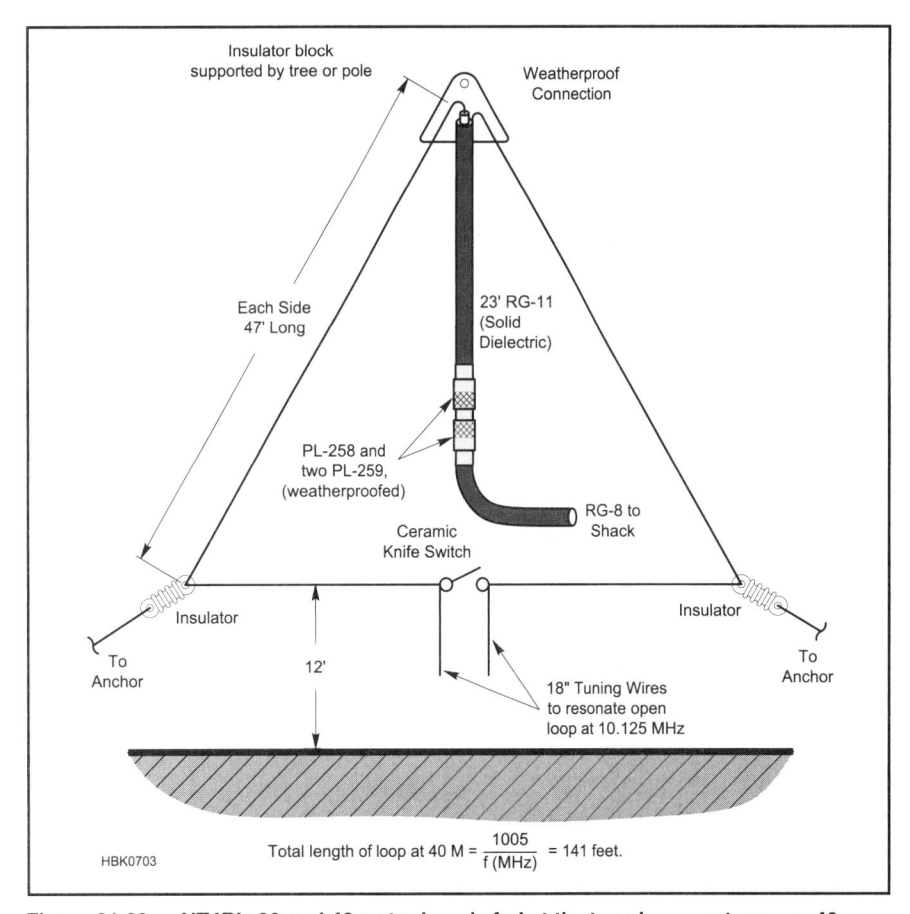

Total length of loop at 40 M = $\frac{1005}{f (MHz)}$ = 141 feet.

Figure 21.62 — NT4B's 30 and 40 meter loop is fed at the top via a quarter-wave 40 meter matching transformer made of 75 Ω coax. Note the 18 inch tuning wires used to lower the antenna's 30 meter resonance from 10.5 to 10.1 MHz. Adjust the length of these wires to set the 30 meter resonant frequency.

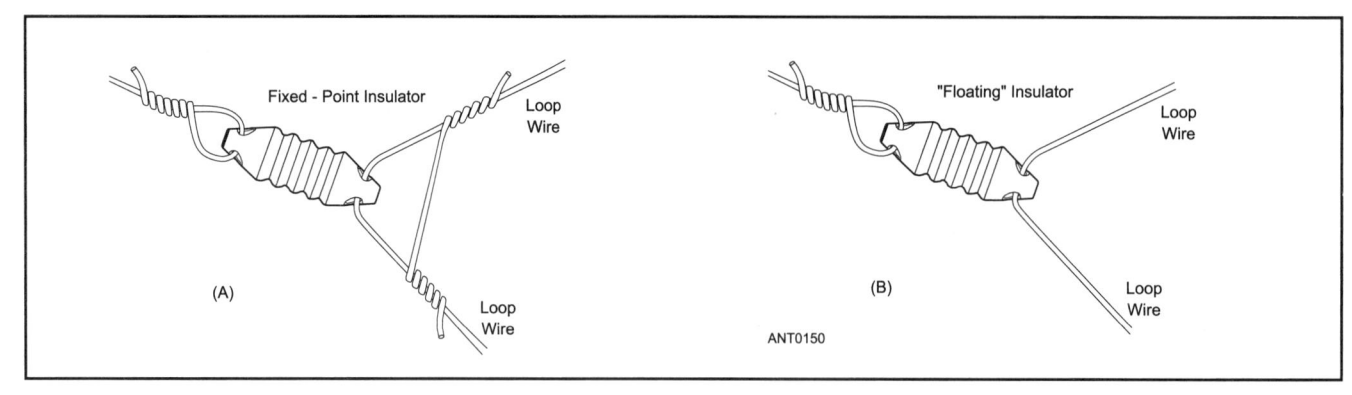

Figure 21.63 — Two methods of installing the insulators at the loop corners.

Project: Multiband Horizontal Loop Antenna

Along with the multiband, non-resonant dipole, many amateurs operate on HF with great success using a horizontal loop antenna. All that is required are at least three supports able to hold the corners of the antenna 20 or more feet above the ground (and even that is negotiable) and enough room for a loop of wire one wavelength or more in circumference at the lowest frequency of operation. (Smaller loops can be used with an impedance-matching unit.)

Start by calculating the total length of wire using Equation 7. You'll need one insulator for each support and lengths of rope that are at least twice the height to which the insulator will be raised. You can feed the antenna at one of the corner insulators or anywhere along the wire with a separate insulator. Examples of corner insulators are shown in **Figure 21.63**. Using floating insulators allows the wire to move as the antenna flexes. One of the insulators should be of the fixed type, or the antenna can be fed at one corner with the loop wires attached to a pair of insulators sharing a common support rope. This holds the antenna feed point in place.

If the loop is only going to be used on the band for which it is resonant, coaxial cable can be used as the feed line, since SWR will be low. A choke balun at the feed point is recommended. For multiband use, open-wire feed line should be used, with an impedance-matching unit in the shack. See Figure 21.15 for an example of how open-wire line can be attached at the feed point.

On its fundamental frequency, the antenna's maximum radiation will be straight up, making it most useful for regional communications at high elevation angles with the occasional DX contact. At higher frequencies, the loop will radiate more strongly at lower angles for better signal strengths at long distances. An example design is shown in **Figure 21.64**.

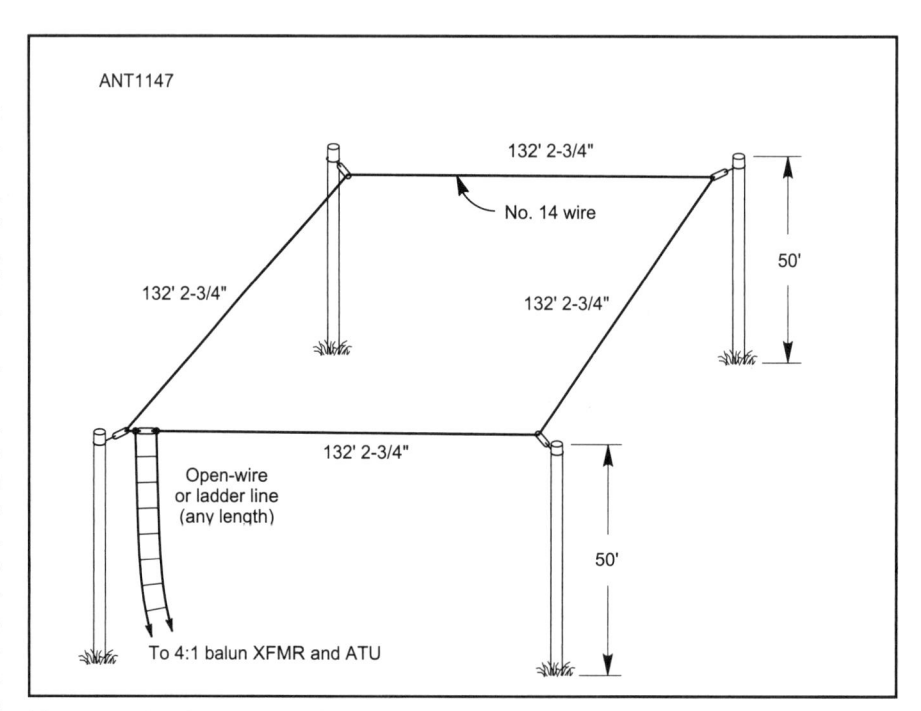

Figure 21.64 — An example of a horizontal full-wave loop designed for 1.9 MHz. The antenna can be fed with any length of open-wire or ladder line form 300 to 600 Ω. The loop is usable on all HF bands..

21.8 HF Mobile Antennas

HF mobile operation has been part of Amateur Radio since the 1930s. Mobile operation has become very popular with advances in antenna design and excellent mobile radios. Material in this section was contributed and updated by Alan Applegate, KØBG, whose website (**www.k0bg.com**) has many useful pages on HF mobile stations and operating.

High frequency (HF) mobile antennas come in every size and shape imaginable, from simple whips to elaborate, computer-controlled behemoths. Regardless of the type and construction, an HF mobile antenna should have a few important attributes.

• Sturdiness: It should be permanently mounted (without altering the vehicle's safety equipment) to stay upright at highway speeds with a minimum of sway.

• Mechanically stable: Sudden stops or sharp turns won't cause it to sway about, endangering others.

• Flexibly mounted: Permits bending around branches and obstacles at low speeds.

• Weatherproof: Withstands the effects of wind, rain, snow and ice.

• Tunable: If multiband operation is desired, be tunable to different HF bands without stopping the vehicle.

• Be easily removable when required.

• Be as efficient as possible.

Of all the antenna choices available, the *whip* antenna — a self-supporting rod or wire mounted at its base — has passed the test of time as providing all of these attributes in one way or another. The following sections discuss the different types of whips, how they are attached to and interact with the vehicle, and how they are connected to the transmitter.

21.8.1 Simple Whips

The simplest of antennas is a quarter-wave whip, but it's only practical on the upper HF bands because of the required length. For example, a 10 meter quarter-wavelength antenna is about 8 feet long. It doesn't require a loading coil, so its efficiency is approximately 80%. The reason efficiency isn't 100% is because of resistive losses in the whip itself, stray capacitance losses in the mounting hardware and ground losses, which we'll cover later. The end result is that the feed point impedance at the antenna's base is very close to 50 Ω.

As we move lower in frequency, the physical length must increase for an equivalent electrical length, but there is a limit. In most localities, the maximum height at the tip of the antenna needs to be less than 13.5 feet (4.1 meters). This generally limits whip length to 10.5 feet (3.2 meters) for an average installation on a vehicle. Creating a resonant antenna below this length on 10 or 12 meters isn't a problem. On the 15 meter and lower frequency bands, 10.5 feet is not long enough for a resonant whip antenna and additional electrical measures are required.

WHIP RADIATION RESISTANCE

The power radiated by the antenna is equal to the radiation resistance times the square of the antenna current. The radiation resistance, R_r, of an electrically small antenna is given by:

$$R_r = 395 \times \left(\frac{h}{\lambda}\right)^2 \qquad (8)$$

where
 h = radiator height in meters
 λ = wavelength in meters = 300 / f in MHz

Since radiation resistance of these electrically small antennas is a function of height, the antenna must be lengthened physically or electrically to increase it. Increasing radiation resistance improves efficiency as shown next.

The efficiency of the antenna, η, equals the radiation resistance, R_r, divided by the resistive component of the feed point impedance, R_{fp}, which for actual antennas includes ground losses and losses in the antenna:

$$\eta = \frac{R_r}{R_{fp}} \times 100\% \qquad (9)$$

Since an electrically short antenna has a low radiation resistance, careful attention must be paid to minimizing losses in the antenna system that can greatly reduce the antenna's effectiveness.

WHIP CAPACITANCE

As we shorten an antenna to less than ¼ λ, its radiation resistance decreases and the capacitance drops as shown in **Table 21.11**. **Figure 21.65** shows that capacitance is not very

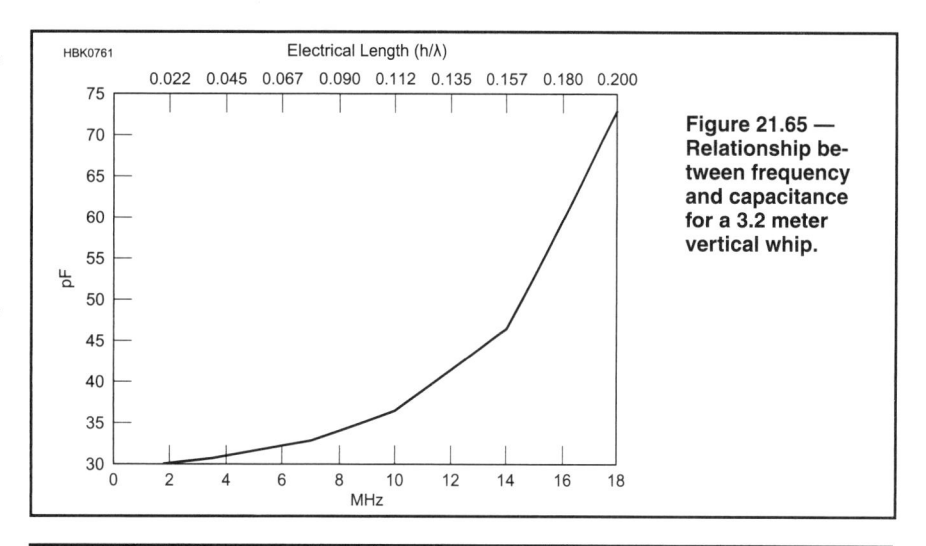

Figure 21.65 — Relationship between frequency and capacitance for a 3.2 meter vertical whip.

Table 21.11
Characteristics of an 8 foot Mobile Whip

f(MHz)	Loading L μH	R_C(Q50) Ω	R_C(Q300) Ω	R_r Ω	Feed R* Ω	Matching L μH
Base Loading						
1.8	345	77	13	0.1	23	3
3.8	77	37	6.1	0.35	16	1.2
7.2	20	18	3	1.35	15	0.6
10.1	9.5	12	2	2.8	12	0.4
14.2	4.5	7.7	1.3	5.7	12	0.28
18.1	3.0	5.0	1.0	10.0	14	0.28
21.25	1.25	3.4	0.5	14.8	16	0.28
24.9	0.9	2.6	—	20.0	22	0.25
29.0	—	—	—	—	36	0.23
Center Loading						
1.8	700	158	23	0.2	34	3.7
3.8	150	72	12	0.8	22	1.4
7.2	40	36	6	3.0	19	0.7
10.1	20	22	4.2	5.8	18	0.5
14.2	8.6	15	2.5	11.0	19	0.35
18.1	4.4	9.2	1.5	19.0	22	0.31
21.25	2.5	6.6	1.1	27.0	29	0.29

R_C = loading coil resistance; R_r = radiation resistance.
*Assuming loading coil Q = 300, and including estimated ground-loss resistance.

sensitive to frequency for h/λ less than 0.075.

The capacitance in pF of an electrically small antenna is given approximately by:

$$C = \frac{55.78 \times h}{[(den1) \times (den2)]} \quad (10)$$

where
(den1) = (ln (h/r) – 1)
(den2) = [1 – (f × h/75)^2]
ln = natural logarithm
r = conductor radius in meters
f = frequency in MHz

Radiation resistance rises in a nonlinear fashion and the capacitance drops just as dramatically with increase in the ratio h/λ. Figure 21.65 can be used for estimating antenna capacitance for other heights and shows that capacitance is not very sensitive to frequency for h/λ less than 0.075 which occurs at 8 MHz in this case.

21.8.2 Coil-Loaded Whips

To bring an electrically-short whip antenna to resonance, we must add inductance in the form of a loading coil. The coil can take many forms, and it may be placed almost anywhere along the length of the radiating element. It cancels out the capacitive reactance by introducing an equal but opposite inductive reactance. Some coils are mounted at the base of the mast — a base-loaded antenna — and some are mounted near the center (center-loaded) or the top (top-loaded).

As the coil is moved higher, the radiation resistance increases (a good thing), but the necessary coil reactance also increases as do resistive losses in the coil. Therefore it becomes a balancing act, which requires a thorough understanding of the parameters involved, to choose the optimal coil location.

Table 21.11 lists the characteristics of an 8 foot (2.4 meter) mobile whip in both base-loaded and center-loaded configurations. The table shows the required loading coil inductance to bring the antenna to resonance on the different bands. The matching coil inductance is placed across the feed point to bring the impedance to 50 Ω.

Note that center-loading approximately doubles both the required inductance and the coil's resistive losses. The radiation resistance also increases, but only in that part of the antenna above the loading coil. If ground losses are included in the calculations, the coil's optimal position changes, but it is typically close to the center of the antenna.

It is important to note that the total amount of stray capacitance from the mounting hardware and proximity of the whip to the vehicle may be much higher depending on where and how the antenna is mounted. The higher the stray capacitance, the less efficient the antenna will be.

Table 21.12 compares different types of HF mobile antennas against an unloaded whip antenna. The simple whip is assumed to be a full-size ¼ wavelength. The effects of mounting are not included.

LOADING COIL Q

Antenna system Q is limited by the Q of the coil. The bandwidth between 2:1 SWR points of the system = 0.36 × f/Q. On 80 meters, the bandwidth of the 10.5 foot whip = 0.36 × 3.5/200 = 6.3 kHz. If we could double the Q of the coil, the efficiency would double and the bandwidth would be halved. The converse is also true. In the interest of efficiency, the highest possible Q should be used!

Loading coil Q is especially important on the lower HF bands where coil losses can exceed ground losses. The factors involved include wire size, wire spacing, length-to-diameter ratio and the materials used in constructing the coil. All of the factors interact with one another, making coil design a compromise — especially when wind loading and weight become major considerations.

In general — the larger the coil, the higher the Q. The more mass within the field of the coil (metal end caps for example) the lower the Q. Short, fat coils are better than long, skinny ones. However, the coil's length-to-diameter ratio (L/D) for the highest Q increases as the inductance increases. It ranges from 1:1 on the upper HF bands to as much as 4:1 on the lower bands where the inductance is large. Practical mechanical considerations for coils with large reactance values above 1000 Ω (160 meter coils for example) require the length-to-diameter ratio to increase, which lowers Q. **Table 21.13** suggests loading coil dimensions that maximize Q.

Another significant factor arises from high Q. Let's assume that we deliver 100 W on 80 meters to the 7.43 Ω at the antenna terminals. The current is 3.67 A and flows through the 1375 Ω reactance of the coil giving rise to 1375 × 3.67 = 5046 V$_{RMS}$ (7137 V$_{peak}$) across the coil! This is a significant voltage and may cause arcing if the coil is wet or dirty.

With only 30.6 pF of antenna capacitance, the presence of significant stray capacitance at the antenna base shunts currents away from the antenna. RG-58 coax presents about 21 pF/foot. A 1.5 foot length of RG-58 would halve the radiation efficiency of our example antenna. For cases like the whip at 3.5 MHz, the matching network has to be right at the antenna!

21.8.3 Base vs Center vs Continuous Loading

There are a few important aspects to be kept in mind when selecting or building an HF mobile antenna. As the antenna becomes longer, less loading inductance is required and the coil Q can become higher, improving efficiency. Also, for longer antennas, the better the mounting location has to be in order to optimize efficiency. We'll cover mounting and efficiency later. (See the section on Physically Short Verticals earlier in this chapter for more on loading vertical antennas.)

Placing the loading coil at the base results in the current distribution shown in **Figure 21.66A**. If we move the coil to the center, the current curve looks like the one in Figure 21.66B. The location of the optimal position between the two extremes depends on the ground losses, and to a lesser degree on loading coil Q and overall length. For

Table 21.12
HF Mobile Antenna Comparison

Antenna Type	Length	Frequency Coverage	Efficiency	Mounting Difficulty	Matching Required
Simple Whip	< 11 ft	15 m & up	Excellent	Easy	No
Base-Loaded	9 to 10.6 ft	160 - 6 m	Fair to good	Average	Yes
Center-Loaded	9 to 10.5 ft	160 - 6 m	Good to excellent	Average	Yes
Top-Loaded	<9 ft	160 - 6 m	Fair	Average	No
Continuous Loading	< 7 feet	80 - 6 m	Poor to fair	Easy	No
Remote-tuned Small	< 7 feet	80 - 6 m	Poor to fair	Easy	No
Remote-tuned Large	9 to 10.5 ft	160 - 6 m	Excellent	Difficult	Yes

Table 21.13
Suggested Loading Coil Dimensions

Req'd L (µH)	Turns	Wire Size	Dia. (Inches)	Length (Inches)
700	190	22	3	10
345	135	18	3	10
150	100	16	2½	10
77	75	14	2½	10
77	29	12	5	4¼
40	28	16	2½	2
40	34	12	2½	4¼
20	17	16	2½	4¼
20	22	12	2½	2¾
8.6	16	14	2	2
8.6	15	12	2½	3
4.5	10	14	2	1¼
4.5	12	12	2½	4
2.5	8	12	2	2
2.5	8	6	2⅜	4½
1.25	6	12	1¾	2
1.25	6	6	2⅜	4½

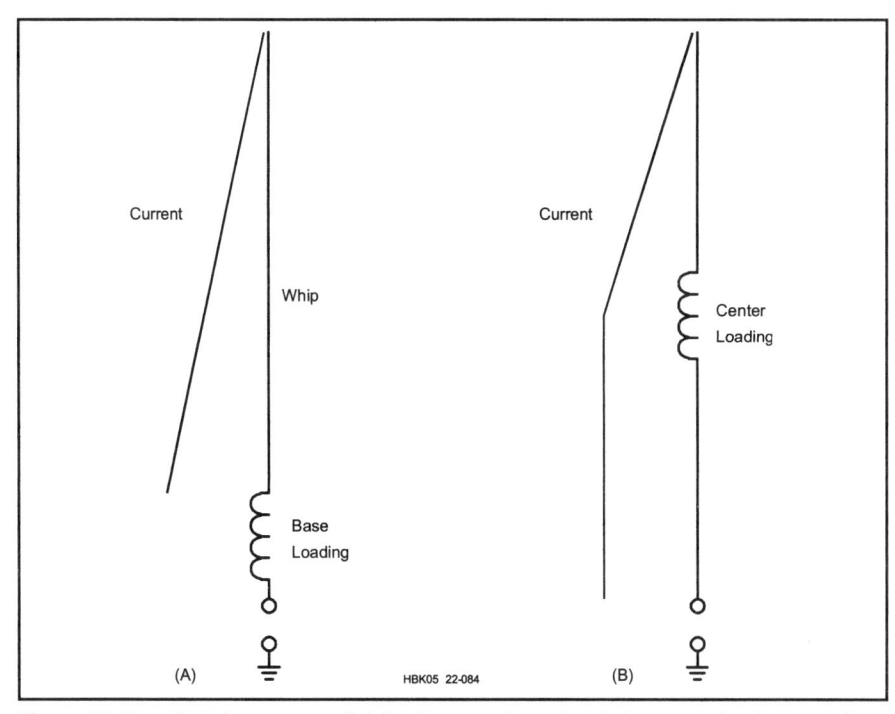

Figure 21.66 — Relative current distribution on a base-loaded antenna is shown at A and for a center-loaded antenna at B.

example, if the ground losses were zero, the best position would be at the bottom. As the ground losses increase, the optimal position gets closer to the center. If the ground losses are high enough, the optimal position is in the top one-third of the antenna's length, but efficiency is very poor.

Center-loading increases the current in the lower half of the whip as shown in Figure 21.66B. Capacitance for the section above the coil can be calculated just as for the base-loaded antenna. This permits calculation of the loading inductance. The center-loaded antenna is often operated without any base matching in which case the resistive component can be assumed to be 50 Ω for purposes of calculating the current rating and selecting wire size for the inductor. The reduced size of the top section results in reduced capacitance which requires a much larger loading inductor.

Because of the high value of inductance required for center-loading, high-Q coils are very large. The large wind resistance necessitates a very sturdy mount for operation at highway speed. One manufacturer of this type of coil does not recommend their use in rain or inclement weather. The higher Q of these large coils results in a lower feed point impedance, necessitating the use of a base matching element in the form of either a tapped inductor or a shunt capacitor to match to 50 Ω. (See this chapter's section on Mobile HF Antenna Matching.) Another manufacturer places the coil above the center and uses a small extendable whip or wand for tuning.

Antennas known by the trade name "Hamsticks" shown in **Figure 21.67** aren't really continuously-loaded. Instead, a small diameter enameled wire loosely wound around a fiberglass tube forms the base section of the antenna. Approximately half way up the antenna, the wire is close wound to form a lumped-element loading coil and a metal whip or stinger is attached at the top to complete the whip. A heat-shrink sleeve covers the wound section of the antenna. The stinger's length can be adjusted to tune the antenna to the desired operating frequency.

In recent years, these lightweight antennas have become very popular. Their input impedance is near 50 Ω in part because of their low-Q base and loading coil sections. Thus they don't require matching once the length of the top whip or stinger is adjusted. They are light in weight (about a pound), short in length (typically 6 to 8 feet) and thus easy to mount. For temporary use, easy mounting may be more important than high efficiency. This type of antenna is most effective on 20 meters and higher frequency bands.

The wound base section of these antennas is a very weak radiator, acting more like a transmission line or distributed element than a linear radiating element. The long and thin coil has low Q, as well, increasing antenna loss. The close-wound section acts like a lumped element and does not radiate.

21.8.4 Top-Loaded Whips

In the interests of efficiency, electrical

Figure 21.67 — Continuously-loaded whip antennas are short and lightweight. The base section consists of a fiberglass tube wound with wire to form the loading inductor. At the top of the base section the length of a steel whip or stinger can be adjusted to bring the antenna to resonance. [Joel Hallas, W1ZR, photo]

length matters because radiation resistance increases as the square of electrical length. Higher radiation resistance in a mobile antenna results in higher efficiency. All else being equal, a 12 foot antenna will have 4 times the radiation resistance than one 6 feet long. As pointed out above, the maximum physical height should be less than 13.5 feet

Designing a Base Loading System

This design procedure was contributed by Jack Kuecken, KE2QJ. To begin, estimate the capacitance, capacitive reactance and radiation resistance as shown at the beginning of this section. Then calculate the expected loss resistance of the loading coil required to resonate the antenna. There is generally additional resistance amounting to about half of the coil loss which must be added in. As a practical matter, it is usually not possible to achieve a coil Q in excess of 200 for such applications.

Using the radiation resistance plus 1.5 times the coil loss and the power rating desired for the antenna, one may select the wire size. For high efficiency coils, a current density of 1000 A/inch^2 is a good compromise. For the 3.67 A of the example we need a wire 0.068 inch diameter, which roughly corresponds to #14 AWG. Higher current densities can lead to a melted coil.

Design the coil with a pitch equal to twice the wire diameter and the coil diameter approximately equal to the coil length. These proportions lead to the highest Q in air core coils.

The circuit of **Figure 21.A4** will match essentially all practical HF antennas on a car or truck. The circuit actually matches the antenna to 12.5 Ω and the transformer boosts it up to 50 Ω. Actual losses alter the required values of both the shunt inductor and the series capacitor. At a frequency of 3.5 MHz with an antenna impedance of 0.55 –j1375 Ω and a base capacitance of 2 pF results in the values shown in **Table 21.B.** Inductor and capacitor values are highly sensitive to coil Q.

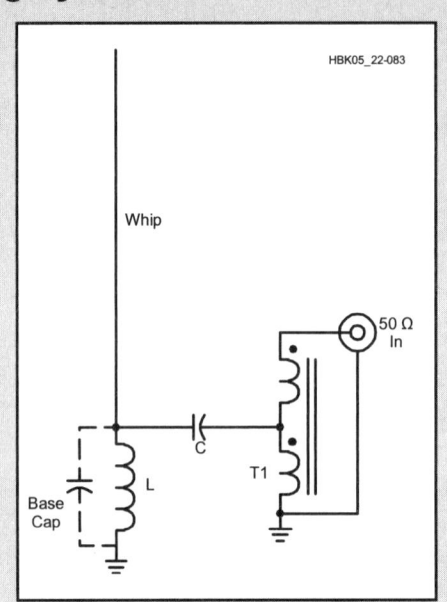

Figure 21.A4 — The base-matched mobile whip antenna

Table 21.B
Values of L and C for the Circuit of Figure 21.A4 on 3.5 MHz

Coil Q	L (µH)	C (pF)	System Efficiency (%)
300	44	11.9	8.3
200	29.14	35	3.72
100	22.2	58.1	1.4

Furthermore, the inductor values are considerably below the 62.5 µH required to resonate the antenna.

This circuit has the advantage that the tuning elements are all at the base of the antenna. The whip radiator itself has minimal mass and wind resistance. In addition, the rig is protected by the fact that there is a dc ground on the radiator so any accidental discharge or electrical contact is kept out of the cable and rig. Variable tuning elements allow the antenna to be tuned to other frequencies.

Connect the antenna, L and C. Start with less inductor than required to resonate the antenna. Tune the capacitor to minimum SWR. Increase the inductance and tune for minimum SWR. When the values of L and C are right, the SWR will be 1:1.

(4.1 meters). As discussed in this chapter's section on Physically Short Antennas, one way to increase the electrical length but not the physical length, is top-loading. A mobile HF antenna is top-loaded by using a *capacitance hat* or "cap hat."

As their name implies, cap hats add capacitance at the top of the antenna, above any loading coil. This increases radiation resistance by as much as four times under ideal conditions, but at the expense of increased weight, wind loading and complexity. Not all antennas, especially small screwdriver types, are sturdy enough to support a large cap hat. For those that are, or if the antenna can be guyed or stiffened, cap hats offer increased efficiency and bandwidth.

The actual placement of the cap hat is important, too. If mounted too close to the loading coil, efficiency is lower than with no cap hat at all. Thus, the best mounting location is at the very top of the antenna.

The physical design of the cap hat is limited by practical concerns. The largest are approximately 3 feet in diameter and require additional bracing or guying of the antenna. Most are constructed of straight radial wires without an outer rim. The loop design shown in **Figure 21.68** is more efficient than straight

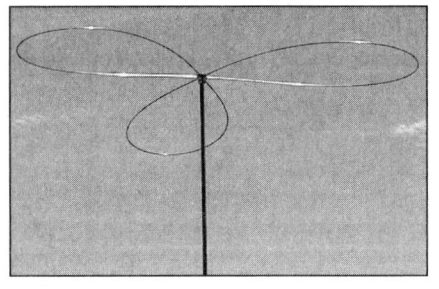

Figure 21.68 — A typical capacitance hat or "cap hat" added at the top of a mobile whip antenna. The antenna is a Scorpion (scorpionantennas.com).

wires, but tends to snag more on errant limbs. See the referenced *QEX* article by Griffith and the *QST* article by Clement for more on capacitance hats and top loading of mobile antennas.

21.8.5 Remotely Controlled HF Mobile Antennas

Remotely controlled (motorized) HF mobile antennas are commonly referred to as *screwdriver antennas*. Don Johnson, W6AAQ (SK), is credited by many as the father of the screwdriver antenna. His design was not the first motorized antenna, but he certainly popularized it. There are now over 50 commercial versions available.

They're called screwdrivers because the first examples used a stripped-down rechargeable electric screwdriver assembly to adjust the resonant frequency of the antenna. The motor turns a threaded rod in and out of a nut attached to the bottom of the coil. This in turn moves the coil in and out of the lower mast section. Contacts at the top of the mast slide on the outside of the coil, thus adjusting the resonance point. Position sensors may be used to keep track of the location of the coil tap. Nowadays, calling them screwdrivers is a bit of a misnomer as the electric screwdriver motors have been replaced with much more reliable gear motors.

There are several remotely controlled HF mobile antennas that don't change length as true screwdrivers do. Both base and center loaded models are available (see **Figure 21.69**). Whether or not they're more efficient is dependent on the factors discussed in the previous section, rather than the method used to adjust the coil.

Figure 21.69 — The screwdriver-style remotely-controlled whip antenna. A small motor in the base mast moves a coil past contacts at the top of the metal base section. The top whip section is attached to the top of the coil. As the coil moves out of the mast, more inductance is connected in series between the base section and top section. Screwdriver antennas are popular because they offer multiband coverage. [Joel Hallas, W1ZR, photo]

Determining the Radiation Efficiency of a Center Loaded Mobile Whip

We can measure the radiation efficiency by measuring ground wave field strength E (dB referenced to µV/m). For the average radio amateur, a field strength meter is not a part of his ham shack gear. We can predict performance using readily available antenna modeling software (one of the many available versions of *NEC*) provided we have a measure of actual losses.

There are a number of loss parameters we do not know. We do not know the Q factor for the center loading coil (R_L), and we do not know the ground-induced loss resistance (R_g). In fact we do not know with certainty the radiation resistance (R_r), since the antenna sees an image of itself in the ground. *NEC* only gives us the sum of the various resistances.

$$R_{as} = R_r + R_C + R_g + R_L$$

R_C, the only parameter not discussed above, is the conductor loss resistance.

We need to know R_r if we are going to compute radiation efficiency, since radiation efficiency is given by:

$$\eta = \frac{R_r}{R_{as}}$$

So what do we do? We can measure R_{as} using the SWR analyzer, by adjusting the tuning so the reactance at the base of the antenna is equal to zero. We can then use *NEC* to predict the base impedance (resistive component), by changing the Q factor of the inductor so that R_{as} predicted equals R_{as} measured. We can then predict the ground field strength (dBµV/m) at say 100 m for a transmitter power of 1 kW. We then reference this predicted field strength to that for an electrically small lossless vertical antenna (129.54 dBµV/m at 100 m for 1 kW transmitter power — which corresponds to the commonly quoted value of 300 mV/m at 1 km). This gives us a pretty good estimate of the radiation efficiency of our mobile whip. — *Jack Belrose, VE2CV*

RF CHOKES

The motors and position sensors of all remotely-controlled antennas operate above vehicle body potential. The amount of RF present on the leads depends on several factors, especially where and how the antenna is mounted and its overall (electrical) length. Thus the RF current coupled onto the leads must be minimized with an RF choke before entering the vehicle. An inadequate choke may result in erratic controller operation and possible interference with transceiver operation.

The choke should have an impedance of at least two orders of magnitude greater than the impedance of the circuit. In other words, at least 5 kΩ, and perhaps two or three times that in some cases (stubby antennas and poor mounting schemes are examples). Mix 31 ferrite split beads are ideal for this application, but it takes eight turns to obtain a 5 kΩ choking impedance. Depending on the wire size and insulation, you'll need to use the ½ or ¾ inch ID cores. Snap-on ferrite beads are available from most Amateur Radio dealers. (More information on this type of RF choke may be found in the **RF Techniques** chapter.)

The choke shown in **Figure 21.70** consists of 13 turns of #18 AWG wire, wound on a ¾ inch ID, mix 31 split bead. It has an impedance of approximately 10 kΩ at 10 MHz. When winding the chokes, try not to overlap or twist the wires as this reduces the effectiveness.

21.8.6 Ground Losses

High frequency mobile ground loss data first appeared in a 1953 issue of *QST*, in an article written by Jack Belrose, VE3BLW (now VE2CV). In the article, Belrose said that the current flowing at the base of the antenna must be returned to the base of the antenna by currents induced in the ground beneath the radiator (antenna). These currents must be collected by the car body and through the capacitance of the car body to the ground. Since the maximum dimension of car body is considerably less than a quarter wavelength on most HF bands, only a portion of these currents will be collected by the car frame itself, and the rest will be collected by ground currents flowing through the capacitance of the car to the ground. Since the ground is not lossless, quite a large loss resistance (R_g) is found.

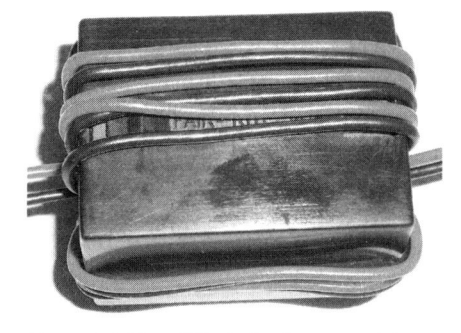

Figure 21.70 — RF choke for screwdriver antenna control and power leads.

From that article, the accepted ground loss figure for HF mobile applications varies between 12 Ω (for 80 meters) and 2 Ω (for 10 meters). However, these figures do not include stray capacitance from the mounting location and method. Stray capacitance has the same effect as ground losses: reduced efficiency. As a result, in the real world, ground losses can be double the accepted values, reducing an otherwise efficient antenna to mediocrity.

21.8.7 Antenna Mounting
PERMANENT OR TEMPORARY

There are many reasons to install any mobile antenna permanently on a vehicle. The decision to drill holes in sheet metal to mount antennas is hotly debated. While no-hole mounts can be used satisfactorily, it is best to look at all sides of the issue before installing any antenna.

A common concern about drilling a hole for an antenna mount is with regard to a leased vehicle. Leases don't necessarily preclude properly installed antenna mounting holes. What lease agreements are primarily concerned with is body damage such as from an accident or mistreatment. Properly installed NMO mounts, for example, are often acceptable. It's always prudent to ask before leasing the vehicle.

Drilled holes and waterproof mounts also help minimize common-mode current on the coaxial feed line. This helps reduce RFI to or from on-board computers and electrical devices. Aside from the hole itself, a permanent mount also minimizes damage to the finish.

Here is an important caveat to keep in mind: While the roof of a vehicle is a very good place to mount an antenna, more and more new vehicles are equipped with side curtain air bags. They typically are mounted along the edges of the headliner, including the rear seat area if there is one. The wiring to these devices is routed through any one (or more) of the roof pillars. Extra care is required when installing antennas in vehicles so equipped. If you are the least bit apprehensive about installing a roof-mounted antenna, seek professional help from your dealer or a qualified installer.

Mobile antenna mounting hardware runs the gamut from mundane to extravagant. Choosing the correct hardware is based on need, as well as on personal preference. There are too many variables with respect to mounting HF mobile antennas on modern vehicles to cover in a short discussion. It is easier to explain what not to do and adapt those guidelines to your own personal circumstances: the antenna mount should:

• Be permanently mounted;
• Be strong enough to support the antenna;
• Have as much metal area under it as possible;
• Be well-grounded to the chassis or body;
• Not interfere with doors, trunks, or access panels and
• Be removable with minimal damage to the vehicle.

Aside from maximizing performance by minimizing ground and stray capacitance losses, there are also safety reasons for using a permanent mount with HF antennas. If you need to use a temporary mount, use the multiple-magnet mounts for their superior holding strength. Any mobile HF antenna attached to a vehicle traveling at highway speed by a single-magnet mount is a tenuous situation at best.

TYPE OF MOUNT

The type of mount is dictated by several conditions. These include a decision whether or not to drill holes, the size, weight and length of the antenna. If you want to operate HF mobile operation regularly, you are better off with a permanent mount. If you're not, a trunk lip, angle bracket, or license plate mount, and a lightweight, continuously-loaded antenna may meet your needs.

Ground plane losses directly affect a mobile antenna's efficiency. From this standpoint, mounts positioned high on the vehicle are preferred over a trailer hitch, bumper or other locations that place the antenna where the vehicle body will be close to the radiating element.

The ground plane of a mobile vertical antenna begins where the coax shield connects. When the feed line shield couples to the vehicle body capacitively as in a mag-mount, or when the mass of the vehicle is far below the feed point (long extension sections attached to trailer hitch mounts), ground losses escalate dramatically. Running a ground strap to the nearest connecting point to the vehicle body does not eliminate ground losses. Remember that the ground connection is part of the antenna system, and it is the efficiency of the whole system that is important.

While it is difficult to mount an HF antenna without at least part of the mast being close to the body, the coil must be kept free and clear

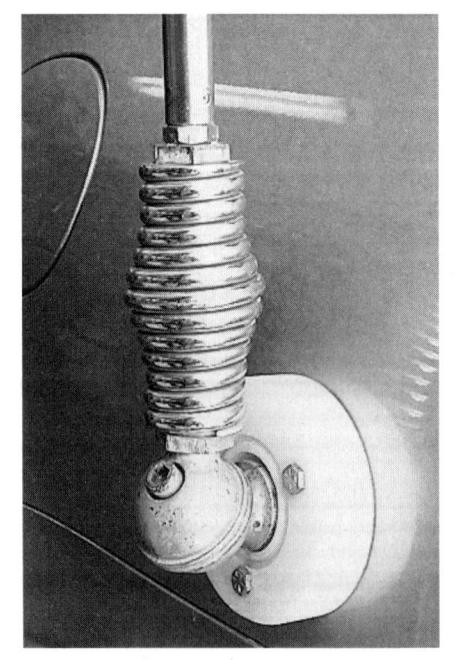

Figure 21.71 — A simple ball mount is sturdy but requires drilling holes in the vehicle body.

or tuning problems and reduced efficiency will result. In some cases, vans and SUVs for example, front-mounting may become necessary to avoid excessive coil-to-body interaction.

One drawback to trunk lip and similar clip mounts is the stress imposed on them as the lids and doors are open and closed. In most cases, angle brackets that attach to the inner surfaces with screws are a better choice.

Sometimes, the only solution is a custom-made bracket like the one shown later in this chapter. Here too, the circumstances dictate the requirements. Keep in mind that removing permanently installed antenna mounts such as the ball mount shown in **Figure 21.71** will always leave some body damage, but temporary ones do, too. Only the severity is in question, and that's in the eyes of the beholder.

21.8.8 Mobile HF Antenna Matching

Modern solid-state transceivers are designed for loads close to 50 Ω impedance. Depending on the design of the antenna (primarily depending on coil position and Q), overall length and the ground losses present, the input impedance is usually closer to 25 Ω but may vary from 18 Ω to more than 50 Ω. Note that a vehicle is an inadequate ground plane for any HF mobile antenna. Typical ground loss varies from 20 Ω (160 meters) to 2 Ω (10 meters). Stray capacitance losses may further increase the apparent ground losses.

It's important to remember two important facts. First, as the coil is moved past the center of the antenna toward the top, the coil's resistive losses begin to dominate, and the input impedance gets closer to 50 Ω. Second, short stubby antennas require more inductance than longer ones, which increases resistive losses in the coil (low Q). While no matching is required in either case, efficiency suffers, and may actually drop below 1% on the lower bands. Another way to look at the situation is that an antenna with no matching required implies a low efficiency.

Ground loss, coil position, coil Q, mast size, whip size and a few other factors determine the feed point impedance, which averages about 25 Ω for a typical quality antenna and mount. This represents an input SWR of 2:1, so some form of impedance matching is required for the transceiver. There are three ways to accomplish the impedance transformation: capacitive, transmission-line transformer and inductive matching as shown in **Figure 21.72**. Each has its own unique attributes and drawbacks.

Transmission line transformers, in this case an unun in Figure 21.72A, do provide a dc ground for the antenna. They can be tapped or switched to match loads as low as a few ohms. Their broadband nature makes them ideal for HF mobile antenna matching. Since a remotely-controlled HF mobile antenna's input impedance varies over a wide range, transmission line transformers are best utilized for matching monoband antennas.

Inductive matching in Figure 21.72B borrows a little capacitance from the antenna (C_a) — the antenna is adjusted to a frequency slightly higher than the operating frequency, making the input impedance capacitive. This forms a high-pass L-network, which transforms the input impedance to the 50 Ω transmission line impedance. It is ideal for use with remotely-controlled antennas, as its reactance increases with frequency. By selecting the correct inductance, a compromise can be reached such that the impedance transformation will result in a low SWR from 160 through 10 meters. The approximate value is 1 µH, but may vary between 0.7 and 1.5 µH.

Adjusting the shunt coil can be done without transmitting by using an antenna analyzer and takes about 10 minutes. (Full instructions for properly adjusting a shunt coil may be found at **www.k0bg.com/coil.html**.) Because no further adjustment is necessary, shunt coil matching is ideal for remotely-controlled HF mobile antennas.

Capacitive matching in Figure 21.72C borrows a little inductance from the antenna (L_a) — the antenna is adjusted to a frequency slightly lower than the operating frequency, making the input impedance inductive. This forms a low-pass L-network, which transforms the input impedance to the 50 Ω transmission line impedance. While it works quite well, it has two drawbacks. First, capacitive matching presents a dc ground for the antenna, which tends to increase the static levels on receive. Second, the capacitance changes with frequency, so changing bands also requires a change in capacitance. This can be a nuisance with a remotely controlled antenna.

An important point should be made about dc grounding in addition to the static issue. If the antenna element should come in contact with a low-hanging high tension wire, or if lightning should strike it, dc grounding offers an additional level of protection for you and your transceiver.

21.8.9 Remotely-Tuned Antenna Controllers

There are three basic types of remote controllers: manual, position sensing and SWR sensing. Manual controllers consist of a DPDT center-off switch that changes the polarity of the current to the motor. Some commercial models include an interface with the radio that causes the radio to transmit a low-power carrier for tuning. Reading the SWR is left to the user. Some manual controllers incorporate a position readout to aid the operator in correctly positioning the antenna.

Position sensing controllers incorporate a magnet attached to the motor output shaft.

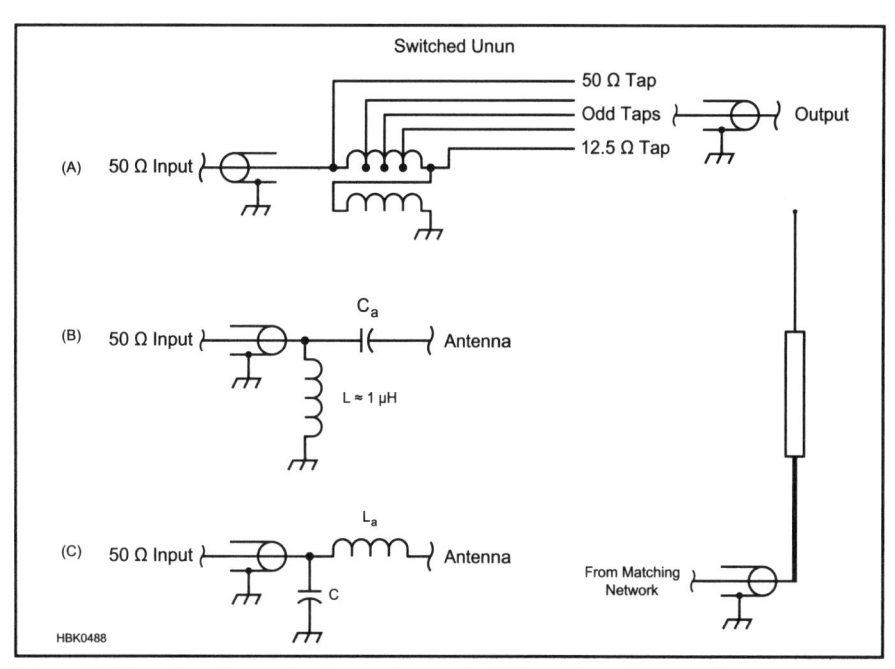

Figure 21.72 — A well-constructed and mounted HF mobile antenna will have an average input impedance around 25 Ω, requiring some matching to the feed line. The unun transmission line transformer (A) is a 4:1 configuration with taps added to match intermediate impedance values between 50 and 12.5 Ω. The high-pass L-network (B) uses some of the antenna's capacitive reactance as part of the network and the low-pass L-network (C) uses some of the antenna's inductive reactance as part of the network. Both (A) and (B) result in an antenna at dc ground, an important safety issue.

Figure 21.73 — A screwdriver antenna controller made to work with the IC-7000 transceiver.

The magnet opens and closes a reed switch. During set up, the antenna is set to one end of its range or the other. Then the resonant points are found (you have to do this yourself) and stored in multiple memory locations. As long as power remains applied to the controller, a simple button push will move the antenna to a specific preset point. Some controllers use band or frequency data from a port on the radio and reset the antenna to the nearest preset based on that information.

SWR-sensing controllers either read data from the radio or from a built-in SWR bridge. Depending on the make and model, a push of the radio's tuner button (or one on the controller) causes the radio to transmit at a reduced power setting. The controller then powers the antenna's tuning motor. When the preset SWR threshold is reached, the controller stops the transmission and shuts off the motor. **Figure 21.73** shows an example of a controller made to work with a specific transceiver.

Antennas 21.47

Automatic controllers are far less distracting than manual ones. Most offer a parking function that collapses the coil of a screwdriver antenna into the mast (highest frequency position, lowest overall length). If you garage your vehicle, this is a welcome feature.

21.8.10 Efficiency

Length matters! All else being equal, a 9 foot antenna will be twice as efficient as a 6 foot antenna, because radiation resistance relates directly to the square of the physical length. Further, longer antennas require less reactance to resonate, hence coil Q is higher, and resistive losses lower.

Mounting methodology matters! It is the mass under the antenna, not alongside, that counts. The higher the mounting, the less capacitive coupling there will be between the antenna and the surface of the vehicle and the lower ground losses will be.

Project: Mounts for Remotely-Tuned Antennas

Remotely tuned antennas have become very popular, but they all have one thing in common: they're difficult to mount. They require both a coaxial feed line and a dc power connection, and no one makes a universal mount for them. The short, stubby ones aren't any more difficult to mount than a small whip antenna, but the "full-sized" ones (8 feet and longer) require special consideration.

These antennas are heavy (up to 18 pounds), so the mounting medium must be extra strong, and well anchored. As a result, many hams opt for a bumper or trailer hitch mount, even though the low mounting position reduces efficiency.

For some, efficiency is paramount which dictates mounting the antenna as high as possible. Doing either low or high mounting often requires custom fabrication. The accompanying photos illustrate the two different strategies that show Amateur Radio ingenuity at its finest.

Figures 21.74 and **21.75** depict the mobile installation of Fokko Vos, PA3VOS. Except for a Hi-Q heavy-duty quick-disconnect, the complete mount was custom engineered by Fokko. The mount bolts to a frame extension, which in turn is bolted to the undercarriage using existing bolts. Note that the rear hatch may be opened without the antenna being removed. Had the trailer hitch been used, this would not be the case.

Figure 21.76 depicts installation on a Ford F350 based motor home owned by Hal Wilson, KE5DKM. Hal designed the bracket, and had a local machine shop do the hard work. It is made of ¼ inch, high-strength aluminum, and the seams are welded. A powder-coat finish tops off the fabrication.

Shown here during installation, the bracket just fits into the right-side hood seam. The piece jutting out from the mount was to be used to further brace the mount. However, after all of the bolts were installed, additional bracing became unnecessary.

Figure 21.74 — The PA3VOS antenna mount easily supports a large screwdriver antenna and is offset to allow the hatch to open and close without removing the antenna.

Figure 21.75 — A close-up of the PA3VOS mount.

Figure 21.76 — The KE5DKM bracket mounts under the hood of a motor home.

Project: Retuning a CB Whip Antenna

The most efficient HF mobile antenna is a full-size quarter-wavelength whip. Wouldn't it be nice if we could use one on every band? Alas, we cannot, but we can use one easily on 10 and 12 meters since the overall length will be less than 10 feet. If we start with a standard-length 102 inch whip and its base spring, we just need to shorten it a little for 10 meters, and lengthen it a little for 12 meters. Here's how to do it.

The formula for calculating the length of a ¼ λ antenna in feet is 234/f, where f is the frequency (MHz). Since the formula is for wire antennas, and the whip is larger in diameter, the resulting length will be slightly too long. This is a good thing because it is easier to remove a little length than it is to add some. This makes tuning easier.

Using the formula, we discover the needed length for 10 meters (28.5 MHz) is 98.5 inches. Thus, we need to remove 3.5 inches and account for the length of the base spring (about 6 inches), for a total of 9.5 inches to be removed. This is best accomplished by filing a notch on opposite sides of the tip of the whip, and snapping it in two. Protect your eyes when you do this, as shards and splinters can fly off the broken ends. If a fiberglass whip is being modified, clip the internal wire at the top of the remaining base section. Remove the plastic cap from the discarded top section and replace it over the new top of the antenna.

Depending on the mount used, the actual resonant frequency will be lower than 28.5 MHz as the mounts adds effective length. A standard CB antenna ball mount will easily support a whip. The finished antenna is shown in **Figure 21.77A**.

Once the antenna is mounted on the vehicle, simply trimming the overall length ½ inch at a time will eventually produce a low SWR at your desired frequency.

LENGTHENING FOR 12 METER OPERATION

Lengthening a CB whip for 12 meters requires a little more work. Thankfully, there's a easy solution if you have a CB radio or truck stop near you. Wilson and other vendors sell short masts designed for the CB market. They have the requisite $3/8 \times 24$ threads to accept a standard whip, and they come with a female-to-female coupler. The 10 inch model is ideal for our use, and costs under $10.

Using our formula 234/f, the overall length needs to be 112.6 inches for 24.93 MHz. Adding 6 inches for the spring, 10 inches for the extension mast, and 102 inches for the whip, gives us 118 inches. So we need to remove 5.4 inches from the whip. Then just trim off ½ inch at a time as above to resonate the antenna. The finished antenna is shown in Figure 21.77B.

FINISHING UP

There are two more things to consider. If a metal whip was modified, you'll need to replace the corona ball at the tip of the antenna. It helps reduce static from corona discharge. It's held on by a set screw and has little effect on tuning. Most CB shops sell them.

The other consideration is ground loss. Theoretically, a ¼ λ vertical will have an input impedance of 36 Ω. In a mobile installation, we have ground losses and stray capacitance losses in the mounting hardware. As a result, the real-world input impedance should be very close to 42 Ω, yielding a rather low SWR and good efficiency.

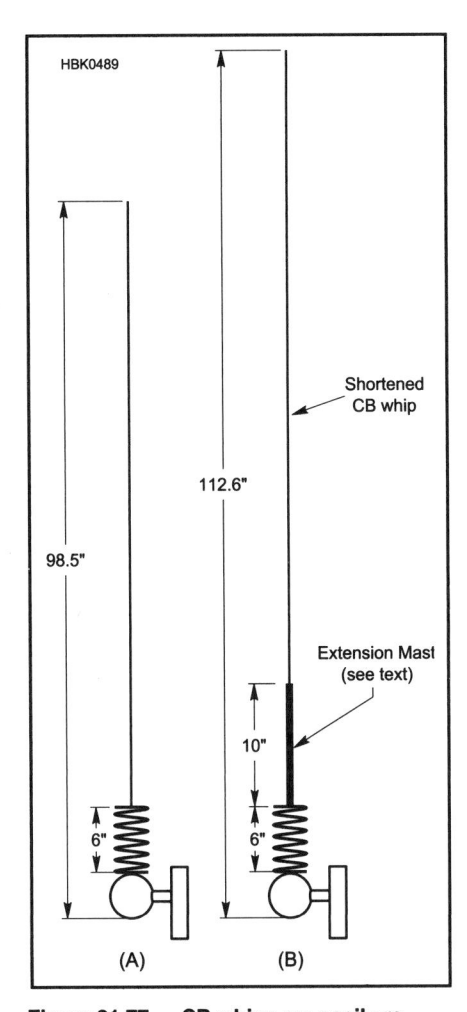

Figure 21.77 — CB whips are easily retuned for 10 meter (A) and 12 meter (B) mobile operation.

21.9 VHF/UHF Mobile Antennas

The simple ¼ λ, ½ λ, and ⅝ λ ground-plane whips are the most common VHF/UHF mobile antennas. Collinear antennas with higher gain are available. However, high gain and the lower radiation angle that goes with it isn't always a desirable attribute.

When using repeaters in urban areas, where higher angles of radiation are preferred, you're typically better off with a unity-gain antenna — a ¼ λ whip. It all depends on the HAAT (height above average terrain) of the repeater being used with respect to the mobile station's HAAT. In mountainous areas you're always better off with a unity gain antenna as the repeaters are much higher in elevation than the mobile station is.

If you're working simplex and living in a suburban or rural area, a high-gain antenna might have a slight edge. However, where, and how the antenna is mounted is more important than gain. A ¼ λ ground plane mounted in the center of the roof will typically out perform a gain antenna mounted on the trunk lid.

Sturdiness is also an important attribute, given the unintended abuse to which mobile antennas are subjected. The simple quarter-wave ground plane has the advantage here, as it isn't much more than a springy piece wire. If you look closely at some of the higher-gain antennas, you'll notice they have very small phasing coils, usually held together by small set screws. Hit one hard enough with a low-hanging limb and your antenna will break whereas a simple quarter-wave whip will only bend. A little straightening and you're back on the air.

21.9.1 VHF/UHF Mobile Antenna Mounts

Without doubt, the best VHF/UHF mobile mount ever devised is the NMO (New Motorola) shown in **Figure 21.78**. When properly installed in vehicle sheet metal, the mount will not leak even when the antenna is removed for car washing. SO-239 and threaded or snap-in mounts often leak even with the antenna attached.

Glass-mounted antennas are rather lossy, especially at lower VHF frequencies (2 meters). Many new vehicles use window glass with a metallic, anti-glare (passivated) coating that interferes with capacitive coupling through the glass. These antennas also transfer mechanical abuse to the glass, risking breaking the glass the antenna is mounted on.

MOUNTING LOCATION

As mentioned above, the center of the roof is an ideal mounting location for a VHF/UHF antenna. However, many mobile operators share a reluctance to drill the proper mounting holes fearing that doing so will depreciate the value of the vehicle. Instead, they rely on a mag-mount which has its own set of negatives including where and how to route the coax cable into the vehicle. They tend to collect metallic road debris, primarily brake pad dust, marring and scratching the painted surface under them, often causing more damage than would the hole for an NMO mount. For these reasons alone, mag-mounts should only be used for temporary installations, such as emergency communication.

Roof mounting has a few caveats. Modern vehicle roofs have strengthening supports to protect the occupants should the vehicle rollover due to a crash. Do not drill through these supports!

The various side pillars supporting the roof contain wiring for lighting, side airbags, and other accessories, which can make routing of the coax difficult. If you're at all reticent about roof mounting, see a dealer or professional installer.

As an alternative, a trunk lip mount may fit the bill. However, they too have some drawbacks. They're stressed every time the trunk is opened or closed, and tend to work loose over time. Thus regular maintenance is required to assure a good electrical ground to the trunk lid. In any case, do not sand the paint down to bare metal as this removes the zinc undercoating which in turn promotes rust. It is also important to bond across the trunk hinges to assure a good ground.

Angle brackets work well, too. They're thin enough to fit into the seam of hoods, trunk lids, and back hatches. Coax routing under or around the weather seals can be a problem with the latter two.

ADJUSTING SWR

Setting the SWR of a VHF/UHF antenna is an important installation procedure, but not one to worry about unless the SWR suddenly makes a large change. Unlike the HF bands, most VHF antennas will cover the whole band segment without the need to retune. That is to say, the SWR will be low across the FM portion of the respective bands. An in-line SWR meter is generally not required as the vertically-polarized antenna is not intended to be used in the weak-signal portion of the bands where horizontal polarization is the norm.

21.9.2 VHF/UHF Mobile Antennas for SSB and CW

Operating SSB and CW on 6 meters, 2 meters, and 70 cm offers some exciting

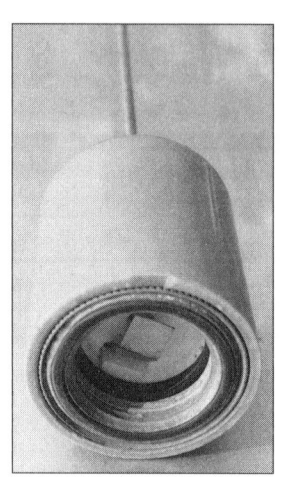

Figure 21.78 — The NMO (New Motorola) mount is widely used for VHF and UHF mobile antennas. It is available in mag-mount, trunk and lip mount and through-body mounting styles.

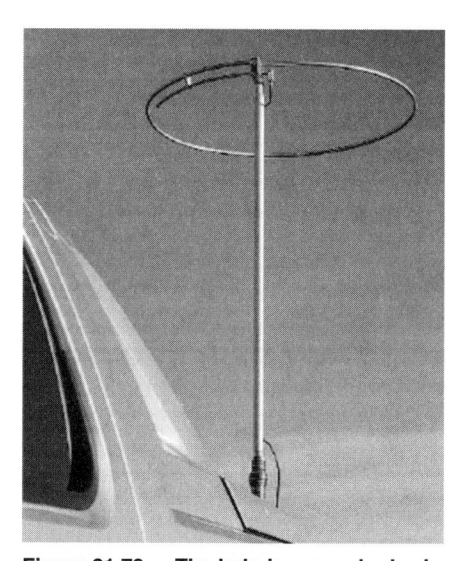

Figure 21.79 — The halo is a popular horizontally polarized mobile antenna for 6 meters through 70 cm. This version was made by Jerry Clement, VE6AB, and the construction article is available online (see text).

prospects for all license classes. While FM communications on the VHF bands are often considered line-of-site, propagation *beyond* line-of-site is common, as discussed in the **Propagation of Radio Waves** chapter.

Modern mobile SSB/CW transceivers usually output 100 W PEP on 6 meters and at least 50 W PEP on 2 meters and 70 cm. Under good band conditions, using horizontally polarized antennas, *beyond* line-of-sight distances can exceed 200 miles even without any sky-wave or tropospheric scatter present!

There's a catch, however. FM communications utilize vertically polarized antennas. Vertical polarization can be used for SSB and CW, but depending on the propagation path, signal strength from a vertically polarized mobile antenna can have a disadvantage of up to 20 dB compared to a horizontally polarized antenna due to cross-polarization.

Fortunately, horizontally-polarized antennas are of manageable size on the VHF and UHF bands, although they are not as simple to construct as vertically polarized whips. Dipoles and small beams present too much wind resistance to withstand the normal mobile environment. The usual solution is a loop antenna.

Figure 21.79 shows a horizontally polarized 6 meter loop called a *halo* that was made by Jerry Clement, VE6AB. (Complete construction plans are available in his article "6 Meter halo Antenna for DXing" in the February 2017 issue of *QST* which is available in this book's downloadable supplemental material.) Square versions, such as those commercially available from M2 Antenna Systems (**www.m2inc.com**) are called *squalos*. Both have a roughly omnidirectional pattern. The "Big Wheel" design is another option and the article "A New Spin on the Big Wheel" by L.B. Cebik, W4RNL, and Bob Cerreto, WA1FXT, from the March 2008 issue of *QST* is included with the downloadable supplemental content, as well. Equivalent antennas for 2 meters and 70 cm are common. Mounting loop antennas on a vehicle can be less cumbersome than mounting an HF antenna because they don't require a ground plane. A simple hitch-mounted mast will suffice, with no body holes needed!

21.10 VHF/UHF Antennas

Improving an antenna system is one of the most productive moves open to the VHF enthusiast. It can increase transmitting range, improve reception, reduce interference problems and bring other practical benefits. The work itself is by no means the least attractive part of the job. Even with high-gain antennas, experimentation is greatly simplified at VHF and UHF because an array is a workable size, and much can be learned about the nature and adjustment of antennas. No large investment in test equipment is necessary.

Whether we buy or build our antennas, we soon find that there is no one *best* design for all purposes. Selecting the antenna best suited to our needs involves much more than scanning gain figures and prices in a manufacturer's catalog. The first step should be to establish priorities for the antenna system as a whole. Once the objectives have been sorted out in a general way, we face decisions on specific design features, such as polarization, length and type of transmission line, matching methods, and mechanical design.

21.10.1 Gain

As has been discussed previously, shaping the pattern of an antenna to concentrate radiated energy, or received signal pickup, in some directions at the expense of others is the only possible way to develop gain. Radiation patterns can be controlled in various ways. One is to use two or more driven elements, fed in phase. Such arrays provide gain without markedly sharpening the frequency response, compared to that of a single element. More gain per element, but with some sacrifice in frequency coverage, is obtained by placing parasitic elements into a Yagi array.

21.10.2 Radiation Pattern

Antenna radiation can be made omnidirectional, bidirectional, practically unidirectional, or anything between these conditions. A VHF net operator may find an omnidirectional system almost a necessity but it may be a poor choice otherwise. Noise pickup and other interference problems tend to be greater with omnidirectional antennas. Maximum gain and low radiation angle are usually prime interests of the weak-signal DX aspirant. A clean pattern, with lowest possible pickup and radiation off the sides and back, may be important in high-activity areas, where the noise level is high, or for challenging modes like EME (Earth-Moon-Earth).

21.10.3 Height Gain

In general, the higher a VHF antenna is installed, the better will be the results. If raising the antenna clears its view over nearby obstructions, it may make dramatic improvements in coverage. Within reason, greater height is almost always worth its cost, but height gain must be balanced against increased transmission line loss. Line losses can be considerable at VHF and above, and they increase with frequency. The best available line may be none too good, if the run is long in terms of wavelength. Consider line losses in any antenna planning.

21.10.4 Physical Size

A given antenna design for 432 MHz, say a 5-element Yagi on a 1 λ boom, will have the same gain as one for 144 MHz, but being only one-third the size it will intercept only one-ninth as much energy in receiving. Thus, to be equal in communication effectiveness, the 432 MHz array should be at least equal in physical size to the 144 MHz one, requiring roughly three times the number of elements. With all the extra difficulties involved in going higher in frequency, it is better to be on the big side in building an antenna for the UHF bands.

21.10.5 Polarization

Whether to position the antenna elements vertically or horizontally has been a question since early VHF operation. Originally, VHF communication was mostly vertically polarized, but horizontal gained favor when directional arrays became widely used. Tests of signal strength and range with different polarizations show little evidence on which to set up a uniform polarization policy. On long paths there is no consistent advantage, either way. Shorter paths tend to yield higher signal levels with horizontal in some kinds of terrain. Man-made noise, especially ignition interference, tends to be lower with horizontal polarization. Vertically polarized antennas, however, are markedly simpler to use in omnidirectional systems and in mobile work, resulting in a standardization on vertical polarization for mobile and repeater operation on FM and for digital communications. Horizontal polarization is the standard for weak signal VHF and UHF operation. (Circular polarization is preferred for satellite work as described below.) A loss in signal strength of 20 dB or more can be expected with cross-polarization so it is important to use antennas with the same polarization as the stations with which you expect to communicate.

21.10.6 Circular Polarization

Polarization is described as *horizontal* or *vertical*, but these terms have no meaning once the reference of the Earth's surface is lost. Many propagation factors can cause polarization change — reflection or refraction and passage through magnetic fields (Faraday rotation), for example. Polarization of VHF waves is often random, so an antenna capable of accepting any polarization is useful. Circular polarization, generated with helical antennas or with crossed elements fed 90° out of phase, will respond to any linear polarization.

The circularly polarized wave in effect threads its way through space, and it can be left- or right-hand polarized. These polarization senses are mutually exclusive, but either will respond to any plane (horizontal or vertical) polarization. A wave generated with right-hand polarization, when reflected from the moon, comes back with left-hand polarization, a fact to be borne in mind in setting up EME circuits. Stations communicating on direct paths should have the same polarization sense.

Both senses can be generated with crossed dipoles, with the aid of a switchable phasing harness. With helical arrays, both senses are provided with two antennas wound in opposite directions.

21.10.7 Transmission Lines

The most common type of transmission line at VHF through the low microwave bands is unbalanced coaxial cable. Small coax such as RG-58 or RG-59 should never be used in VHF work if the run is more than a few feet. Half-inch lines (RG-8 or RG-11) work fairly well at 50 MHz, and runs of 50 feet or less are acceptable at 144 MHz. Lines with foam rather than solid insulation have about 30% less loss. Low-loss cable is required for all but the shortest runs above 222 MHz and *waveguide* is used on microwave frequencies. (See the **Transmission Lines** chapter for a discussion of waveguides.)

Solid aluminum-jacketed *hardline* coaxial cable with large inner conductors and foam insulation are well worth the cost. Hardline can sometimes even be obtained for free from local Cable TV operators as *end runs* — pieces at the end of a roll. The most common CATV variety is ½ inch OD 75 Ω hardline. Hardline is considered *semi-rigid* in that it can be bent, but only with a large radius to avoid kinking and repeated bending should be avoided.

Waterproof commercial connectors for hardline are fairly expensive, but enterprising amateurs have *home-brewed* low-cost connectors. If they are properly waterproofed, connectors and hardline can last almost indefinitely. See *The ARRL Antenna Book* for details on connectors and techniques for working with hardline.

Properly-built open-wire line can operate with very low loss in VHF and even UHF installations. A line made of #12 AWG wire, spaced ¾ inch or less with Teflon spreaders, and running essentially straight from antenna to station, can be better than anything but the most expensive hardline at a fraction of the cost. Line loss under 2 dB per 100 feet at 432 MHz is readily obtained. This assumes the use of high-quality baluns to match into and out of the balanced line, with a short length of low-loss coax for the rotating section from the top of the tower to the antenna. Such an open-wire line could have a line loss under 1 dB at 144 MHz.

Effects of weather on transmission lines should not be ignored. A well-constructed open-wire line works well in nearly any weather, and it stands up well. TV-type twin-lead is almost useless in heavy rain, wet snow or icing conditions. The best grades of coax and hardline are impervious to weather. They can be run underground, fastened to metal towers without insulation, or bent into almost any convenient position, with no adverse effects on performance. However, beware of bargain coax. Lost transmitter power can be made up to some extent by increasing power, but once lost in the transmission line a weak signal can never be recovered in the receiver.

21.10.8 Impedance Matching

Theory and practice in impedance matching are discussed in detail in the **Transmission Lines** chapter, and in theory, at least, are the same for frequencies above 50 MHz. Practice may be similar, but physical size can be a major modifying factor in choice of methods.

DELTA MATCH

Probably the first impedance match was made when the ends of an open line were fanned out and tapped onto a half-wave antenna at the points of most efficient power transfer, as in **Figure 21.80A**. Both the side length and the points of connection either side of the center of the element must be adjusted for minimum reflected power in the line, but the impedances need not be known. The delta

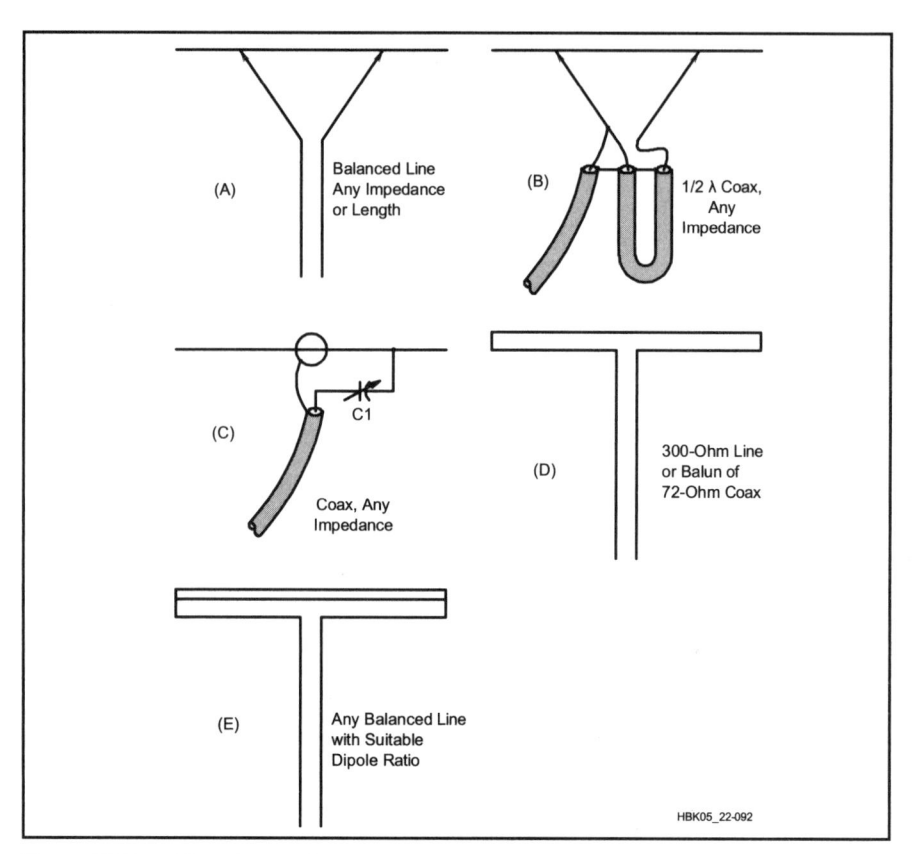

Figure 21.80 — Matching methods commonly used in VHF antennas. In the delta match, A and B, the line is fanned out to tap on the dipole at the points of best impedance match. The gamma match, C, is for direct connection of coax. C1 tunes out inductance in the arm. Folded dipole of uniform conductor size, D, steps up antenna impedance by a factor of four. Using a larger conductor in the unbroken portion of the folded dipole, E, gives higher orders of impedance transformation.

makes no provision for tuning out reactance, so the length of the dipole is pruned for best SWR.

Once thought to be inferior for VHF applications because of its tendency to radiate if adjusted improperly, the delta has come back to favor now that we have good methods for measuring the effects of matching. It is very handy for phasing multiple-bay arrays with low-loss open lines, and its dimensions in this use are not particularly critical.

GAMMA MATCH

The gamma match is shown in Figure 21.80C and is covered in more detail in the preceding section on HF Yagi antennas and in the **Transmission Lines** chapter. The center of a half-wave dipole being electrically neutral, the outer conductor of the coax is connected to the element at this point, which may also be the junction with a metallic or non-conductive boom. The inner conductor is connected to the element at the matching point. Inductance of the connection to the element is canceled by means of C1. Both the point of contact with the element and the setting of the capacitor are adjusted for minimum SWR using an antenna analyzer or SWR bridge.

The capacitor C1 can be a variable unit during adjustment and then replaced with a suitable fixed unit when the required capacitance value is found. Maximum capacitance should be about 100 pF for 50 MHz and 35 to 50 pF for 144 MHz. The capacitor and arm can be combined with the arm connecting to the driven element by means of a sliding clamp, and the inner end of the arm sliding inside a sleeve connected to the inner conductor of the coax. It can be constructed from concentric pieces of tubing, insulated by plastic sleeving or shrink tubing. RF voltage across the capacitor is low, once the match is adjusted properly, so with a good dielectric, insulation presents no great problem. A clean, permanent, high-conductivity bond between arm and element is important, as the RF current is high at this point.

Because it is inherently somewhat unbalanced, the gamma match can sometimes introduce pattern distortion, particularly on long-boom, highly directive Yagi arrays. The T-match, essentially two gamma matches in series creating a balanced feed system, has become popular for this reason. (See the preceding discussion on T-matches in the HF Yagi section.) A coaxial balun like that shown in Figure 21.80B is used from the balanced T-match to the unbalanced coaxial line going to the transmitter. To maintain a symmetrical pattern, the feed line should be run along the antenna boom at the centerline of the elements to the mast. A choke balun is often used to minimize currents that might be induced on the outer surface of the feed line shield.

FOLDED DIPOLE

The impedance of a half-wave dipole feed point at its center is 72 Ω. If a single conductor of uniform size is folded to make a half-wave dipole, as shown in Figure 21.80D, the impedance is stepped up four times. Such a folded dipole can thus be fed directly with 300 Ω line with no appreciable mismatch. Coaxial feed line of 70 to 75 Ω impedance may then be used with a 4:1 impedance transformer. Higher impedance step-up can be obtained if the unbroken portion is made larger in cross-section than the fed portion, as in Figure 21.80E. The folded dipole is discussed further in the *ARRL Antenna Book*.

21.10.9 Baluns and Impedance Transformers

Conversion from balanced loads to unbalanced lines, or vice versa, can be performed with electrical circuits, or their equivalents made of coaxial line. A balun made from flexible coax is shown in **Figure 21.81A**. The looped portion is an electrical half-wave. This type of balun gives an impedance step-up of 4:1, 50 to 200 Ω, or 75 to 300 Ω typically. See the **RF Techniques** and **Transmission Lines** chapters for a detailed discussion of baluns and impedance transformers.

The physical length of the line section depends on the propagation factor of the line used, so it is best to check its resonant frequency, as shown at B. One end of the line is left open and an antenna analyzer used to find the lowest frequency at which the impedance at the other end of the line is a minimum, the frequency at which the section of line is ¼ λ long. Multiply the frequency by two to find the frequency at which the section is ½ λ long.

Coaxial baluns giving a 1:1 impedance transfer are shown in **Figure 21.82**. The coaxial sleeve, open at the top and connected to the outer conductor of the line at the lower

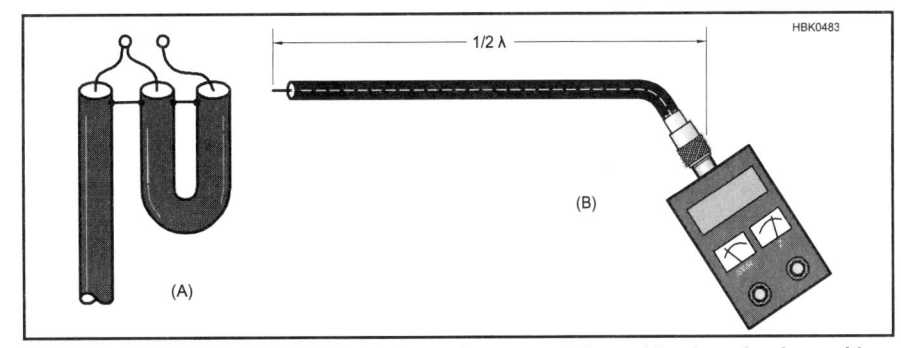

Figure 21.81 — Conversion from unbalanced coax to a balanced load can be done with a half-wave coaxial balun, A. The half-wave balun gives a 4:1 impedance step up. Electrical length of the looped section should be checked with an antenna analyzer with the far end of the line open, as in B. The lowest frequency at which the line impedance is a minimum is the frequency at which the line is ¼ λ long. Multiply that frequency by two to obtain the ½ λ frequency.

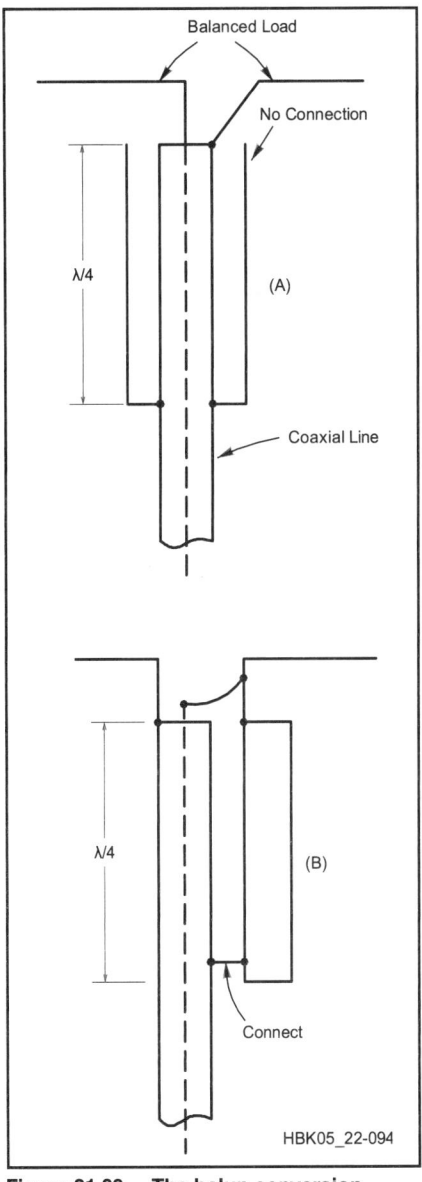

Figure 21.82 — The balun conversion function, with no impedance change, is accomplished with quarter-wave lines, open at the top and connected to the coax outer conductor at the bottom. The coaxial sleeve shown at A is preferred.

end (Figure 21.82A) is the preferred type. A conductor of approximately the same size as the line is used with the outer conductor to form a quarter-wave stub, in Figure 21.82B. Another piece of coax, using only the outer conductor, will serve this purpose. Both baluns are intended to present a high impedance to any RF current that might otherwise tend to flow on the outer conductor of the coax. Choke baluns made of ferrite beads of the proper material type or mix may also be used. See the **RF Techniques** chapter for information about ferrite use at VHF and UHF.

Project: Simple, Portable Ground-Plane Antenna

The ground-plane antenna is shown in **Figure 21.83** and uses a female chassis-mount connector to support the element and two radials. With only two radials, it is essentially two dimensional, which makes it easier to store when not in use. UHF connectors work well for 144 and 222 MHz, but you may prefer to use Type N connectors. N connectors are recommended for 440 MHz and higher frequencies. BNC connectors can be used for the shorter antennas on 915 and 1280 MHz but are not particularly sturdy.

If the antenna is sheltered from weather, copper wire is sufficiently rigid for the radiating element and radials. Antennas exposed to the wind and weather can be made from brazing rod, which is available at welding supply stores. Alternatively, #12 or #14 AWG copper-clad steel wire could be used to construct this antenna.

To eliminate sharp ends, it's a good idea to bend the element and radial ends into a circle or to terminate them with a crimp terminal as in **Figure 21.84**. The crimp terminal approach is easier with stiff wire. Crimp and then solder the terminal to the wire. Make the overall length of the element and radials the same as shown in Figure 21.83, measuring to the outer tip of the loop or terminal.

Radials may be attached directly to the mounting holes of the coaxial connector.

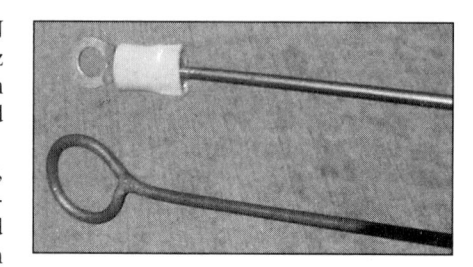

Figure 21.84 — Alternate methods for terminating element and radial tips on the simple ground-plane antenna. See text. *(Photo by K8CH)*

Bend a hook at one end of each radial for insertion through the connector. Solder the radials to the connector using a large soldering iron or propane torch.

Solder the element to the center pin of the connector. If the element does not fit inside the solder cup, use a short section of brass tubing as a coupler (a slotted ⅛ inch ID tube will fit over an SO-239 or N receptacle center pin).

If necessary, prune the antenna to raise the frequency of minimum SWR. Then adjust the radial droop angle for minimum SWR — this should not affect the frequency at which the minimum SWR occurs.

One mounting method for fixed-station antennas appears in Figure 21.83. The feed line and connector are inside the mast, and a hose clamp squeezes the slotted mast end to tightly grip the plug body. Once the antenna is mounted and tested, thoroughly seal the open side of the coaxial connector with silicone sealant, and weatherproof the connections with rust-preventative paint.

A related simple antenna is the crossed-dipole which has an omnidirectional pattern and requires no ground plane. Paul Wade, W1GHZ, rescaled a design found in an IEEE journal that was originally designed for 1.7 GHz. His construction article from the *Proceedings of Microwave Update 2016* is included with the downloadable supplemental information for this book.

Project: Coaxial Dipole for VHF or UHF

(The following antenna was originally described in July 2009 *QST* by John Portune, W6NBC, and was also reprinted in *The ARRL Antenna Compendium Volume 8*.)

Here is a homebrew coaxial dipole built from a small stainless whip, a length of threaded table-lamp tubing and some ¾ inch copper and PVC fittings. The one shown is for 440 MHz but it can readily be scaled for 146 or 222 MHz.

For homebrew vertical VHF antennas, coaxial dipoles often play second fiddle to J-poles. That's because the center connection to coax is often difficult to fabricate in the

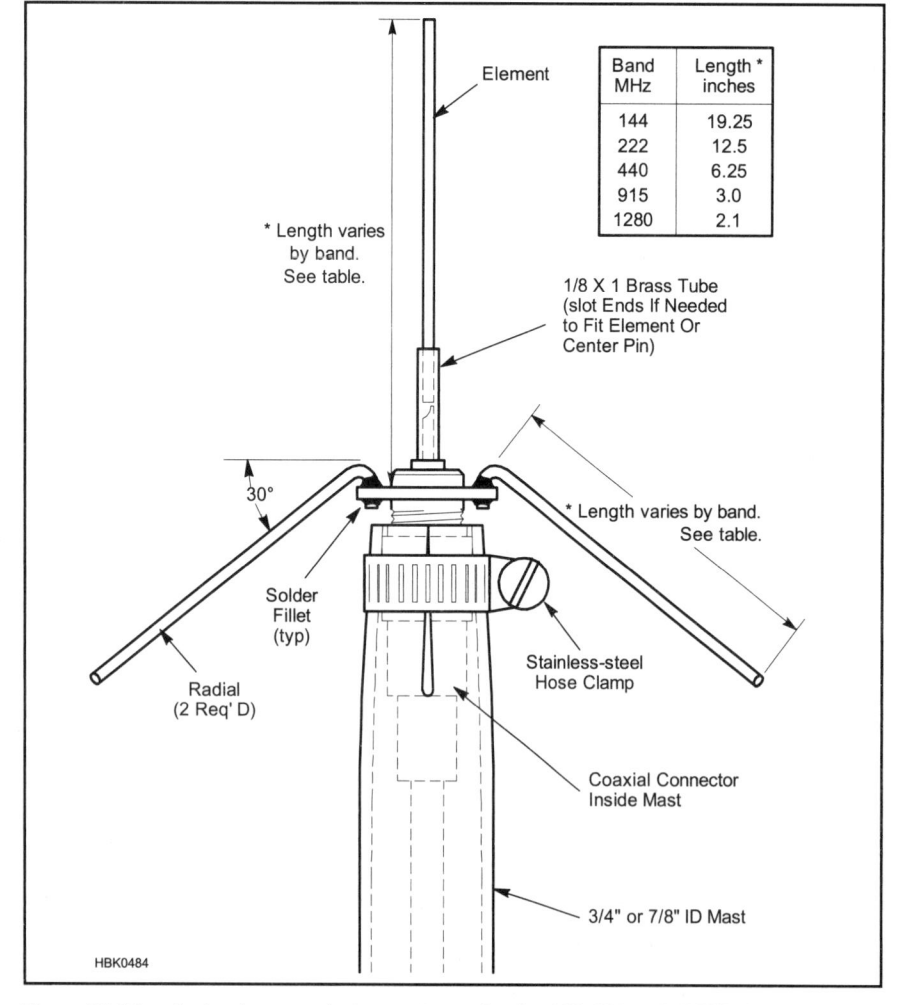

Band MHz	Length * inches
144	19.25
222	12.5
440	6.25
915	3.0
1280	2.1

Figure 21.83 — A simple ground-plane antenna for the 144, 222 or 440 MHz bands. The feed line and connector are inside the mast, and a hose clamp squeezes the slotted mast end to tightly grip the plug body. Element and radial dimensions given in the drawing are good for the entire band.

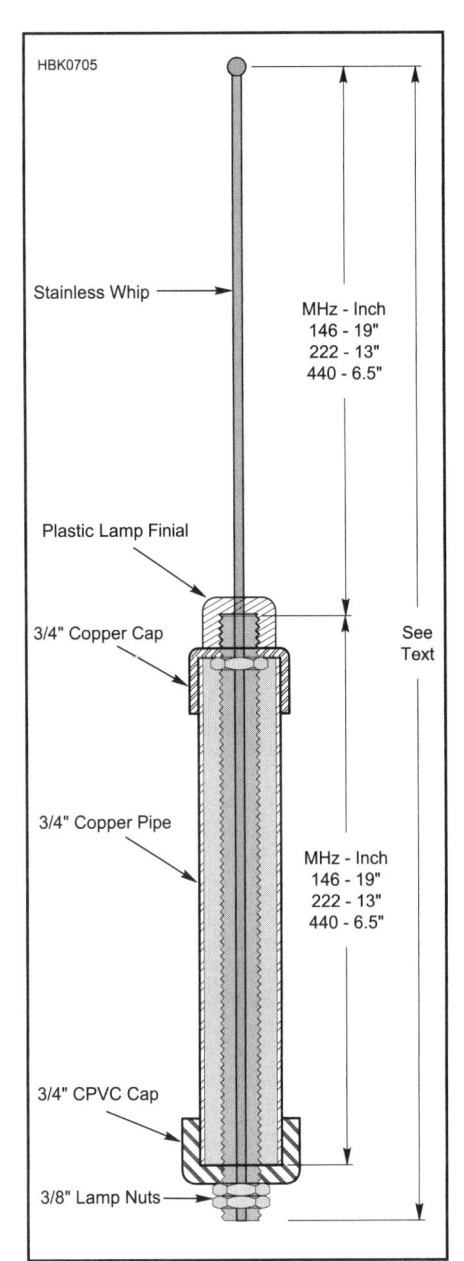

Figure 21.85 — Dimensioned drawing of coaxial dipole for three bands.

Labels on figure:
- HBK0705
- Stainless Whip
- Plastic Lamp Finial
- 3/4" Copper Cap
- 3/4" Copper Pipe
- 3/4" CPVC Cap
- 3/8" Lamp Nuts
- MHz - Inch / 146 - 19" / 222 - 13" / 440 - 6.5"
- MHz - Inch / 146 - 19" / 222 - 13" / 440 - 6.5"
- See Text

home workshop. Yet both antennas have the same performance. They're both full sized, half wave vertical dipoles, and the coaxial is shorter.

MAKING A COAXIAL DIPOLE

If you start with a common half wave ($\lambda/2$) stainless whip and extend it all the way down through a $\lambda/2$ long support tubing, here made from a threaded table lamp tube, the lower part of the whip becomes the center conductor of a short length of rigid coax feeding the center of the antenna. Now connection to normal coax is easily made below the antenna. To form the rigid coax section, you'll need to insulate the center conductor (lower part of the stainless whip) from the lamp tubing with some 1/4 inch inside diameter (ID) polyethylene tubing. Hardware stores normally carry it. This short length of rigid coax formed in this way isn't precisely 50 Ω characteristic impedance, but the difference is totally insignificant. The drawing in **Figure 21.85** shows the details.

Assembly Details

The bottom half ($\lambda/4$) of the radiating dipole is a coaxial sleeve made from 3/4 inch copper pipe and a pipe cap. The coax feed runs up its center to the connector at the bottom of the lamp tubing. Support and insulation of the bottom of the sleeve is provided by a 3/4 inch CPVC plastic pipe cap. For those not familiar with CPVC fittings, they're made to mate with copper pipe and can handle high water temperatures. That's not true of common PVC fittings. Most hardware stores now carry CPVC. Drill a 3/8 inch hole in the center top of the copper and the CPVC caps for the lamp tubing to pass through.

The whole antenna is held together by two lamp tubing nuts and a plastic lamp finial, also readily available at hardware stores (see **Figure 21.86**). Note that a lamp tubing nut is also required inside the copper pipe cap. Drill a small hole in the middle of the lamp finial for the stainless whip. On the bottom of lamp tubing below the antenna install a 1¼ inch common PVC pipe cap, and secure it with two more lamp tubing nuts. This gives you a way to easily mount the antenna on top of any convenient length of 1/4 inch PVC pipe. Run the coax feed down through the PVC pipe. (Note that lamp parts are generally not intended for use outside and may rust or corrode without being painted or otherwise protected against the weather.)

Hooking it Up

A conventional PL-259 UHF type coax connector for RG-8 coax will actually screw onto the bottom of the lamp tubing. The threads are not a perfect fit, but will tighten satisfactorily. The stainless whip runs down all the way to the very tip of the PL-259 connector. Solder it in there. Before doing so, however, install all the pieces of the antenna onto the threaded lamp tubing.

Many hams may think that stainless steel won't solder. It definitely will with a hot iron and acid flux. Scrape the end of the whip and dip it in hydrochloric swimming pool acid. With a little action from the tip of the soldering iron the whip will tin perfectly well. Before soldering, however, grind two or three small side notches in the bottom end of the whip. A Dremel tool works well for this. The notches will help the solder securely lock the whip into the tip of the PL-259 connector. Neutralize any leftover acid with baking soda solution.

Figure 21.86 — Details of final assembly of coaxial dipole (A) and the finished product (B).

Perhaps surprising to some, it really isn't necessary to solder any other parts of the antenna. There is adequate mating surface at the joints for the RF to cross over efficiently. Do, however, seal all possible water access spots with common silicone sealant and or plastic electrical tape.

MAKE IT FOR THE BAND YOU LIKE

There isn't an exact length required for the lamp tubing or the stainless whip. These merely need to provide enough space for all the pieces of the antenna to go together. The author had a 48 inch whip on hand that he used uncut for the 146 MHz coaxial dipole and a similar 17 inch uncut whip for 440 MHz. He cut the lamp tubing to an appropriate length to fit the whips. What does matter, however, is the length of the whip above the top of the lamp tubing as well as the length of the coaxial sleeve. These need to be close to a λ/4 — for 440 MHz, 6½ inches; for 222 MHz, 13 inches; and 19 inches for 146 MHz. These antennas are quite broad band and will cover the entire band in each case with these sizes. No cutting or pruning is necessary.

For ruggedness, or perhaps for stealth, you can install the whole antenna inside of 2 inch PVC water or ABS soil pipe and close the ends with end caps. The author lives in a mobile home park where antennas are not permitted, but the landlord thinks these coaxial dipoles (in ABS pipe) are vent pipes.

Try out one of these homebrew coaxial dipoles. You may find you prefer its smaller size, less obvious appearance and superior weatherproofing as compared to a J-pole.

21.11 VHF/UHF Beams

Without doubt, the Yagi is king of home-station antennas these days. Today's best designs are computer optimized. For years amateurs as well as professionals designed Yagi arrays experimentally. Now we have powerful (and inexpensive) personal computers and sophisticated software for antenna modeling. These have brought us antennas with improved performance, with little or no element pruning required. A more complete discussion of Yagi design can be found earlier in this chapter and in the *ARRL Antenna Book*.

21.11.1 Stacking Yagis

Where suitable provision can be made for supporting them, two Yagis mounted one above the other and fed in-phase may be preferable to one long Yagi having the same theoretical or measured gain. The pair will require a much smaller turning space for the same gain, and their lower radiation angle can provide interesting results. On long ionospheric paths a stacked pair occasionally may show an apparent gain much greater than the 2 to 3 dB that can be measured locally as the gain from stacking.

Optimum spacing for Yagis with booms longer than 1 λ is one wavelength, but this may be too much to handle for many builders of 50 MHz antennas. Worthwhile results are possible with separations of as little as ½ λ (10 feet), but ⅝ λ (12 feet) is markedly better. At 50 MHz, the difference between 12 and 20 foot spacing may not be worth the added structural problems.

The closer spacings give lowered measured gain, but the antenna patterns are cleaner (less power in the high-angle elevation lobes) than with 1 λ spacing. Extra gain with wider spacings is usually the objective on 144 MHz and higher bands, where the structural problems are not quite as severe as on 50 MHz.

One method for feeding two 50 Ω antennas, as might be used in a stacked Yagi array, is shown in **Figure 21.87**. The transmission lines from each antenna, with a balun feeding each antenna (not shown in the drawing for simplicity), to the common feed point must be equal in length and an odd multiple of ¼ λ. This line acts as a quarter-wave (Q-section) impedance transformer, raises the feed impedance of each antenna to 100 Ω, and forces current to be equal in each driven element. When the feed lines are connected in parallel at the coaxial tee connector, the resulting impedance is close to 50 Ω.

Project: Three and Five-Element Yagis for 6 Meters

Boom length often proves to be the deciding factor when one selects a Yagi design. Dean Straw, N6BV, created the designs shown in **Table 21.14**. Straw generated the designs in the table for convenient boom lengths (6

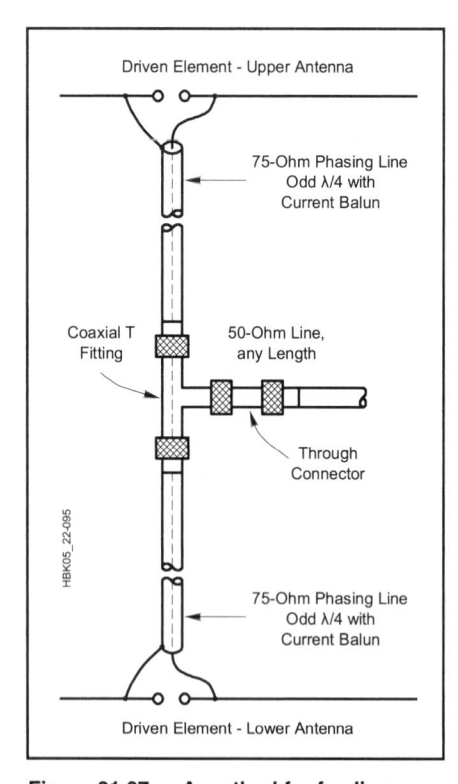

Figure 21.87 — A method for feeding a stacked Yagi array. Note that baluns at each antenna are not specifically shown. Good practice is to use choke baluns made up of ferrite beads slipped over the outside of the coax and taped to prevent movement. See the RF Techniques and Transmission Lines chapter for details.

Table 21.14
Optimized 6 Meter Yagi Designs

	Spacing From Reflector (in.)	Seg 1 Length (in.)	Seg 2 Length (in.)	Midband Gain F/R
306-06				
Refl	0	36	23.500	8.1 dBi
DE	24	36	16.000	28.3 dB
Dir 1	66	36	15.500	
506-12				
OD		0.750	0.625	
Refl	0	36	23.625	10.0 dBi
DE	24	36	17.125	26.8 dB
Dir 1	36	36	19.375	
Dir 2	80	36	18.250	
Dir 3	138	36	15.375	

Note: For all antennas, telescoping tube diameters (in inches) are: Seg1=0.750, Seg2=0.625.
Boom length should be 6 inches longer than the maximum Refl-Dir spacing to allow 3 inches on each end for element mounting hardware.

and 12 feet). The 3 element design has about 8 dBi gain, and the 5 element version has about 10 dBi gain. Both antennas exhibit better than 22 dB front-to-rear ratio, and both cover 50 to 51 MHz with better than 1.6:1 SWR.

Element lengths and spacings are given in the table. Elements can be mounted to the boom as shown in **Figure 21.88**. Two muffler clamps hold each aluminum plate to the boom, and two U bolts fasten each element to the plate, which is 0.25 inches thick and 4.4 inches square. Stainless steel is the best choice for hardware. However, galvanized hardware can be substituted. Automotive muffler clamps do not work well in this application, because they are not galvanized and quickly rust once exposed to the weather.

The driven element is mounted to the boom on a phenolic plate of similar dimension to the other mounting plates. A 12 inch piece of Plexiglas rod is inserted into the driven element halves. The Plexiglas allows the use of a single clamp on each side of the element and also seals the center of the elements against moisture. Self-tapping screws are used for electrical connection to the driven element.

Refer to **Figure 21.89** for driven element and hairpin match details. A bracket made from a piece of aluminum is used to mount the three SO-239 connectors to the driven element plate. A 4:1 transmission-line balun connects the two element halves, transforming the 200 Ω resistance at the hairpin match to 50 Ω at the center connector. Note that the electrical length of the balun is λ/2, but the physical length will be shorter due to the velocity factor of the particular coaxial cable used. The hairpin is connected directly across the element halves. The exact center of the hairpin is electrically neutral and should be fastened to the boom. This has the advantage of placing the driven element at dc ground potential.

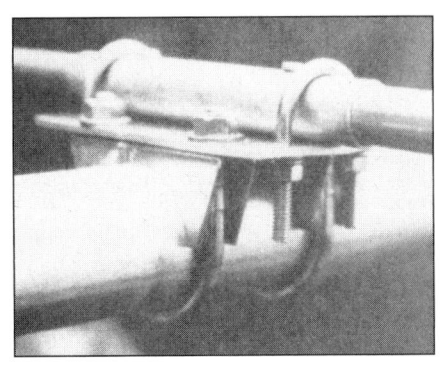

Figure 21.88 — The boom-to-element clamp. Galvanized U-bolts are used to hold the element to the plate, and 2 inch galvanized muffler clamps hold the plates to the boom.

The hairpin match requires no adjustment as such. However, you may have to change the length of the driven element slightly to obtain the best match in your preferred portion of the band. Changing the driven-element length will not adversely affect antenna performance. *Do not adjust the lengths or spacings of the other elements — they are optimized already*. If you decide to use a gamma match, add three inches to each side of the driven element lengths given in the table for both antennas.

Project: Medium-Gain 2 Meter Yagi

This project was designed and built by L. B. Cebik, W4RNL (SK). Practical Yagis for 2 meters abound. What makes this one a bit different is the selection of materials. The elements, of course, are high-grade aluminum. However, the boom is PVC and there are only two #6 nut-bolt sets and two #8 sheet metal screws in the entire antenna. The remaining fasteners are all hitch-pin clips. The result is a very durable six-element Yagi that you can disassemble with fair ease for transport. The antenna is shown in **Figure 21.90**. The complete construction details and more discussion of the antenna are included with the downloadable supplemental content.

THE BASIC ANTENNA DESIGN

The 6 element Yagi presented here is a derivative of the *optimized wide-band antenna* (OWA) designs developed for HF use by NW3Z and WA3FET. **Figure 21.91** shows the general outline. The reflector and first director largely set the impedance. The next 2 directors contribute to setting the operating bandwidth. The final director (Dir. 4) sets the gain. This account is over-simplified, since every element plays a role in every facet of

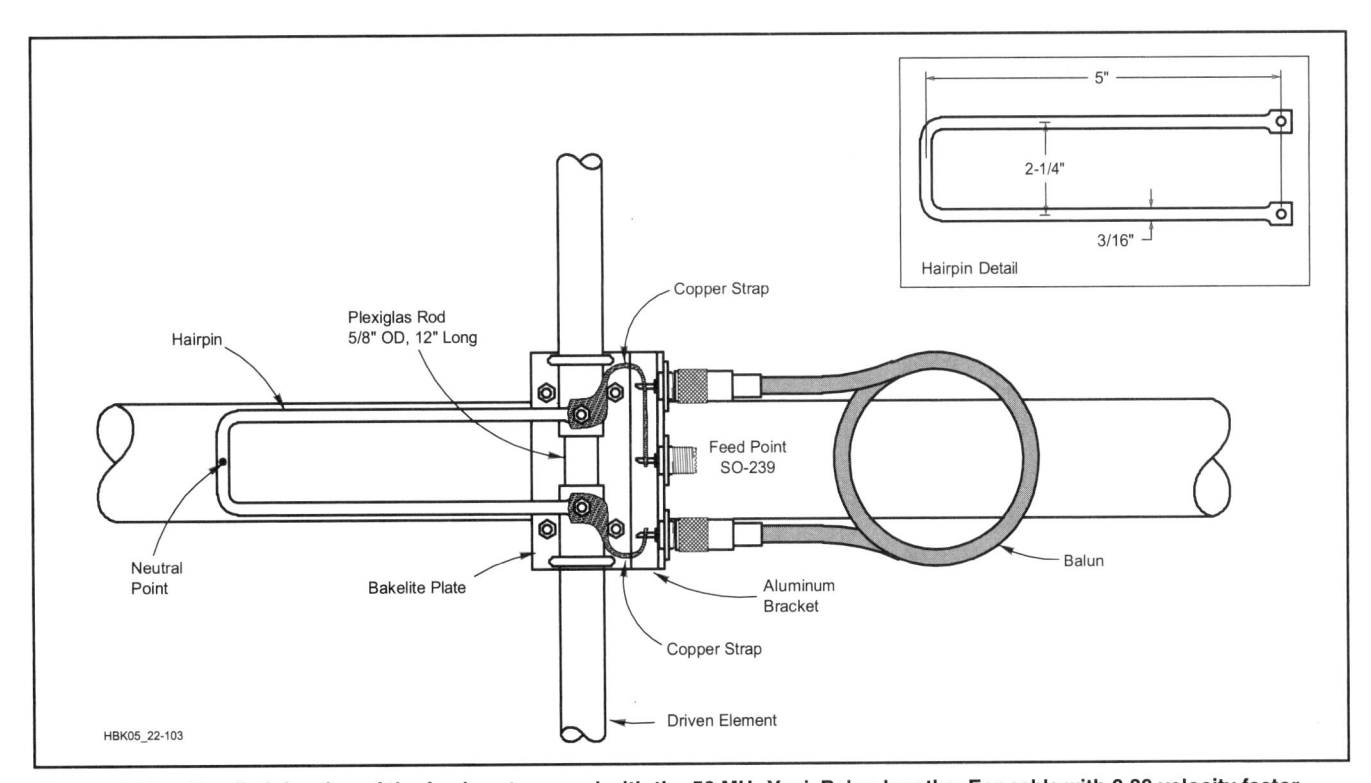

Figure 21.89 — Detailed drawing of the feed system used with the 50 MHz Yagi. Balun lengths: For cable with 0.80 velocity factor — 7 feet, 10⅜ inches. For cable with 0.66 velocity factor — 6 feet, 5¾ inches

Figure 21.90 — The completed 2 meter Yagi is shown with the PVC boom and mast mount.

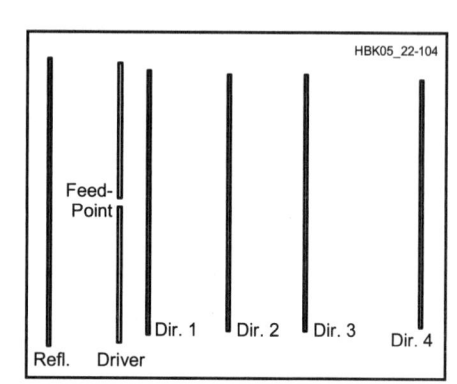

Figure 21.91 — The general outline of the 2 meter, 6 element OWA Yagi. Dimensions are given in Table 21.15.

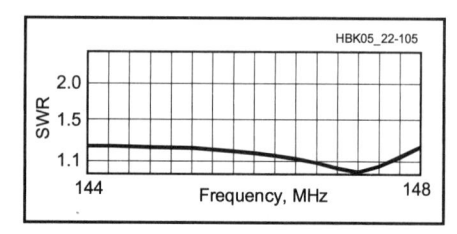

Figure 21.92 — SWR curve for the 2 meter, 6 element OWA Yagi as modeled using *NEC-4*.

Table 21.15
2 Meter OWA Yagi Dimensions

Element	Element Length (in)	Spacing from Reflector (in)	Element Diameter (in)
Version described here:			
Refl.	40.52	—	0.1875
Driver	39.70	10.13	0.5
Alt. Driver	*39.96*	*10.13*	*0.1875*
Dir. 1	37.36	14.32	0.1875
Dir. 2	36.32	25.93	0.1875
Dir. 3	36.32	37.28	0.1875
Dir. 4	34.96	54.22	0.1875
Version using ⅛-inch diameter elements throughout:			
Refl.	40.80	—	0.125
Driver	40.10	10.20	0.125
Dir. 1	37.63	14.27	0.125
Dir. 2	36.56	25.95	0.125
Dir. 3	36.56	37.39	0.125
Dir. 4	35.20	54.44	0.125

Yagi performance. However, the notes give some idea of which elements are most sensitive in adjusting the performance figures.

Designed using *NEC-4*, the antenna uses 6 elements on a 56 inch boom. **Table 21.15** gives the specific dimensions for the version described in these notes. The parasitic elements are all ³⁄₁₆ inch aluminum rods. For ease of construction, the driver is ½ inch aluminum tubing. Do not alter the element diameters without referring to a source, such as RSGB's *The VHF/UHF DX Book*, edited by Ian White, G3SEK, (Chapter 7), for information on how to recalculate element lengths.

The OWA design provides about 10.2 dBi of free-space gain with better than 20 dB front-to-back (or front-to-rear) ratio across the entire 2 meter band. Azimuth (or E-plane) patterns show solid performance across the entire band. This applies not only to forward gain but rejection from the rear.

One significant feature of the OWA design is its direct 50 Ω feed point impedance that requires no matching network. Of course, a choke balun to suppress any currents on the feed line is desirable, and a simple ferrite bead balun (see the **Transmission Lines** chapter) works well in this application. The SWR, shown in **Figure 21.92**, is very flat across the band and never reaches 1.3:1. The SWR and the pattern consistency together create a very useful utility antenna for 2 meters, whether installed vertically or horizontally. The only remaining question is how to effectively build the beam in the average home shop.

The six-element OWA Yagi for 2 meters performs well. It serves as a good utility antenna with more gain and directivity than the usual three-element general-use Yagi. When vertically polarized, the added gain confirms the wisdom of using a longer boom and more elements. With a length under five feet, the antenna is still compact. The ability to disassemble the parts simplifies moving the antenna to various portable sites.

Project: Cheap Yagis by WA5VJB

If you're planning to build an EME array, don't use these antennas. But if you want to put together a VHF rover station with less than $500 in the antennas, read on as Kent Britain, WA5VJB, shows you how to put together a VHF/UHF Yagi with QRO performance at a QRP price. (This material is adapted from Kent's on-line paper "Controlled Impedance 'Cheap' Antennas" at **www.wa5vjb.com/references.html**.) First, a bit of history on the design of these antennas. In 1993 at the Oklahoma City Central States VHF Society Conference, Arnie, CO2KK, spoke on the difficulties building VHF antennas in non-industrialized nations. Just run down to the store and pick up some Delrin insulators and 0.141 inch Teflon coax? Arnie's tales were the motivation to use advanced technology

21.58   Chapter 21

to come up with something simple.

The simplified feed uses the structure of the antenna itself for impedance matching. So the design started with the feed and the elements were built around it. The antennas were designed with *YagiMax*, tweaked in *NEC*, and the driven elements experimentally determined on the antenna range.

Typically a high-gain antenna is designed in the computer, then you try to come up with a driven element matching arrangement for whatever feed point impedance the computer comes up with. In this design, compromises for the feed impedance, asymmetrical feed, simple measurements, wide bandwidth, the ability to grow with the same spacing, and trade-offs for a very clean pattern cost many dB of gain. But you can build these antennas for about $5!

Construction of the antennas is straightforward. The boom is ¾ inch square, or ½ inch by ¾ inch wood. To install an element, drill a hole through the boom and insert the element. A drop of cyanoacrylate "super glue," epoxy, or silicone adhesive is used to hold the elements in place. There is no boom-to-mast plate — drill holes in the boom and use a U-bolt to attach it to the mast!

The life of the antenna is determined by what you coat it with. The author had a 902 MHz version, varnished with polyurethane, in the air for two years with little deterioration.

The parasitic elements on prototypes have been made from silicon-bronze welding rod, aluminum rod, brass hobby tubing, and #10 or #12 AWG solid copper ground wire. So that you can solder to the driven element, use the welding rod, hobby tubing, or copper wire. The driven element is folded at one end with its ends inserted through the boom.

Figure 21.93 shows the basic plan for the antenna and labels the dimensions that are

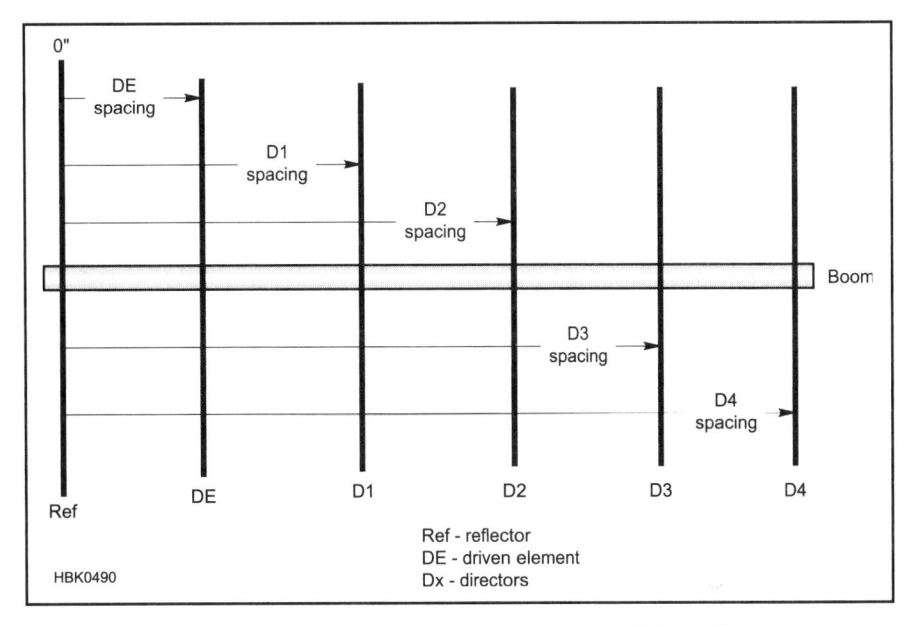

Figure 21.93 — Element spacing for the Cheap Yagis. Refer to Tables 21.16 to 21.23 for exact dimensions for the various bands.

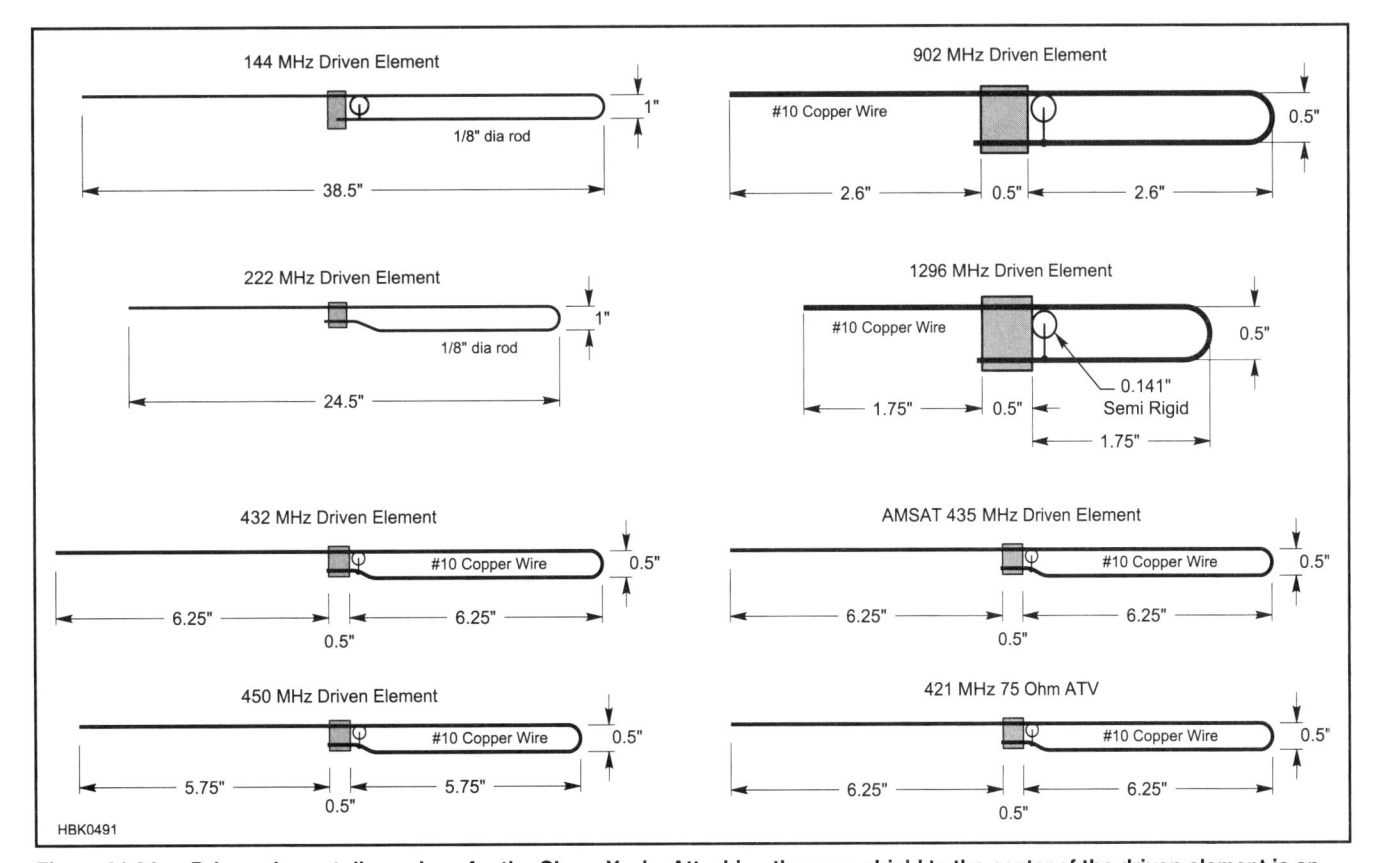

Figure 21.94 — Driven element dimensions for the Cheap Yagis. Attaching the coax shield to the center of the driven element is appropriate because that is the lowest impedance point of the element.

Antennas 21.59

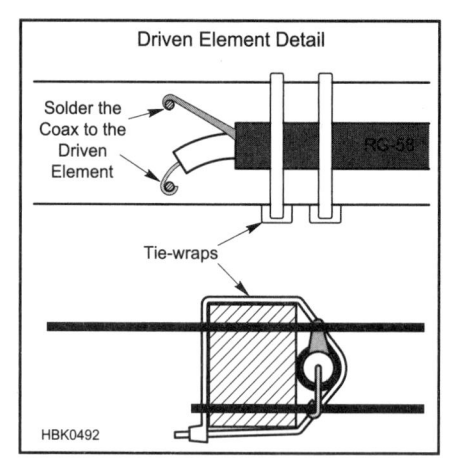

Figure 21.95 — Construction details and feed line attachment for the Cheap Yagi driven element.

given in the table for each band. All table dimensions are given in inches.

Figure 21.94 shows how the driven element is constructed for each antenna. Trim the free end of the driven element to tune it for minimum SWR at the desired frequency. **Figure 21.95** shows how to attach coaxial cable to the feed point. Sliding a quarter-wave sleeve along the coax had little effect, so there's not much RF on the outside of the coax. You may use a ferrite bead choke balun if you like, but these antennas are designed for minimum expense!

144 MHz Yagi

While others have reported good luck with 16 element long-boom wood antennas, six elements was about the maximum for most rovers. The design is peaked at 144.2 MHz, but performance is still good at 146.5 MHz. All parasitic elements are made from ³⁄₁₆ inch aluminum rod and the driven element is made from ⅛ inch rod. Lengths and spacings are given in **Table 21.16**.

222 MHz Yagi

This antenna is peaked at 222.1 MHz, but performance has barely changed at 223.5 MHz. You can drill the mounting holes to mount it with the elements horizontal or vertical. All parasitic elements are made from ³⁄₁₆ inch aluminum rod and the driven element is made from ⅛ inch rod. Lengths and spacings are given in **Table 21.17**.

432 MHz Yagi

At this band the antenna is getting very practical and easy to build. All parasitic elements are made from ⅛ inch diameter rod and the driven element is made from #10 AWG solid copper wire. Lengths and spacings are given in **Table 21.18**.

435 MHz Yagi for AMSAT

KA9LNV provided help and motivation for these antennas. A high front-to-back ratio (F/B) was a major design consideration of all versions. The model predicts 30 dB F/B for the six-element and over 40 dB for the others. For gain, *NEC* predicts 11.2 dBi for the six-element, 12.6 dBi for the eight-element, and 13.5 dBi for the 10 element, and 13.8 dBi for the 11 element.

Using ¾ inch square wood for the boom makes it easy to build two antennas on the

Table 21.16
WA5VJB 144 MHz Yagi Dimensions

		Ref	DE	D1	D2	D3	D4
3-element	Length	41.0	—	37.0			
	Spacing	0	8.5	20.0			
4-element	Length	41.0	—	37.5	33.0		
	Spacing	0	8.5	19.25	40.5		
6-element	Length	40.5	—	37.5	36.5	36.5	32.75
	Spacing	0	7.5	16.5	34.0	52.0	70.0

Dimensions in inches.

Table 21.17
WA5VJB 222 MHz Yagi Dimensions

		Ref	DE	D1	D2	D3	D4
3-element	Length	26.0	—	23.75			
	Spacing	0	5.5	13.5			
4-element	Length	26.25	—	24.1	22.0		
	Spacing	0	5.0	11.75	23.5		
6-element	Length	26.25	—	24.1	23.5	23.5	21.0
	Spacing	0	5.0	10.75	22.0	33.75	45.5

Dimensions in inches.

Table 21.18
WA5VJB 432 MHz Yagi Dimensions

		Ref	DE	D1	D2	D3	D4	D5	D6	D7	D8	D9
6-element	Length	13.5	—	12.5	12.0	12.0	11.0					
	Spacing	0	2.5	5.5	11.25	17.5	24.0					
8-element	Length	13.5	—	12.5	12.0	12.0	12.0	12.0	11.25			
	Spacing	0	2.5	5.5	11.25	17.5	24.0	30.75	38.0			
11-element	Length	13.5	—	12.5	12.0	12.0	12.0	12.0	12.0	11.75	11.75	11.0
	Spacing	0	2.5	5.5	11.25	17.5	24.0	30.75	38.0	45.5	53.0	59.5

Dimensions in inches.

Table 21.19
WA5VJB 435 MHz Yagi Dimensions

		Ref	DE	D1	D2	D3	D4	D5	D6	D7	D8	D9
6-element	Length	13.4	—	12.4	12.0	12.0	11.0					
8-element	Length	13.4	—	12.4	12.0	12.0	12.0	12.0	11.1			
10-element	Length	13.4	—	12.4	12.0	12.0	12.0	12.0	11.75	11.75	11.1	
11-element	Length	13.4	—	12.4	12.0	12.0	12.0	12.0	11.75	11.75	11.75	11.1
	Spacing	0	2.5	5.5	11.25	17.5	24.0	30.5	37.75	45.0	52.0	59.5

Dimensions in inches.

same boom for cross-polarization. Offset the two antennas 6½ inches along the boom and feed them in-phase for circular polarization, or just use one for portable operations. All parasitic elements are made from ⅛ inch diameter rod and the driven element is made from #10 AWG solid copper wire. Lengths and spacings are given in **Table 21.19**. The same element spacing is used for all four versions of the antenna.

450 MHz Yagi

For FM, this six-element Yagi is a good, cheap antenna to get a newcomer into a repeater or make a simplex-FM QSO during a contest. The author used ⅛ inch diameter aluminum ground wire in the prototype for all the elements except the driven element, which is made from #10 AWG solid copper wire. Other ⅛ inch diameter material could be used. Lengths and spacings are given in **Table 21.20**.

902 MHz Yagi

This was the first antenna the author built using the antenna to control the driven element impedance. The 2.5 foot length has proven very practical. All parasitic elements are made from ⅛ inch diameter rod and the driven element is made from #10 AWG solid copper wire. Lengths and spacings are given in **Table 21.21**.

1296 MHz Yagi

This antenna is the veteran of several "Grid-peditions" and has measured 13.5 dBi on the Central States VHF Society antenna range. Dimensions must be followed with great care. The driven element is small enough to allow 0.141 inch semi-rigid coax to be used. The prototype antennas use ⅛ inch silicon-bronze welding rod for the elements, but any ⅛ inch-diameter material can be used. The driven element is made from #10 AWG solid copper wire. Lengths and spacings are given in **Table 21.22**.

421.25 MHz 75 Ω Yagi for ATV

421 MHz vestigial sideband video is popular in North Texas for receiving the FM video input repeaters. These antennas are made for 421 MHz use and the driven element is designed for 75 Ω. RG-59 or an F adapter to RG-6 can be directly connected to a cable-TV converter or cable-ready TV on channel 57. All parasitic elements are made from ⅛ inch diameter rod and the driven element is made from #10 AWG solid copper wire. Lengths and spacings are given in **Table 21.23**. The same spacing is used for all versions.

Project: Fixed Moxons for Satellite Operation

The following project is based on the article, "A Simple Fixed Antenna for VHF/UHF Satellite Work" by the late L.B. Cebik, W4RNL, from the August 2001 issue of *QST*. The complete article is available with the downloadable supplemental content. This design produces a simple, reliable, fixed antenna that provides nearly hemispherical coverage for satellite operation on 145 and 435 MHz.

Many fixed-position satellite antennas for VHF and UHF have used a version of the *turnstile*. The word "turnstile" actually refers to two different ideas. One is a particular antenna: two crossed dipoles fed 90° out of phase, usually with a reflecting screen behind the dipoles. The other is the principle of obtaining omnidirectional patterns by diving almost any crossed antennas 90° out of phase. The second idea opens the door to adapting many possible antenna designs to omnidirectional coverage.

Figure 21.96 shows a general method of obtaining the 90° phase shift for omnidirectional patterns. Note that the coax center conductor connects to only one of the two crossed elements. A ¼-λ section of transmission line that has the same characteristic impedance as the natural feed point impedance of the first antenna element alone connects one element to the next. The opposing ends of the two elements go to the shield at each end of the

---

Table 21.20
WA5VJB 450 MHz Yagi Dimensions

		Ref	DE	D1	D2	D3	D4
6-element	Length	13.0	—	12.1	11.75	11.75	10.75
	Spacing	0	2.5	5.5	11.0	18.0	28.5

Dimensions in inches.

Table 21.21
WA5VJB 902 MHz Yagi Dimensions

		Ref	DE	D1	D2	D3	D4	D5	D6	D7	D8
10-element	Length	6.2	—	5.6	5.5	5.5	5.4	5.3	5.2	5.1	5.1
	Spacing	0	2.4	3.9	5.8	9.0	12.4	17.4	22.4	27.6	33.0

Dimensions in inches.

Table 21.22
WA5VJB 1296 MHz Yagi Dimensions

		Ref	DE	D1	D2	D3	D4	D5	D6	D7	D8
10-element	Length	4.3	—	3.9	3.8	3.75	3.75	3.65	3.6	3.6	3.5
	Spacing	0	1.7	2.8	4.0	6.3	8.7	12.2	15.6	19.3	23.0

Dimensions in inches.

Table 21.23
WA5VJB 421.25 MHz 75-Ω Yagi Dimensions

		Ref	DE	D1	D2	D3	D4	D5	D6	D7	D8	D9
6-element	Length	14.0	—	12.5	12.25	12.25	11.0					
9-element	Length	14.0	—	12.5	12.25	12.25	12.0	12.0	11.25			
11-element	Length	14.0	—	12.5	12.25	12.25	12.0	12.0	12.0	11.75	11.75	11.5
	Spacing	0	3.0	6.5	12.25	17.75	24.5	30.5	36.0	43.0	50.25	57.25

Dimensions in inches.

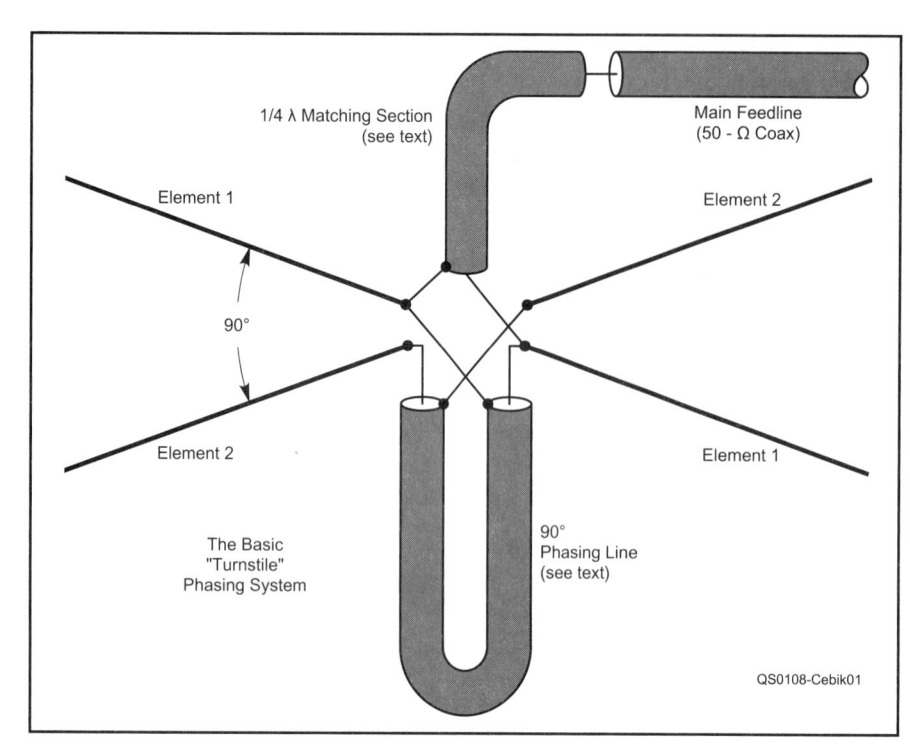

Figure 21.96 — The basic turnstile phasing (and matching) system for any antenna set requiring a 90° phase shift between driven elements in proximity.

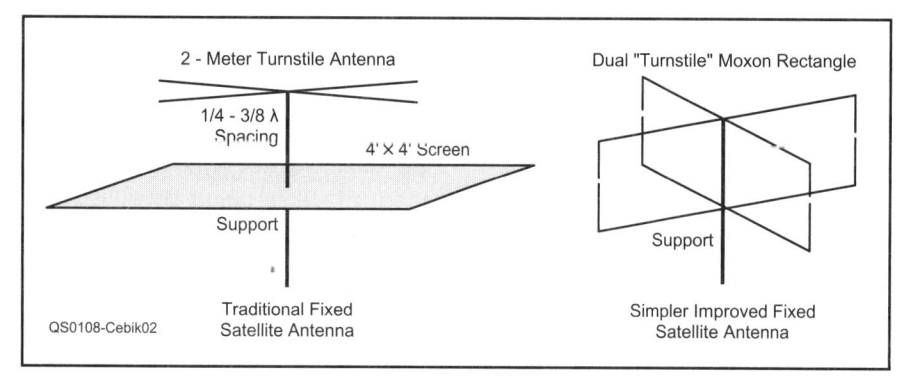

Figure 21.97 — Alternative schemes for fixed-position satellite antennas: the traditional turnstile-and-screen and a pair of "turnstiled" Moxon rectangles.

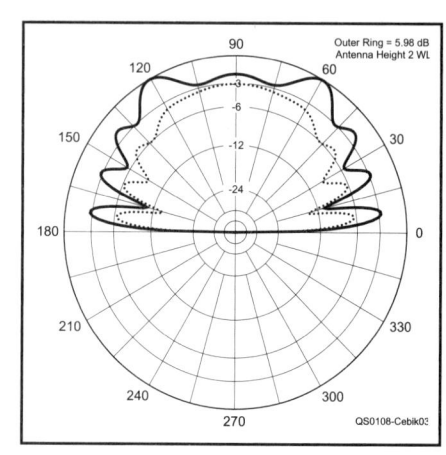

Figure 21.98 — A comparison of elevation patterns for the turnstile-and- screen system (with ⅜ λ wavelength spacing, shown by the solid black line) and a Moxon pair (dashed line), both at 2 λ height.

transmission line. The resulting impedance at the overall antenna feed point will be exactly half the impedance of one element alone. If dipoles are used, the feed point impedance will be approximately 35 Ω.

The dual Moxon rectangle array, shown in outline form on the right of **Figure 21.98**, offers some advantages over the traditional turnstile. (The article "Having a Field Day with the Moxon Rectangle," by L.B. Cebik describes the Moxon in detail and is included with the downloadable supplemental content.) First, it yields a somewhat better dome-like pattern. Second, it is relatively easy to build and compact to install. The Moxon pair, with lower but smoother gain across the dome of the sky, offers the fixed-antenna user the chance to build a successful beginning satellite antenna.

Figure 21.98 shows the elevation patterns of a turnstile-and-screen and of a pair of Moxon rectangles when both are 2 λ above the ground. A 1 λ height will reduce the low angle ripples even more, if that height is feasible. The elevation patterns show the considerably smoother pattern dome of the Moxon pair over the traditional turnstile. The middle of the turnstile dome has nearly 2 dB less gain than its peaks, while the top valleys are nearly 3 dB lower than the peaks. The peaks and valleys can make the difference between successful communications and broken-up transmissions.

Without requiring a reflecting screen which would narrow the antenna's beamwidth, the azimuthal pattern will be circular within under a 0.2-dB difference for 145.5 to 146.5 MHz, and within 0.5 dB for the entire 2 meter band. Since satellite work is concentrated in the 145.8 to 146.0 MHz region, the broadbanded antenna will prove fairly easy to build with success. A 435.6 MHz version, designed to cover the 435 to 436.2 MHz region of satellite activity will have an even larger bandwidth.

Like the dipole-based turnstile, the Moxons are fed 90° out of phase with a ¼-λ phasing line of 50-Ω coaxial cable as shown in Figure 21.96. Since the natural feed point impedance of a single Moxon rectangle of the design used here is 50 Ω, the pair will show a 25-Ω feed-point impedance. Paralleled ¼-λ sections of 70- to 75-Ω coaxial cable, such as RG-59, will transform the low impedance to a good match for the main 50-Ω coaxial feed line.

Figure 21.99 shows the critical dimensions for a Moxon rectangle. The lettered references are keys to the dimensions in **Table 21.24**. The design frequencies for the two satellite antenna pairs are 145.9 MHz and 435.5 MHz, the centers of the satellite activity on these two bands. The 2 meter Moxon prototype uses ³⁄₁₆-inch diameter rod, while the 435 MHz version uses #12 AWG wire with a nominal 0.0808-inch diameter. Going one small step up or down in element diameter will still produce a usable antenna, but major diameter changes will require that the dimensions be recalculated. (Complete construction details and drawings are available with the downloadable supplemental content.)

The antennas can be mounted on the same mast. However, for similar patterns, they should each be the same number of wavelengths above ground. For example, if the

21.62   Chapter 21

Table 21.24
Dimensions for Moxon Rectangles for Satellite Use
Two are required for each antenna. The phase-line is 50-Ω coaxial cable and the matching line is parallel sections of 75-Ω coaxial cable. Low power cables less than 0.15 inches in outer diameter were used in the prototypes. See Figure 21.99 for letter references. All dimensions are in inches.

Dimension	145.9 MHz	435.6 MHz
A	29.05	9.72
B	3.81	1.25
C	1.40	0.49
D	5.59	1.88
E (B + C + D)	10.80	3.62
¼ wavelength	20.22	6.77
Phasing and matching lines (0.66 velocity factor)	13.35	4.47

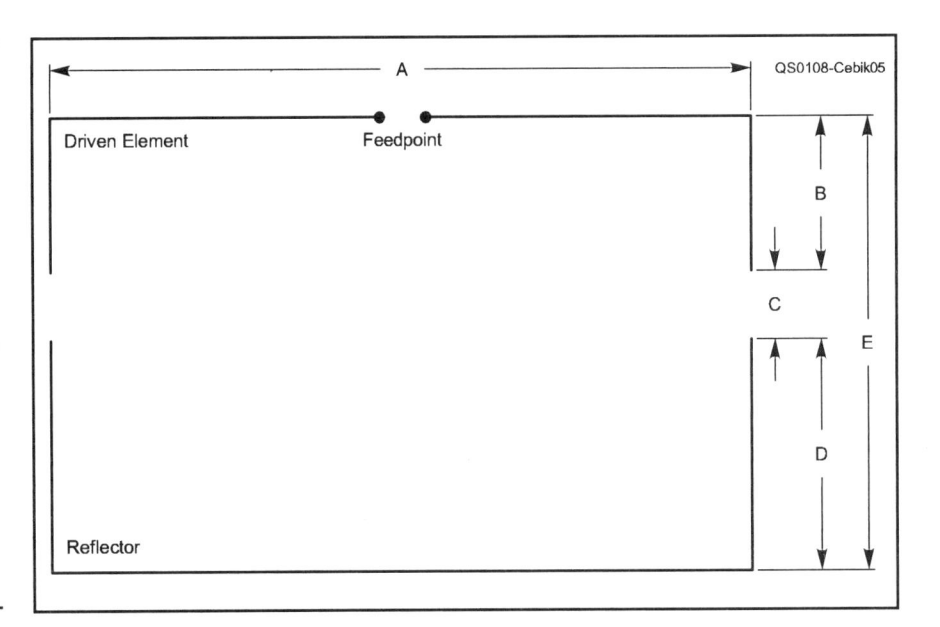

Figure 21.99 — The basic dimensions of a Moxon rectangle. Two identical rectangles are required for each "turnstiled" pair. See Table 21.24 for letter references.

2 meter antenna is about two wavelengths up at about 14 feet or so, then the bottom of the 435-MHz antenna should be only about 4.5 feet above the ground. Placing the higher-frequency antenna below the 2 meter assembly will create some small irregularities in the desired dome pattern, but not serious enough to affect general operation.

There is no useful adjustment to these antennas except for making the gap between the drivers and reflectors as accurate as possible. Turnstile antennas show a very broad SWR curve. Across 2 meters, for example, the highest SWR is under 1.1:1. However, serious errors in the phasing line length can result in distortions to the desired circular pattern. There is no substitute for checking the lengths of the phasing line and the matching section several times before cutting. The correct length is from one junction to the next, including the portions of exposed cable interior.

21.12 Radio Direction Finding Antennas

Radio direction finding (RDF) is almost as old as radio communication. It gained prominence when the British Navy used it to track the movement of enemy ships in World War I. Since then, governments and the military have developed sophisticated and complex RDF systems. Fortunately, simple equipment, purchased or built at home, is quite effective in Amateur Radio RDF.

In European and Asian countries, direction-finding contests are foot races. The object is to be first to find four or five transmitters in a large wooded park. Young athletes have the best chance of capturing the prizes. This sport is known as *foxhunting* (after the British hill-and-dale horseback events) or *ARDF* (Amateur Radio direction finding). It is growing in popularity here in North America. Today, most competitive hunts worldwide are for 144 MHz FM signals, though other VHF bands are also used. Some international foxhunts include 3.5 MHz events.

In North America and England, most RDF contests involve mobiles — cars, trucks, and vans, even motorcycles. It may be possible to drive all the way to the transmitter, or there may be a short hike at the end, called a *sniff*. These competitions are also called foxhunting by some, while others use *bunny hunting*, *T-hunting* or the classic term *hidden transmitter hunting*.

Even without participating in RDF contests, you will find knowledge of the techniques useful. They simplify the search for a neighborhood source of power-line interference or TV cable leakage. RDF must be used to track down emergency radio beacons, which signal the location of pilots and boaters in distress. Amateur Radio enthusiasts skilled in transmitter hunting are in demand by agencies such as the Civil Air Patrol and the US Coast Guard Auxiliary for search and rescue support. RDF is an important part of the evidence-gathering process in interference cases.

The most basic RDF system consists of a directional antenna and a method of detecting and measuring the level of the radio signal, such as a receiver with signal strength indicator. RDF antennas range from a simple tuned loop of wire to an acre of antenna elements with an electronic beam-forming network. Other sophisticated techniques for RDF use the Doppler effect or measure the time of arrival difference of the signal at multiple antennas.

All of these methods have been used from 2 to 500 MHz and above. However, RDF practices vary greatly between the HF and VHF/UHF portions of the spectrum. For practical reasons, high gain beams, Dopplers and switched dual antennas find favor on VHF/UHF, while loops and phased arrays are the most popular choices on 6 meters and below. Signal propagation differences between HF and VHF also affect RDF practices. But many basic transmitter-hunting techniques, discussed later in this chapter, apply to all bands

Antennas 21.63

and all types of portable RDF equipment.

Several RDF projects may be found with the downloadable supplemental content along with a thorough article on Direction-Finding Techniques and mobile RDF system installation, including some examples of mobile RDF antenna mounting.

21.12.1 RDF Antennas for HF Bands

Below 50 MHz, gain antennas such as Yagis and quads are of limited value for RDF. The typical tribander installation yields only a general direction of the incoming signal, due to ground effects and the antenna's broad forward lobe. Long monoband beams at greater heights work better, but still cannot achieve the bearing accuracy and repeatability of simpler antennas designed specifically for RDF.

RDF LOOPS

An effective directional HF antenna can be as uncomplicated as a small loop of wire or tubing, tuned to resonance with a capacitor. When immersed in an electromagnetic field, the loop acts much the same as the secondary winding of a transformer. The voltage at the output is proportional to the amount of flux passing through it and the number of turns. If the loop is oriented such that the greatest amount of area is presented to the magnetic field, the induced voltage will be the highest. If it is rotated so that little or no area is cut by the field lines, the voltage induced in the loop is zero and a null occurs.

To achieve this transformer effect, the loop must be small compared with the signal wavelength. In a single-turn loop, the conductor should be less than 0.08λ long. For example, a 28 MHz loop should be less than 34 inches in circumference, giving a diameter of approximately 10 inches. The loop may be smaller, but that will reduce its voltage output. Maximum output from a small loop antenna is in directions corresponding to the plane of the loop; these lobes are very broad. Sharp nulls, obtained at right angles to that plane, are more useful for RDF.

For a perfect bidirectional pattern, the loop must be balanced electrostatically with respect to ground. Otherwise, it will exhibit two modes of operation, the mode of a perfect loop and that of a non-directional vertical antenna of small dimensions. This dual-mode condition results in mild to severe inaccuracy, depending on the degree of imbalance, because the outputs of the two modes are not in phase.

The theoretical true loop pattern is illustrated in **Figure 21.100A**. When properly balanced, there are two nulls exactly 180° apart. When the unwanted antenna effect is appreciable and the loop is tuned to resonance, the loop may exhibit little directivity, as shown in Figure 21.100B. By detuning the loop to shift the phasing, you may obtain a useful pattern similar to Figure 21.100C. While not symmetrical, and not necessarily at right angles to the plane of the loop, this pattern does exhibit a pair of nulls.

By careful detuning and amplitude balancing, you can approach the unidirectional pattern of Figure 21.100D. Even though there may not be a complete null in the pattern, it resolves the 180° ambiguity of Figure 21.100A. Korean War era military loop antennas, sometimes available on today's surplus market, use this controlled antenna effect principle.

An easy way to achieve good electrostatic balance is to shield the loop, as shown in **Figure 21.101**. The shield, represented by the dashed lines in the drawing, eliminates the antenna effect. The response of a well-constructed shielded loop is quite close to the ideal pattern of Figure 21.100A.

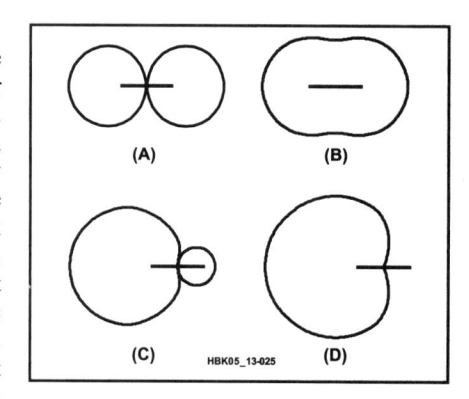

Figure 21.100 — Small loop field patterns with varying amounts of antenna effect — the undesired response of a loop acting merely as a mass of metal connected to the receiver antenna terminals. The horizontal lines show the plane of the loop turns.

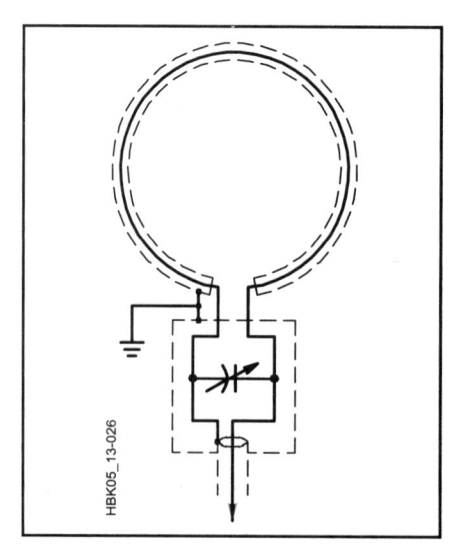

Figure 21.101 — Electrostatically-shielded loop for RDF. To prevent shielding of the loop from magnetic fields, leave the shield unconnected at one end.

For 160 through 30 meters, single-turn loops that are small enough for portability are usually unsatisfactory for RDF work. Multi-turn loops are generally used instead. They are easier to resonate with practical capacitor values and give higher output voltages. This type of loop may also be shielded. If the total conductor length remains below 0.08λ, the directional pattern is that of Figure 21.100A.

FERRITE ROD ANTENNAS

Another way to get higher loop output is to increase the permeability of the medium in the vicinity of the loop. By winding a coil of wire around a form made of high-permeability material, such as ferrite rod, much greater flux is obtained in the coil without increasing the cross-sectional area.

Modern magnetic core materials make compact directional receiving antennas practical. Most portable AM broadcast receivers use this type of antenna, commonly called a *loopstick*. The loopstick is the most popular RDF antenna for portable/mobile work on 160 and 80 meters.

Like the shielded loop discussed earlier, the loopstick responds to the magnetic field of the incoming radio wave, and not to the electrical field. For a given size of loop, the output voltage increases with increasing flux density, which is obtained by choosing a ferrite core of high permeability and low loss at the frequency of interest. For increased output, the turns may be wound over two rods taped together. A practical loopstick antenna is described later in this chapter.

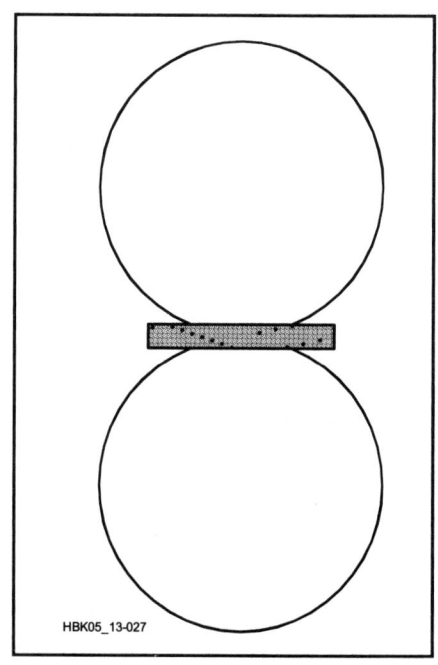

Figure 21.102 — Field pattern for a ferrite-rod antenna. The dark bar represents the rod on which the loop turns are wound.

A loop on a ferrite core has maximum signal response in the plane of the turns, just as an air core loop. This means that maximum response of a loopstick is broadside to the axis of the rod, as shown in **Figure 21.102**. The loopstick may be shielded to eliminate the antenna effect; a U-shaped or C-shaped channel of aluminum or other form of "trough" is best. The shield must not be closed, and its length should equal or slightly exceed the length of the rod.

SENSE ANTENNAS

Because there are two nulls 180° apart in the directional pattern of a small loop or loopstick, there is ambiguity as to which null indicates the true direction of the target station. For example, if the line of bearing runs east and west from your position, you have no way of knowing from this single bearing whether the transmitter is east of you or west of you.

If bearings can be taken from two or more positions at suitable direction and distance from the transmitter, the ambiguity can be resolved and distance can be estimated by triangulation, as discussed later in this chapter. However, it is almost always desirable to be able to resolve the ambiguity immediately by having a unidirectional antenna pattern available.

You can modify a loop or loopstick antenna pattern to have a single null by adding a second antenna element. This element is called a *sense antenna*, because it senses the phase of the signal wavefront for comparison with the phase of the loop output signal. The sense element must be omnidirectional, such as a short vertical. When signals from the loop and the sense antenna are combined with 90° phase shift between the two, a heart-shaped (cardioid) pattern results, as shown in **Figure 21.103A**.

Figure 21.103B shows a circuit for adding a sense antenna to a loop or loopstick. For the best null in the composite pattern, signals from the loop and sense antennas must be of equal amplitude. R1 adjusts the level of the signal from the sense antenna.

In a practical system, the cardioid pattern null is not as sharp as the bidirectional null of the loop alone. The usual procedure when transmitter hunting is to use the loop alone to obtain a precise line of bearing, then switch in the sense antenna and take another reading to resolve the ambiguity.

PHASED ARRAYS AND ADCOCK ANTENNAS

Two-element phased arrays are popular for amateur HF RDF base station installations. Many directional patterns are possible, depending on the spacing and phasing of the elements. A useful example is two ½ λ elements spaced ¼ λ apart and fed 90° out of phase. The resultant pattern is a cardioid, with a null off one end of the axis of the two antennas and a broad peak in the opposite direction. The directional frequency range of this antenna is limited to one band, because of the critical length of the phasing lines.

The best-known phased array for RDF is the Adcock, named after the man who invented it in 1919. It consists of two vertical elements fed 180° apart, mounted so the array may be rotated. Element spacing is not critical, and may be in the range from 0.1 to 0.75 λ. The two elements must be of identical lengths, but need not be self-resonant; shorter elements are commonly used. Because neither the element spacing nor length is critical in terms of wavelengths, an Adcock array may operate over more than one amateur band.

Figure 21.104 is a schematic of a typical Adcock configuration, called the H-Adcock because of its shape. Response to a vertically polarized wave is very similar to a conven-

Figure 21.103 — At A, the directivity pattern of a loop antenna with sensing element. At B is a circuit for combining the signals from the two elements. Adjust C1 for resonance with T1 at the operating frequency.

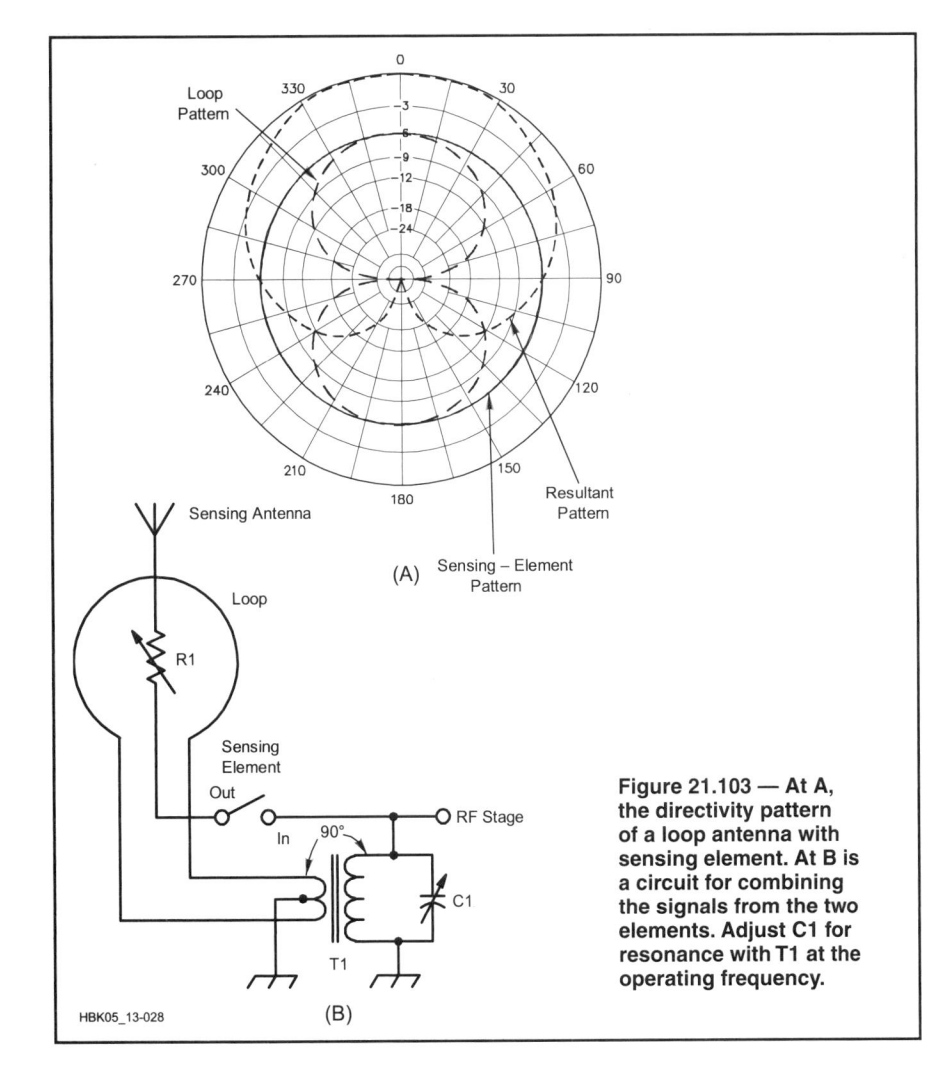

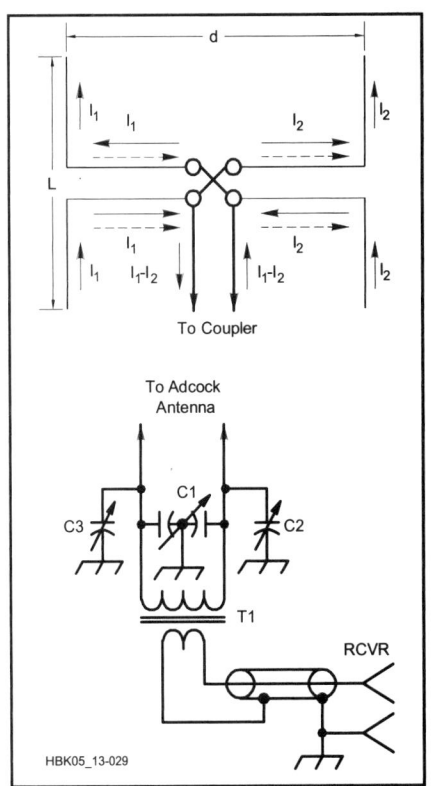

Figure 21.104 — A simple Adcock antenna and its coupler.

Antennas 21.65

tional loop. The passing wave induces currents I1 and I2 into the vertical members. The output current in the transmission line is equal to their difference. Consequently, the directional pattern has two broad peaks and two sharp nulls, like the loop. The magnitude of the difference current is proportional to the spacing (d) and length (l) of the elements. You will get somewhat higher gain with larger dimensions. The Adcock of **Figure 21.105**, designed for 40 meters, has element lengths of 12 feet and spacing of 21 feet (approximately 0.15 λ).

Figure 21.106 shows the radiation pattern of the Adcock. The nulls are broadside to the axis of the array, becoming sharper with increased element spacing. When element spacing exceeds ¾ λ, however, the antenna begins to take on additional unwanted nulls off the ends of the array axis.

The Adcock is a vertically polarized antenna. The vertical elements do not respond to horizontally polarized waves, and the currents induced in the horizontal members by a horizontally polarized wave (dotted arrows in Figure 21.104) tend to balance out regardless of the orientation of the antenna.

Since the Adcock uses a balanced feed system, a coupler is required to match the unbalanced input of the receiver. T1 is an air-wound coil with a two-turn link wrapped around the middle. The combination is resonated with C1 to the operating frequency. C2 and C3 are null-clearing capacitors. Adjust them by placing a low-power signal source some distance from the antenna and exactly broadside to it. Adjust C2 and C3 until the deepest null is obtained.

While you can use a metal support for the mast and boom, wood is preferable because of its non-conducting properties. Similarly, a mast of thick-wall PVC pipe gives less distortion of the antenna pattern than a metallic mast. Place the coupler on the ground below the wiring harness junction on the boom and connect it with a short length of 300 Ω twin-lead-feed line.

LOOPS VS PHASED ARRAYS

Loops are much smaller than phased arrays for the same frequency, and are thus the obvious choice for portable/mobile HF RDF. For base stations in a triangulation network, where the 180° ambiguity is not a problem, Adcocks are preferred. In general, they give sharper nulls than loops, but this is in part a function of the care used in constructing and feeding the individual antennas, as well as of the spacing of the elements. The primary construction considerations are the shielding and balancing of the feed line against unwanted signal pickup and the balancing of the antenna for a symmetrical pattern. Users report that Adcocks are somewhat less sensitive to proximity effects, probably because their larger aperture offers some space diversity.

Skywave Considerations

Until now we have considered the directional characteristics of the RDF loop only in the two-dimensional azimuthal plane. In three-dimensional space, the response of a vertically oriented small loop is doughnut-shaped. The bidirectional null (analogous to a line through the doughnut hole) is in the line of bearing in the azimuthal plane and toward the horizon in the vertical plane. Therefore, maximum null depth is achieved only on signals arriving at 0° elevation angle.

Skywave signals usually arrive at nonzero wave angles. As the elevation angle increases, the null in a vertically oriented loop pattern becomes shallower. It is possible to tilt the loop to seek the null in elevation as well as azimuth. Some amateur RDF enthusiasts report success at estimating distance to the target by measurement of the elevation angle with a tilted loop and computations based on estimated height of the propagating ionospheric layer. This method seldom provides high accuracy with simple loops, however.

Most users prefer Adcocks to loops for skywave work, because the Adcock null is present at all elevation angles. Note, however, that an Adcock has a null in all directions from signals arriving from overhead. Thus for very high angles, such as under-250-mile skip on 80 and 40 meters, neither loops nor Adcocks will perform well.

ELECTRONIC ANTENNA ROTATION

State-of-the-art fixed RDF stations for government and military work use antenna arrays of stationary elements, rather than mechanically rotatable arrays. The best-known type is the *Wullenweber antenna*. It has a large number of elements arranged in a circle, usually outside of a circular reflecting screen. Depending on the installation, the circle may be anywhere from a few hundred feet to more than a quarter of a mile in diameter. Although the Wullenweber is not practical for most amateurs, some of the techniques it uses may be applied to amateur RDF.

The device, which permits rotating the antenna beam without moving the elements, has the classic name *radio goniometer*, or simply *goniometer*. Early goniometers were RF transformers with fixed coils connected to the array elements and a moving pickup coil connected to the receiver input. Both amplitude and phase of the signal coupled into the pickup winding are altered with coil rotation in a way that corresponded to actually rotating the array itself. With sufficient elements and a goniometer, accurate RDF measurements can be taken in all compass directions.

Beam Forming Networks

By properly sampling and combining signals from individual elements in a large array, an antenna beam is electronically rotated or steered. With an appropriate number and arrangement of elements in the system, it is possible to form almost any desired antenna pattern by summing the sampled signals in appropriate amplitude and phase relationships. Delay networks and/or attenuation are added in line with selected elements before summation to create these relationships.

To understand electronic beam forming, first consider just two elements, shown as A and B in **Figure 21.107**. Also shown is the wavefront of a radio signal arriving from a distant transmitter. The wavefront strikes element A first, then travels somewhat farther before it strikes element B. Thus, there is an interval between the times that the wavefront reaches elements A and B.

We can measure the differences in arrival

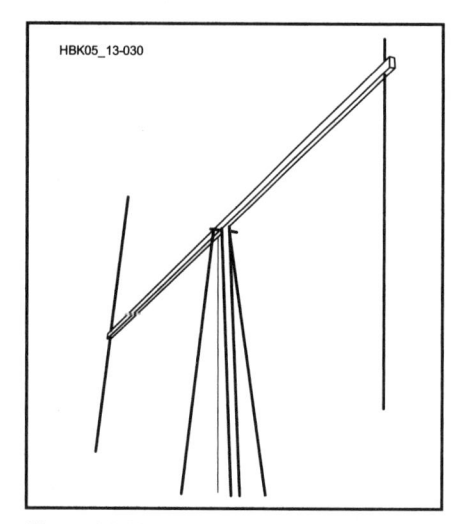

Figure 21.105 — An experimental Adcock antenna on a wooden frame.

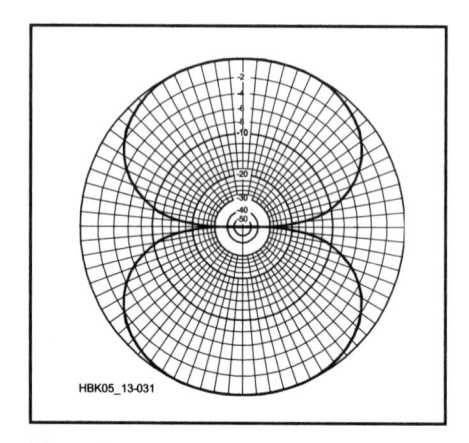

Figure 21.106 — The pattern of an Adcock array with element spacing of ½ wavelength. The elements are aligned with the vertical axis.

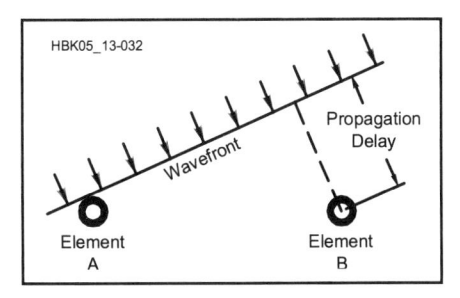

Figure 21.107 — One technique used in elec-tronic beam forming. By delaying the sig-nal from element A by an amount equal to the propagation delay, two signals are summed precisely in phase, even though the signal is not in the broadside direction.

times by delaying the signal received at element A before summing it with that from element B. If two signals are combined directly, the amplitude of the sum will be maximum when the delay for element A exactly equals the propagation delay, giving an in-phase condition at the summation point. On the other hand, if one of the signals is inverted and the two are added, the signals will combine in a 180° out-of-phase relationship when the element A delay equals the propagation delay, creating a null. Either way, once the time delay is determined by the amount of delay required for a peak or null, we can convert it to distance. Then trigonometry calculations provide the direction from which the wave is arriving.

Altering the delay in small increments steers the peak (or null) of the antenna. The system is not frequency sensitive, other than the frequency range limitations of the array elements. Lumped-constant networks are suitable for delay elements if the system is used only for receiving. Delay lines at installations used for transmitting and receiving employ rolls of coaxial cable of various lengths, chosen for the time delay they provide at all frequencies, rather than as simple phasing lines designed for a single frequency.

Combining signals from additional elements narrows the broad beamwidth of the pattern from the two elements and suppress unwanted sidelobes. Electronically switching the delays and attenuations to the various elements causes the formed beam to rotate around the compass. The package of electronics that does this, including delay lines and electronically switched attenuators, is the beam-forming network.

21.12.2 Methods for VHF/UHF RDF

Three distinct methods of mobile RDF are commonly in use by amateurs on VHF/UHF bands: directional antennas, switched dual antennas and Dopplers. Each has advantages over the others in certain situations.

Many RDF enthusiasts employ more than one method when transmitter hunting.

DIRECTIONAL ANTENNAS

Ordinary mobile transceivers and handhelds work well for foxhunting on the popular VHF bands. If you have a lightweight beam and your receiver has an easy-to-read S meter, you are nearly ready to start. All you need is an RF attenuator and some way to mount the setup in your vehicle.

Amateurs seldom use fractional wavelength loops for RDF above 60 MHz because they have bidirectional characteristics and low sensitivity, compared to other practical VHF antennas. Sense circuits for loops are difficult to implement at VHF, and signal reflections tend to fill in the nulls. Typically VHF loops are used only for close-in sniffing where their compactness and sharp nulls are assets, and low gain is of no consequence.

Phased Arrays

The small size and simplicity of two-element driven arrays make them a common choice of newcomers at VHF RDF. Antennas such as phased ground planes and ZL Specials have modest gain in one direction and a null in the opposite direction. The gain is helpful when the signal is weak, but the broad response peak makes it difficult to take a precise bearing.

As the signal gets stronger, it becomes possible to use the null for a sharper S meter indication. However, combinations of direct and reflected signals (called *multipath*) will distort the null or perhaps obscure it completely. For best results with this type of antenna, always find clear locations from which to take bearings.

Parasitic Arrays

Parasitic arrays are the most common RDF antennas used by transmitter hunters in high competition areas such as Southern California. Antennas with significant gain are a necessity due to the weak signals often encountered on weekend-long T-hunts, where the transmitter may be over 200 miles distant. Typical 144 MHz installations feature Yagis or quads of three to six elements, sometimes more. Quads are typically home-built, using data from *The ARRL Antenna Book* and *Transmitter Hunting* (see Bibliography).

Two types of mechanical construction are popular for mobile VHF quads. One model uses thin gauge wire (solid or stranded), suspended on wood dowel or fiberglass rod spreaders. It is lightweight and easy to turn rapidly by hand while the vehicle moves. Many hunters prefer to use larger gauge solid wire (such as #10 AWG) on a PVC plastic pipe frame. This quad is more rugged and has somewhat wider frequency range, at the expense of increased weight

and wind resistance. It can get bent going under a branch, but it is easily reshaped and returned to service.

Yagis are a close second to quads in popularity. Commercial models work fine for VHF RDF, provided that the mast is attached at a good balance point. Lightweight and small-diameter elements are desirable for ease of turning at high speeds.

A well-designed mobile Yagi or quad installation includes a method of selecting wave polarization. Although vertical polarization is the norm for VHF-FM communications, horizontal polarization is allowed on many T-hunts. Results will be poor if a VHF RDF antenna is cross-polarized to the transmitting antenna, because multipath and scattered signals (which have indeterminate polarization) are enhanced, relative to the cross-polarized direct signal. The installation of **Figure 21.108** features a slip joint at the boom-to-mast junction, with an actuating cord to rotate the boom, changing the polarization. Mechanical stops limit the boom rotation to 90°.

Parasitic Array Performance for RDF

The directional gain of a mobile beam (typically 8 dB or more) makes it unexcelled for both weak signal competitive hunts and for locating interference such as TV cable leakage. With an appropriate receiver, you can get bearings on any signal mode, including FM, SSB, CW, TV, pulses and noise. Because only the response peak is used, the null-fill problems and proximity effects of loops and phased arrays do not exist.

You can observe multiple directions of arrival while rotating the antenna, allowing you to make educated guesses as to which signal peaks are direct and which are from

Figure 21.108 — The mobile RDF installation of WB6ADC features a thin wire quad that can be switched between vertical and horizontal polarization.

non-direct paths or scattering. Skilled operators can estimate distance to the transmitter from the rate of signal strength increase with distance traveled. The RDF beam is useful for transmitting, if necessary, but use care not to damage an attenuator in the coax line by transmitting through it.

The 3 dB beamwidth of typical mobile-mount VHF beams is on the order of 80°. This is a great improvement over 2 element driven arrays, but it is still not possible to get pinpoint bearing accuracy. You can achieve errors of less than 10° by carefully reading the S meter. In practice, this is not a major hindrance to successful mobile RDF. Mobile users are not as concerned with precise bearings as fixed station operators, because mobile readings are used primarily to give the general direction of travel to "home in" on the signal. Mobile bearings are continuously updated from new, closer locations.

Amplitude-based RDF may be very difficult when signal level varies rapidly. The transmitter hider may be changing power, or the target antenna may be moving or near a well-traveled road or airport. The resultant rapid S meter movement makes it hard to take accurate bearings with a quad. The process is slow because the antenna must be carefully rotated by hand to "eyeball average" the meter readings.

SWITCHED ANTENNA RDF UNITS

Three popular types of RDF systems are relatively insensitive to variations in signal level. Two of them use a pair of vertical dipole antennas, spaced ½ λ or less apart, and alternately switched at a rapid rate to the input of the receiver. In use, the indications of the two systems are similar, but the principles are different.

Switched Pattern Systems

The switched pattern RDF set (**Figure 21.109**) alternately creates two cardioid antenna patterns with lobes to the left and the right. The patterns are generated in much the same way as in the phased arrays described above. PIN RF diodes select the alternating patterns. The combined antenna outputs go to a receiver with AM detection. Processing after the detector output determines the phase or amplitude difference between the patterns' responses to the signal.

Switched pattern RDF sets typically have a zero center meter as an indicator. The meter swings negative when the signal is coming from the user's left, and positive when the signal source is on the right. When the plane of the antenna is exactly perpendicular to the direction of the signal source, the meter reads zero.

The sharpness of the zero crossing indication makes possible more precise bearings than those obtainable with a quad or Yagi.

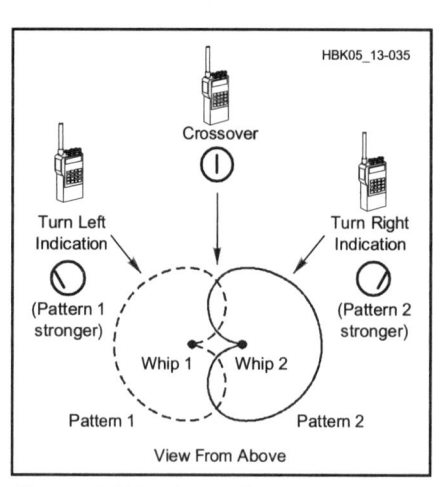

Figure 21.109 — In a switched pattern RDF set, the responses of two cardioid antenna patterns are summed to drive a zero center indicator.

Under ideal conditions with a well-built unit, null direction accuracy is within 1°. Meter deflection tells the user which way to turn to zero the meter. For example, a negative (left) reading requires turning the antenna left. This solves the 180° ambiguity caused by the two zero crossings in each complete rotation of the antenna system.

Because it requires AM detection of the switched pattern signal, this RDF system finds its greatest use in the 120 MHz aircraft band, where AM is the standard mode. Commercial manufacturers make portable RDF sets with switched pattern antennas and built-in receivers for field portable use. These sets can usually be adapted to the amateur 144 MHz band. Other designs are adaptable to any VHF receiver that covers the frequency of interest and has an AM detector built in or added.

Switched pattern units work well for RDF from small aircraft, for which the two vertical antennas are mounted in fixed positions on the outside of the fuselage or simply taped inside the windshield. The left-right indication tells the pilot which way to turn the aircraft to home in. Since street vehicles generally travel only on roads, fixed mounting of the antennas on them is undesirable. Mounting vehicular switched-pattern arrays on a rotatable mast is best.

Time-of-Arrival Systems

Another kind of switched antenna RDF set uses the difference in arrival times of the signal wavefront at the two antennas. This narrow-aperture Time-Difference-of-Arrival (TDOA) technology is used for many sophisticated military RDF systems. The rudimentary TDOA implementation of **Figure 21.110** is quite effective for amateur use. The signal from transmitter 1 reaches antenna A before antenna B. Conversely, the signal from transmitter 3 reaches antenna B before antenna A. When the plane of the antenna is perpendicular to the signal source (as transmitter 2 is in the figure), the signal arrives at both antennas simultaneously.

If the outputs of the antennas are alternately switched at an audio rate to the receiver input, the differences in the arrival times of a continuous signal produce phase changes that are detected by an FM discriminator. The resulting short pulses sound like a tone in the receiver output. The tone disappears when the antennas are equidistant from the signal source, giving an audible null.

The polarity of the pulses at the discriminator output is a function of which antenna is closer to the source. Therefore, the pulses can be processed and used to drive a left-right zero-center meter in a manner similar to the switched pattern units described above. Left-right LED indicators may replace the meter for economy and visibility at night.

RDF operations with a TDOA dual antenna RDF are done in the same manner as with a switched antenna RDF set. The main difference is the requirement for an FM receiver in the TDOA system and an AM receiver in the switched pattern case. No RF attenuator is needed for close-in work in the TDOA case.

Popular designs for practical do-it-yourself TDOA RDF sets include the Simple Seeker (described elsewhere in this chapter) and the W9DUU design (see article by Bohrer in the Bibliography). Articles with plans for the Handy Tracker, a simple TDOA set with a delay line to resolve the dual-null ambiguity instead of LEDs or a meter, are listed in the Bibliography.

Performance Comparison

Both types of dual antenna RDFs make good on-foot "sniffing" devices and are excellent performers when there are rapid amplitude variations in the incoming signal. They

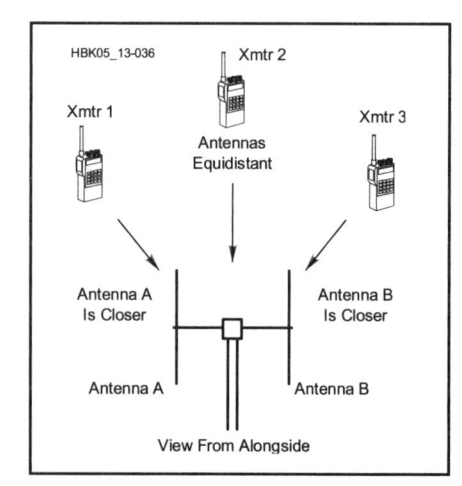

Figure 21.110 — A dual-antenna TDOA RDF system has a similar indicator to a switched pattern unit, but it obtains bearings by determining which of its antennas is closer to the transmitter.

are the units of choice for airborne work. Compared to Yagis and quads, they give good directional performance over a much wider frequency range. Their indications are more precise than those of beams with broad forward lobes.

Dual-antenna RDF sets frequently give inaccurate bearings in multipath situations, because they cannot resolve signals of nearly equal levels from more than one direction. Because multipath signals are a combined pattern of peaks and nulls, they appear to change in amplitude and bearing as you move the RDF antenna along the bearing path or perpendicular to it, whereas a non-multipath signal will have constant strength and bearing.

The best way to overcome this problem is to take large numbers of bearings while moving toward the transmitter. Taking bearings while in motion averages out the effects of multipath, making the direct signal more readily discernible. Some TDOA RDF sets have a slow-response mode that aids the averaging process.

Switched antenna systems generally do not perform well when the incoming signal is horizontally polarized. In such cases, the bearings may be inaccurate or unreadable. TDOA units require a carrier type signal such as FM or CW; they usually cannot yield bearings on noise or pulse signals.

Unless an additional method is employed to measure signal strength, it is easy to "overshoot" the hidden transmitter location with a TDOA set. It is not uncommon to see a TDOA foxhunter walk over the top of a concealed transmitter and walk away, following the opposite 180° null, because there is no display of signal amplitude.

DOPPLER RDF SETS

RDF sets using the Doppler principle are popular in many areas because of their ease of use. They have an indicator that instantaneously displays direction of the signal source relative to the vehicle heading, either on a circular ring of LEDs or a digital readout in degrees. A ring of four, eight or more antennas picks up the signal. Quarter-wavelength monopoles on a ground plane are popular for vehicle use, but half-wavelength vertical dipoles, where practical, perform better.

Radio signals received on a rapidly moving antenna experience a frequency shift due to the Doppler effect, a phenomenon well-known to anyone who has observed a moving car with its horn sounding. The horn's pitch appears higher than normal as the car approaches, and lower as the car recedes. Similarly, the received radio frequency increases as the antenna moves toward the transmitter and vice versa. An FM receiver will detect this frequency change.

Figure 21.111 shows a ¼ λ vertical antenna being moved on a circular track around point

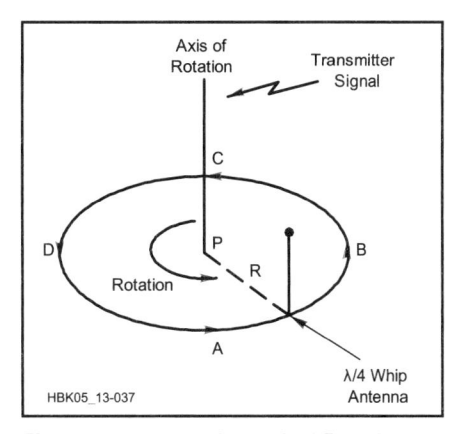

Figure 21.111 — A theoretical Doppler antenna circles around point P, continuously moving toward and away from the source at an audio rate.

P, with constant angular velocity. As the antenna approaches the transmitter on its track, the received frequency is shifted higher. The highest instantaneous frequency occurs when the antenna is at point A, because tangential velocity toward the transmitter is maximum at that point. Conversely, the lowest frequency occurs when the antenna reaches point C, where velocity is maximum away from the transmitter.

Figure 21.112 shows a plot of the component of the tangential velocity that is in the direction of the transmitter as the antenna moves around the circle. Comparing Figures 21.111 and 21.112, notice that at B in Figure 21.112, the tangential velocity is crossing zero from the positive to the negative and the antenna is closest to the transmitter. The Doppler shift and resulting audio output from the receiver discriminator follow the same plot, so that a negative-slope zero-crossing detector, synchronized with the antenna rotation, senses the incoming direction of the signal.

The amount of frequency shift due to the Doppler effect is proportional to the RF frequency and the tangential antenna velocity. The velocity is a function of the radius of rotation and the angular velocity (rotation rate). The radius of rotation must be less than ¼ λ to avoid errors. To get a usable amount of FM deviation (comparable to typical voice modulation) with this radius, the antenna must rotate at approximately 30,000 RPM (500 Hz). This puts the Doppler tone in the audio range for easy processing.

Mechanically rotating a whip antenna at this rate is impractical, but a ring of whips, switched to the receiver in succession with RF PIN diodes, can simulate a rapidly rotating antenna. Doppler RDF sets must be used with receivers having FM detectors. The Dopple ScAnt and Roanoke Doppler (see Bibliography) are mobile Doppler RDF sets designed for inexpensive home construction.

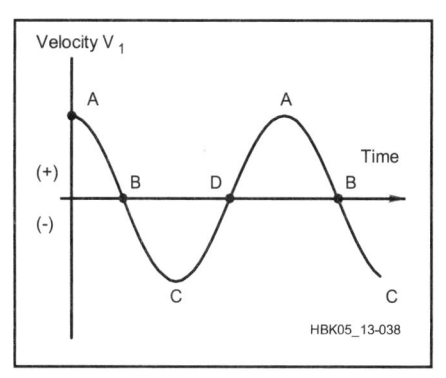

Figure 21.112 — Frequency shift versus time produced by the rotating antenna movement toward and away from the signal source.

Doppler Advantages and Disadvantages

Ring-antenna Doppler sets are the ultimate in simplicity of operation for mobile RDF. There are no moving parts and no manual antenna pointing. Rapid direction indications are displayed on very short signal bursts.

Many units lock in the displayed direction after the signal leaves the air. Power variations in the source signal cause no difficulties, as long as the signal remains above the RDF detection threshold. A Doppler antenna goes on top of any car quickly, with no holes to drill. Many Local Interference Committee members choose Dopplers for tracking malicious interference, because they are inconspicuous (compared to beams) and effective at tracking the strong vertically polarized signals that repeater jammers usually emit.

A Doppler does not provide superior performance in all VHF RDF situations. If the signal is too weak for detection by the Doppler unit, the hunt advantage goes to teams with beams. Doppler installations are not suitable for on-foot sniffing. The limitations of other switched antenna RDFs also apply: (1) poor results with horizontally polarized signals, (2) no indication of distance, (3) carrier type signals only and (4) inadvisability of transmitting through the antenna.

Readout to the nearest degree is provided on some commercial Doppler units. This does not guarantee that level of accuracy, however. A well-designed four-monopole set is typically capable of ±5° accuracy on 2 meters, if the target signal is vertically polarized and there are no multipath effects.

The rapid antenna switching can introduce cross modulation products when the user is near strong off-channel RF sources. This self-generated interference can temporarily render the system unusable. While not a common problem with mobile Dopplers, it makes the Doppler a poor choice for use in remote RDF installations at fixed sites with high power VHF transmitters nearby.

21.13 Rotators

The rotator is an important component of directional antenna systems, turning the antenna to any direction with a repeatable accuracy of a few degrees. Once in position, the rotator must hold the antenna in place against the wind. The rotator must do this while supporting the weight of the mast and all of the antennas.

Although mechanical details vary, a rotator consists of a base assembly mounted to a fixed mast or tower and a rotating assembly atop it with a clamp in which the antenna support mast is held. The turning motor and gear train, brake, position indicator, and limit switches are installed in or on the base. The rotating assembly sits on a bearing race resting on the base assembly. A ring gear is the most common method of transferring the motor's rotation to the rotating housing, although worm gears are also used.

Rotators are usually installed inside a lattice tower section that uses a sleeve or thrust bearing to hold a mast and stabilize it against sideways torque. The sleeve is part of the tower's top section. A thrust bearing is mounted on a bearing plate at the top of the tower. The rotator is mounted on a rotator shelf that sits inside the tower and is sold as an accessory by the tower manufacturer. Smaller rotators usually come with a mast clamp so they can be mounted on a pipe or similar mast with the antenna directly above them. **Figure 21.113** shows typical installations.

21.13.1 Rotator Ratings

Rotators are expected to work for many years over a very wide range of temperatures while exposed to the elements, with little or no maintenance. To achieve those performance goals, the rotator's specifications and installation requirements must be respected.

There are three primary rotator ratings: *wind load*, *braking ability*, and *turning torque*. Many rotators also specify a maximum *vertical load* in pounds or kilograms. **Table 21.25** lists manufacturers for rotators intended for fixed-station installations and **Table 21.26** shows the primary ratings for common rotators.

Wind load is specified both with the rotator mounted inside a tower and with the rotator outside a tower mounted on a mast (see Figure 21.113). When mounted inside a tower section, the tower holds the mast in place straight above the rotator, often using a thrust bearing to hold the mast in place. This eliminates any sideways load on the rotating assembly relative to the base. Wind load ratings are given as a maximum antenna area in

---

Table 21.25
Rotator Manufacturers and Service (Fixed Station)

Manufacturers
Alpha-Spid	www.alfaradio.ca
Channel Master	www.channelmaster.com
Hy-Gain	www.hy-gain.com
M²	www.m2inc.com
TIC	www.ticgen.com
Yaesu	www.yaesu.com

Service
C.A.T.S.	www.rotor-doc.com
Norm's Rotor Service	www.rotorservice.com
RK Radio Electronics	rotordoctor.com

"Rotator" or "Rotor"?

The piece of equipment installed on the tower that makes the antennas turn is a "rotator." A "rotor" is the rotary part of a motor or vehicle. For example, the blades of a helicopter form its rotor and the spinning shaft and armature of an electric motor form its rotor. The rotator includes the entire machine, both the stationary and moving parts, making the antenna system turn. Amateurs use both words, rotator and rotor, somewhat interchangeably, regardless.

Table 21.26
Common Rotator Specifications

Mfr	Model	Wind Load (in tower, sq ft)	Wind Load (outside tower, sq ft)	Turning Torque (in-lb)	Braking Ability (in-lb)	Effective Moment (ft-lb)	Brake Type	Notes
Alpha-Spid	RAK1			1400	>14,000		Worm gear	Heavy-duty
Channel Master	9521HD			100				Light-duty
Hy-Gain	T2X	20	10	1000	9000	3400	Wedge	Heavy-duty
	AR-40	3	1.5	350	450	300	Disc	Light-duty
	CD-45II	8.5	5	600	800	1200	Disc	Medium-duty
	HAM-IV	15	7.5	800	5000	2800	Wedge	Medium-duty
	HDR-300A	25	n/a	5000	7500		Solenoid lock	Heavy-duty
M²	OR2800	35	n/a	3200	17000		Gear reduction	Heavy-duty
TIC	1022D			6500	6500		Gear reduction	Heavy-duty, ring mount
	1032D			7881	7530		Gear reduction	Heavy-duty, ring mount
Yaesu	G-450A	10.8	5.4	516	2604		Gear reduction	Light-duty
	G-800DXA	21.5	8	955	3472		Mech and elec	Medium-duty
	G-1000DXA	23.7	8	955	5207		Mech and elec	Medium-duty
	G-2800DXA	32.3	10.8	2170	21700		Mech and elec	Heavy-duty
Az-El Rotators								
Yaesu	G-5500	10.8	10.8	428	3468		Gear reduction	
Alpha-Spid	RAS-1	30		1400	14,000s		Worm gear	At 12 V
	RAS-2			1400	14,000s		Worm gear	
	REAL-1			1400	14,000s		Worm gear	

> ### What is an Armstrong Rotator?
> The term "armstrong" refers to anything turned or lifted manually, requiring a "strong arm." There are many examples of hams using gears or cranks to turn antennas but the most common is a rope tied to the antenna's boom and pulled from ground level. The antenna's mast turns freely in the tower or the antenna mount turns on the mast. This is a common temporary solution during antenna system repair or when operating during Field Day and portable.

square feet, and antenna manufacturers specify the area of their beams for this reason. In the US, wind load calculations are based on the standard EIA/TIA-222-G:2005-08-02. In Europe, EN 1991-1-4 is the current standard, corresponding to the German standard DIN 1055-4.

Braking ability is the maximum twisting force the rotator can withstand when stopped. This force is primarily created by the wind. The rotator's braking action is provided either by a solenoid-controlled wedge or bar inside the housing, or by a worm-gear drive that does not allow backward rotation of the mast under load. Turning torque is the maximum amount of torque the rotator can produce to turn the antennas. Both braking ability and turning torque are given in inch-pounds.

Effective moment is the product of antenna weight in pounds (or kilograms) and turning radius in feet (or meters). Heavy antennas and bigger antennas are harder to turn and to hold in place against the wind, requiring a higher effective moment rating for the rotator. Hy-Gain uses effective moment as a maximum rating for its line of rotators.

It is important not to overload a rotator. If you live in a location that is prone to high winds, persistent winds, or large gusts, include a safety factor when selecting a rotator. Persistent twisting from winds can wear out a rotator's brake wedge or housing indentations that hold the brake in place. This can cause the brake to slip or jam. Rotators are not inexpensive, and a failed rotator brake can allow an antenna to "freewheel," damaging the feed line as well. A thrust bearing at the top of the tower can be used to hold the weight of a large antenna array, leaving only the turning load on the rotator.

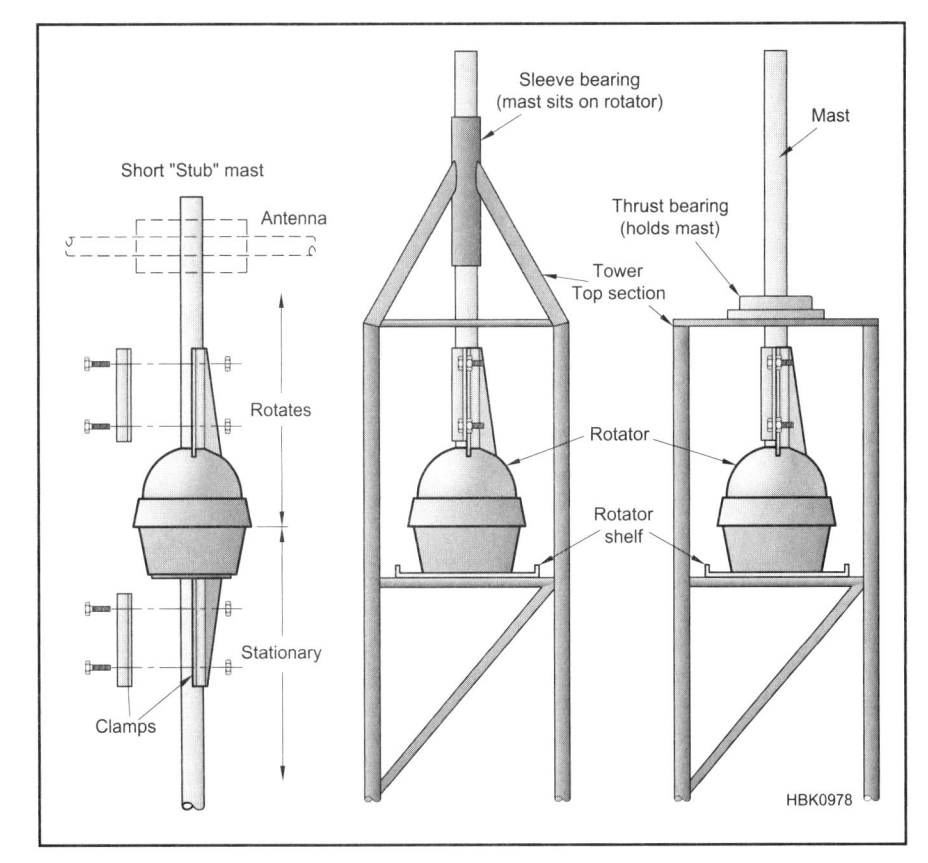

Figure 21.113 — Rotators can be mounted directly on masts or inside lattice-style towers. Rotators can also be mounted directly on the top of towers (not shown).

21.13.2 Types of Rotators

Amateur rotators range from very light-duty models intended for TV antennas all the way to reconditioned "prop-pitch" rotators designed originally to control the pitch or angle of aircraft propeller blades. There are also models for portable and temporary use.

Light-duty antenna rotators are suitable for small VHF and UHF Yagis or log-periodic antennas. They should not be used with HF antennas, large microwave dishes, or antenna systems with a significant wind load.

Medium-duty rotators can handle a single, mid-sized HF tribander or log-periodic. A small VHF/UHF Yagi can be stacked with the HF beam. These rotators are also good choices for a stack of VHF/UHF antennas. Dish antennas should be evaluated to be sure they won't overload these rotators.

Heavy-duty rotators are able to handle the biggest amateur HF Yagis, including stacks of two or three antennas. Instead of a solenoid brake, some of these rotators use a gear train or worm-drive to provide the braking action. Be sure the tower and supporting hardware are rated to handle the antenna and mast load. These rotators are somewhat larger than the more common medium-duty models and may be difficult to install in smaller lattice-style towers.

Ring rotators, or orbital ring rotators, are a special type of rotator installed outside the tower, attached to its legs. The antenna is carried by a motorized cradle that moves around the tower on a circular, toothed track that acts as a drive gear. Ring rotators are generally used at big stations which use large, stacked HF Yagis.

It is also possible to simply rotate the entire tower with a variety of antennas mounted directly on the tower. The guy wires are attached to bearing rings, allowing the tower to turn inside them.

21.13.3 Rotator Control

TURNING CONTROL

There are two steps in controlling turning; releasing the brake, if any, and energizing a motor to turn in the desired direction.

An electrically controlled brake consists of a heavy-duty solenoid and a spring-loaded brake wedge or bar that fits into indentations inside the rotating assembly. The rotator's braking torque is determined by how securely the brake is held by the indentations or, if worm gears are used, by the resistance to the gears turning backward under load. To turn the rotator, the solenoid is energized, pulling the brake out of the indentations. Energizing the solenoid is usually the largest current draw of the rotator.

The most common rotator motor is a 2-phase ac motor with a starting capacitor.

One Control for All

Each rotator family (Ham-IV, Yaesu, M², and so on) comes with a custom control unit for turning and position display. There are also after-market control units that operate with any of the common rotators. The most widely used are the Green Heron controllers (**www.greenheronengineering.com**) and the EA4TX interfaces (**ea4tx.com**). Both can control most available models of rotators, allowing you to standardize in the shack and customize on the tower.

The capacitor is switched between phases to control direction of rotation. Because of gear reduction, the motor can be fairly small and does not draw much current. Unless blocked by an obstruction, rotators turn a full 360 degrees. Limit switches open at the ends of rotation, removing power from the motor at the extreme ends of travel to prevent feed line damage.

When rotation is complete, the solenoid is de-energized and the brake re-engages the indentations, holding the mast in place. Over time, the indentations or brake can wear out, allowing the rotating housing to slip under heavy loads. Wear is accelerated by de-energizing the solenoid while the mast is still turning, causing the brake to impact the sides of the indentations. To reduce the impact of sudden stops, some controllers allow the mast to stop turning before de-energizing the solenoid. Typical brake delays are about 5 seconds. (Retrofit delay modules are available for the Hy-Gain family of rotators.) If your rotator does not have a brake delay, practice keeping the brake energized for a few seconds after you release the turning controls to allow the antennas to stop moving first.

POSITION INDICATION

There are two basic types of position indication — resistance and pulse counting. The most common circuit is a potentiometer ("pot") contained in the rotator's housing and turned in sync with the rotator motor. Current through the pot (typically only a few milliamps) drives an analog meter in the control unit calibrated in degrees. Rotators using pulse counters use a switch to generate pulses that the control unit counts to calculate the number of degrees from one end of travel.

Most rotator controllers in North America are configured as "North center," meaning they can turn an antenna from pointing directly south at one limit, through north at mid-travel, and all the way to south again at the opposite limit. North is the center position on the meter displaying the antenna's direction. (South center meter scales are an option for most rotators.)

To calibrate a pot-indicator rotator's direction, assuming North center, first adjust any meter calibration controls to mid-scale. Then move the rotator to its mid-travel orientation. Loosen the antenna mast clamp and rotate the mast until the antennas point directly north and re-tighten the clamp. (Using a compass or landmark is sufficient resolution for most

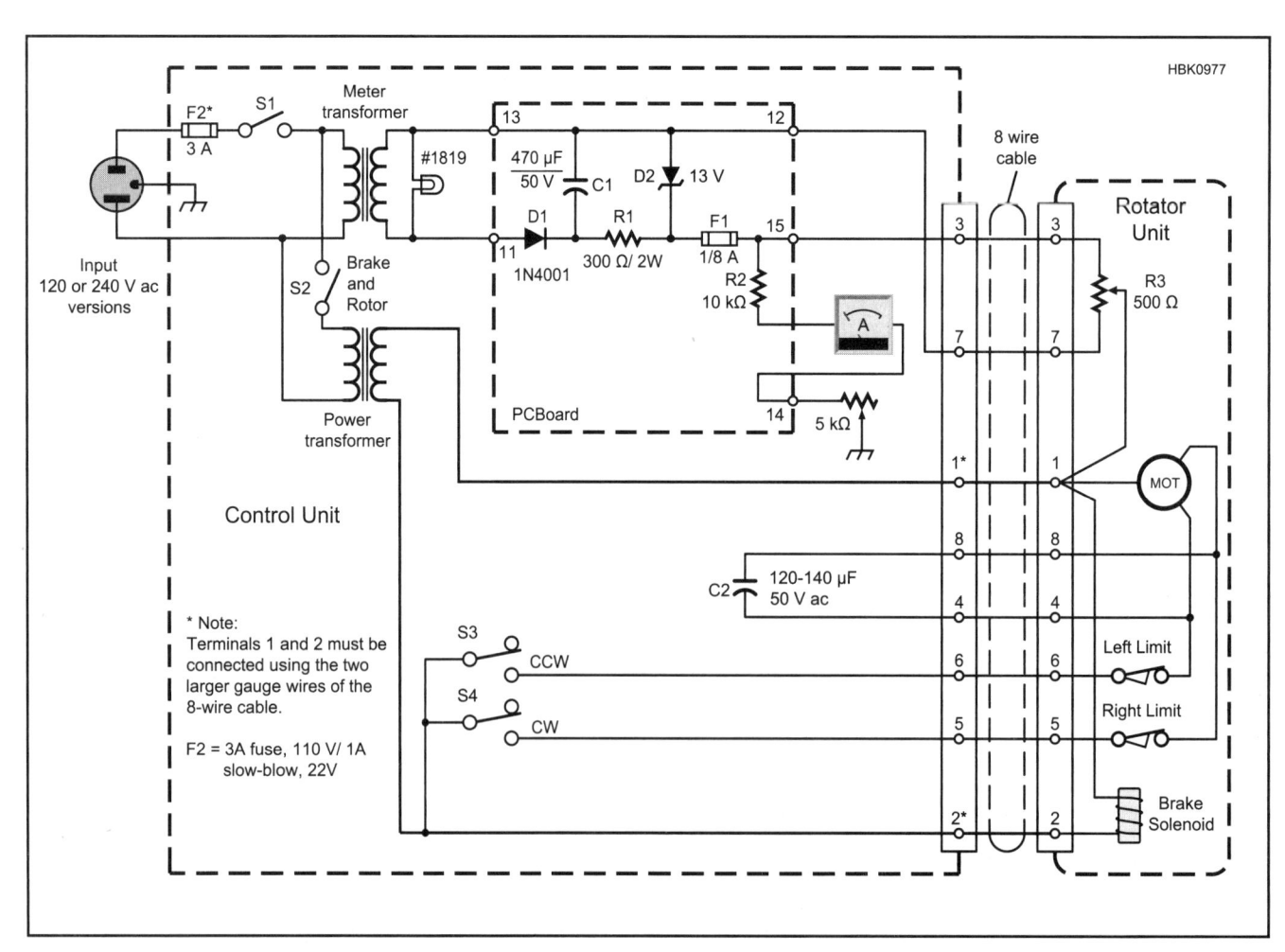

Figure 21.114 — The Hy-Gain Ham-IV/IVX control unit schematic. This control unit will also work with T2X rotators. (Circuit provided courtesy of Hy-Gain, Inc.)

Table 21.27
Ham-IV/IVX Connector and Cable Wiring
Pin numbers, colors, and resistance values from Ham-IV/IVX Instruction Manual

Pin	Color	Circuit
1	Black (heavy wire)	Solenoid and common
2	White (heavy wire)	Solenoid
3	Green	Position pot element, + end
4	Blue	Motor winding 1
5	Orange	Right limit switch
6	Yellow	Left limit switch
7	Brown	Position pot element, – end
8	Red	Motor winding 2

Resistance Checks — Read Between Terminals

1-2	Brake solenoid	0.75 Ω + cable or leads
1-8	½ Motor winding	2.5 Ω + cable or leads
1-4	½ Motor winding	2.5 Ω + cable or leads
1-6	½ Motor + switch	2.5 Ω + cable or leads
1-5	½ Motor + switch	2.5 Ω + cable or leads
8-4	Entire motor	5 Ω + cable or leads
8-5	Right limit switch	0 Ω + cable or leads
4-6	Left limit switch	0 Ω + cable or leads
3-7	Entire pot element	500 Ω
3-1	Pot wiper to element end 1	0 to 500 Ω
7-1	Pot wiper to element end 2	0 to 500 Ω

Note: readings 3-1 and 7-1 should add to 3-7 reading

Rotator Software Control

Recently-designed rotator control units have RS-232 or USB interfaces which act as COM ports to PC software. There are several different protocols, the Yaesu protocol being the most common. The Rotor-EZ and ERC interfaces can be added to most rotators that don't have a software interface. Logging software often supports several different protocols and standalone software packages and utilities are also available - Internet searches for "antenna rotator software control" will find many programs.

---

amateur antennas.) When storing or testing a rotator, make a practice of leaving it set to mid-travel for ease of position calibration and mark or tag it for later reference. For a pulse-count rotator, the manufacturer's manual will provide the necessary directions.

ROTATOR WIRING

The ARRL appreciates being granted permission by the Hy-Gain Company to reproduce the wiring diagram of the control unit for its widely used Ham-IV and Tailtwister T2X rotators as a convenience for readers. (See **Figure 21.114**.)

The connection from the control unit to the rotator requires a multi-conductor control cable (no shield necessary). Most rotators require either 6- or 8-conductor cable. Solenoid brake circuits need heavier wire due to the higher current. If the wire used is too small, the extra resistance may cause enough voltage drop to result in erratic brake operation or slow turning. Check the manufacturer's recommendation for minimum wire size, which depends on the length of the cable. For the popular Ham-IV series, minimum recommended wire sizes are:

- Up to 125 feet: #18 (solenoid), #20 (all others)
- 125 to 200 feet: #16 (solenoid), #18 (all others)
- 200 to 300 feet: #14 (solenoid), #16 (all others)

Other rotators have similar requirements — consult the manufacturer's instructions.

At the rotator, connections can be made directly to a terminal strip under the unit or to a weatherproofed connector at the end of a short "pigtail." A nearby junction box where the pigtail and cable are attached can also be used. Retrofit kits to replace terminal strips are available from several vendors. The Ham-IV family suggests an 8-pin Cinch-Jones connector with wiring and color code as shown in **Table 21.27**.

For terminal strip connections, use a weatherproofing grease found at electrical and automotive stores. Run the connecting cable down and away from the rotator to guide water away from it. Use a consistent color code at the rotator and the control unit.

Lightning protection is also recommended for rotator control cables. Several vendors make 8-line lightning protectors for rotators. The protector must be well-grounded and should be installed at a common entry point for all antenna system cables. See the **Safety** chapter for more about grounding and lightning protection practices.

Troubleshooting a rotator electrically can be done from the ground through resistance checks. Table 21.27 shows the nominal resistance values for the Ham-IV family of rotators. When making resistance checks, the control unit must be disconnected. Include the resistance of the cable or test leads when making resistance checks.

21.14 Glossary

Antenna — An electrical conductor or array of conductors that radiates signal energy (transmitting) or collects signal energy (receiving).

Antenna tuner — A device containing variable reactances (and perhaps a balun) used to convert an antenna or feed line impedance to 50 Ω. (Also called transmatch, impedance-matching unit, matchbox).

Apex angle — The included angle between the legs of an inverted-V antenna.

Azimuth (azimuthal) pattern — A radiation pattern in a plane oriented parallel to the Earth's surface or at a specified angle to the Earth's surface.

Balanced feed line — A two-conductor feed line with each conductor having the same impedance with respect to a reference potential, usually an earth connection (also called open-wire line, ladder line, window line, twin-lead).

Balun — A device that transfers energy between a balanced and unbalanced system. A balun may or may not change the impedance ratio between the systems.

Base loading — Adding a coil to the base of a ground-plane antenna to increase its electrical length.

Beamwidth — The width in degrees of the major lobe of a directive antenna between the two angles at which the relative radiated power is equal to one-half its value (–3 dB) at the peak of the lobe.

Capacitance hat — A conducting structure with a large surface area that is added to an antenna to add capacitive reactance at that point on the antenna.

Center loading — Adding a coil near the center of a ground-plane antenna to increase its electrical length.

Coaxial cable (coax) — A coaxial transmission line with a center conductor surrounded by a layer of insulation and then a tubular shield conductor and covered by an insulating jacket. (see also *unbalanced feed line*)

Delta loop — A full-wavelength loop, usually in the vertical plane, shaped like a triangle or delta.

Delta match — Center-feed technique used with antenna elements that are not split at the center in which the transmission line is spread apart and connected to the element symmetrically, forming a triangle or delta.

Dipole — An antenna, usually one-half wavelength long, divided into two parts at a feed point. An *off-center-fed (OCF) dipole* has a feed point offset from the center.

Directivity — The property of an antenna that concentrates the radiated energy to form one or more major lobes.

Director — An antenna element in a parasitic array that causes radiated energy from the driven element to be focused along the line from the driven element to the director.

Doublet — A more general name for a wire antenna fed in the center and that may or may not be resonant at the operating frequency.

Driven array — An array of antenna elements which are all driven or excited by means of a transmission line.

Driven element — An antenna element excited by means of a transmission line.

E-plane — The plane in which the electric field of an electromagnetic wave is maximum.

Efficiency (antenna) — The ratio of radiated power to input power.

Elements — The conductive parts of an antenna system that determine the antenna's characteristics.

Elevation pattern — A radiation pattern in a plane perpendicular to the Earth's surface.

End effect — The effect of capacitance at the end of an antenna element that acts to electrically lengthen the element.

End-fed Half Wave (EFHW) — A half-wavelength antenna fed at one end, usually with open-wire feed line.

Feed line — See *transmission line*

Feed point — location at which a transmission line delivers power to an antenna.

Front-to-back ratio — The ratio in dB of the radiation from an antenna in a favored direction to that in the opposite direction.

Front-to-rear ratio — The ratio in dB of the radiation from an antenna is a favored direction to an average of the radiation in the opposite direction across some specified angle.

Front-to-side ratio — The ratio in dB of the radiation from an antenna in a favored direction to that at right angles to the favored direction.

Gain — The increase in radiated power with respect to a reference antenna in the desired direction of the major lobe.

Gamma match — A matching system used with driven antenna elements in which a conductor is placed near the element and connected to the feed line with an adjustable capacitor at the end closest to the center and connected to the element at the other.

Ground plane — A system of conductors configured to act as a substitute for an earth ground to an antenna element and connected to one side of the transmission line.

H-plane — The plane in which the magnetic field of an electromagnetic wave is maximum.

Hairpin match — A U-shaped inductor that is connected across the feed point of a driven element for the purpose of creating a match to a feed line.

Impedance — The ratio of voltage to current in a feed line or along an antenna.

Inverted-V — A dipole antenna supported at its mid-point with halves angled down toward the ground.

Isotropic — An imaginary antenna that radiates and receives equally well in all directions.

Ladder line — See *balanced line*.

Line loss — The power lost in a transmission line, specified in dB per unit of length.

Load — The electrical system or component to which power is delivered.

Lobe — A region of increased radiation in an antenna's radiation pattern between two nulls. A *main lobe* is the largest lobe in the pattern and all other lobes are *side lobes*.

Matching — The process by which power at one impedance is transferred to a system having a different impedance.

Monopole — An antenna with a single element that functions in concert with a ground-plane.

Null — A point of minimum radiation in an antenna's radiation pattern.

Open-wire line — See *balanced line*.

Parasitic array — A set of elements that form a radiation pattern through coupling and re-radiation of energy from one or more driven elements.

Polarization — The orientation of an antenna or electromagnetic field, referring to the orientation of the E field.

Q section — A quarter-wavelength section of transmission line used for impedance-matching purposes.

Quad — A directive antenna based on the Yagi with elements that consist of one-wavelength loops.

Radiation pattern — The characteristics of an antenna's distribution of energy in a single plane. (See also elevation pattern and azimuth pattern.)

Radiation resistance — A resistance that represents the work done by the current in an antenna to radiate power.

Reflector — An antenna element in a parasitic array that causes radiated energy from the driven element to be focused along the line from the driven element away from the reflector.

Sense Antenna — An antenna added to a bidirectional array or loop that samples the incoming signal's phase for comparison to that of the main receiving antenna.

Stacking — Arranging two or more directive antennas such that their radiation pattern characteristics reinforce each other.

SWR (VSWR) — Standing-wave ratio. A measure of the match between a transmission line and a load such as an antenna.

T-match — A symmetrical version of the gamma match for a balanced antenna system.

Top loading — Addition of a reactance, usually capacitive, at the top of a ground-plane antenna so as to increase its electrical length.

Transmatch — See *antenna tuner*.

Trap — A parallel LC-circuit used to isolate sections of an antenna.

Twin-lead — See *balanced line*.

Unbalanced feed line — A transmission line such as coaxial cable with conductors that have different impedances with respect to a reference potential, usually an earth connection. One conductor is usually connected directly to the reference. (see also *balanced line*)

Unipole — See *monopole*.

Yagi — A parasitic array consisting of a driven element and one or more director and reflectors.

Zepp — (see *End-fed Half Wave*)

21.15 References and Bibliography

J. S. Belrose, VE2CV, "Short Antennas for Mobile Operation," *QST*, Sep 1953, pp 30-35.

B. Black, W4SSY, "The W4SSY Spudgun," *QST*, Mar 2009, pp 67-69.

G. H. Brown, "The Phase and Magnitude of Earth Currents Near Radio Transmitting Antennas," *Proc IRE*, Feb 1935.

G. H. Brown, R. F. Lewis and J. Epstein, "Ground Systems as a Factor in Antenna Efficiency," *Proc IRE*, Jun 1937, pp 753-787.

G. H. Brown and O. M. Woodward, Jr, "Experimentally Determined Impedance Characteristics of Cylindrical Antennas," *Proc IRE*, April 1945.

C. L. Buchanen, W3DZZ, "The Multimatch Antenna System," *QST*, Mar 1955, p 22.

L.B. Cebik, W4RNL, "A Simple Fixed Antenna for VHF/UHF Satellite Work," *QST*, Aug 2001, pp 38-42.

A. Christman, "Elevated Vertical Antenna Systems," *QST*, Aug 1988, pp 35-42.

J. Clement, VE6AB, "Gain Twist 75 Meter Mobile Monobander," *QST*, Jul 2011, pp 39-42.

J. Devoldere, ON4UN's *Low-Band DXing*, 5th ed (Newington: ARRL, 2011).

R. B. Dome, "Increased Radiating Efficiency for Short Antennas," *QST*, Sep 1934, pp 9-12.

A. C. Doty, Jr, J. A. Frey and H. J. Mills, "Characteristics of the Counterpoise and Elevated Ground Screen," Professional Program, Session 9, Southcon '83 (IEEE), Atlanta, GA, Jan 1983.

A. C. Doty, Jr, J. A. Frey and H. J. Mills, "Efficient Ground Systems for Vertical Antennas," *QST*, Feb 1983, pp 20-25.

A. C. Doty, Jr, technical paper presentation, "Capacitive Bottom Loading and Other Aspects of Vertical Antennas," Technical Symposium, Radio Club of America, New York City, Nov 20, 1987.

A. C. Doty, Jr, J. A. Frey and H. J. Mills, "Vertical Antennas: New Design and Construction Data," *The ARRL Antenna Compendium, Volume 2* (Newington: ARRL, 1989), pp 2-9.

R. Fosberg, "Some Notes on Ground Systems for 160 Meters," *QST*, Apr 1965, pp 65-67.

G. Grammer, "More on the Directivity of Horizontal Antennas; Harmonic Operation — Effects of Tilting," *QST*, Mar 1937, pp 38-40, 92, 94, 98.

H. E. Green, "Design Data for Short and Medium Length Yagi-Uda Arrays," *Trans IE Australia*, Vol EE-2, No. 1, Mar 1966.

A. Griffith, W4ULD, "Capacitance Hats for HF Mobile Antennas," *QEX*, Jul/Aug 1996, p 16.

K. McCleish, W7TX, "Why An Antenna Radiates," *QST*, Nov 1992, pp. 59-63.

H. J. Mills, technical paper presentation, "Impedance Transformation Provided by Folded Monopole Antennas," Technical Symposium, Radio Club of America, New York City, Nov 20, 1987.

B. Myers, "The W2PV Four-Element Yagi," *QST*, Oct 1986, pp 15-19.

L. Richard, "Parallel Dipoles of 300-Ohm Ribbon," *QST*, Mar 1957.

J. H. Richmond, "Monopole Antenna on Circular Disc," *IEEE Trans on Antennas and Propagation*, Vol. AP-32, No. 12, Dec 1984.

S.A. Schelkunoff, "Theory of Antennas of Arbitrary Size and Shape," Proc. IRE, Sep. 1941; corrections Nov. 1941 and Jan. 1943. Republished in Proc. IRE, September 1984.

W. Schulz, "Designing a Vertical Antenna," *QST*, Sep 1978, pp 19- 21.

J. Sevick, "The Ground-Image Vertical Antenna," *QST*, Jul 1971, pp 16-17, 22.

J. Sevick, "The W2FMI 20-Meter Vertical Beam," *QST*, Jun 1972, pp 14-18.

J. Sevick, "The W2FMI Ground-Mounted Short Vertical," *QST*, Mar 1973, pp 13-18, 41.

J. Sevick, "A High Performance 20-, 40- and 80-Meter Vertical System," *QST*, Dec 1973.

J. Sevick, "Short Ground-Radial Systems for Short Verticals," *QST*, Apr 1978, pp 30-33.

C. E. Smith and E. M. Johnson, "Performance of Short Antennas," *Proc IRE*, Oct 1947.

J. Stanley, "Optimum Ground Systems for Vertical Antennas," *QST*, Dec 1976, pp 13-15.

S. Stearns, K6OIK, "Antenna Modeling for Radio Amateurs," presented at ARRL Pacificon Antenna Seminar, 2017, archived at **www.fars.k6ya.org/docs**.

R. E. Stephens, "Admittance Matching the Ground-Plane Antenna to Coaxial Transmission Line," Technical Correspondence, *QST*, Apr 1973, pp 55-57.

D. Sumner, "Cushcraft 32-19 'Boomer' and 324-QK Stacking Kit," Product Review, *QST*, Nov 1980, pp 48-49.

B Sykes, "Skeleton Slot Aerials," *RSGB Bulletin*, Jan 1953.

C. T. Tai and S. A. Long, "Dipoles and Monopoles," Chapter 4 in *Antenna Engineering Handbook, 3rd edition*, R. C. Johnson editor, McGraw-Hill, 1993.

W. van B. Roberts, "Input Impedance of a Folded Dipole," *RCA Review*, Jun 1947.

E. M. Williams, "Radiating Characteristics of Short-Wave Loop Aerials," *Proc IRE*, Oct 1940.

B. Witvliet et al, "Near Vertical Incidence Skywave Propagation: Elevation Angles and Optimum Antenna Height for Horizontal Dipole Antennas," *IEEE Antennas and Propagation Magazine*, Vol 57, No. 1, Feb 2015, pp 129-146.

TEXTBOOKS ON ANTENNAS

C. A. Balanis, *Antenna Theory, Analysis and Design* (New York: Harper & Row, 1982).

D. S. Bond, *Radio Direction Finders*, 1st ed. (New York: McGraw-Hill Book Co).

W. N. Caron, *Antenna Impedance Matching* (Newington: ARRL, 1989).

L. B. Cebik, "Antennas from the Ground Up, Vol 1 and 2," MFJ Publishing, 2000.

K. Davies, *Ionospheric Radio Propagation* — National Bureau of Standards Monograph 80 2(Washington, DC: U.S. Government Printing Office, Apr 1, 1965).

R. S. Elliott, *Antenna Theory and Design* (Englewood Cliffs, NJ: Prentice Hall, 1981).

A. E. Harper, *Rhombic Antenna Design* (New York: D. Van Nostrand Co, Inc, 1941).

K. Henney, *Principles of Radio* (New York: John Wiley and Sons, 1938), p 462.

C. Hutchinson and R. D. Straw, *Simple and Fun Antennas for Hams* (Newington: ARRL, 2002).

H. Jasik, *Antenna Engineering Handbook*, 1st ed. (New York: McGraw-Hill, 1961).

W. C. Johnson, *Transmission Lines and Networks*, 1st ed. (New York: McGraw-Hill Book Co, 1950).

Johnson and Jasik, *Antenna Engineering Handbook*, 2nd ed. (New York: McGraw-Hill).

R. C. Johnson, *Antenna Engineering Handbook*, 3rd ed. (New York: McGraw-Hill, 1993).

E. C. Jordan and K. G. Balmain, *Electromagnetic Waves and Radiating Systems*, 2nd ed. (Englewood Cliffs, NJ: Prentice-Hall, Inc, 1968).

R. Keen, *Wireless Direction Finding*, 3rd ed. (London: Wireless World).

R. W. P. King, *Theory of Linear Antennas* (Cambridge, MA: Harvard Univ. Press, 1956).

R. W. P. King, H. R. Mimno and A. H. Wing, *Transmission Lines, Antennas and Waveguides* (New York: Dover Publications, Inc, 1965).

King, Mack and Sandler, *Arrays of Cylindrical Dipoles* (London: Cambridge Univ Press, 1968).

M. G. Knitter, ed., *Loop Antennas — Design and Theory* (Cambridge, WI: National Radio Club, 1983).

M. G. Knitter, ed., *Beverage and Long Wire Antennas — Design and Theory* (Cambridge, WI: National Radio Club, 1983).

J. D. Kraus, *Electromagnetics* (New York: McGraw-Hill Book Co).

J. D. Kraus, *Antennas*, 2nd ed. (New York: McGraw-Hill Book Co, 1988).

E. A. Laport, *Radio Antenna Engineering* (New York: McGraw-Hill Book Co, 1952).

J. L. Lawson, *Yagi-Antenna Design*, 1st ed. (Newington: ARRL, 1986).

P. H. Lee, *The Amateur Radio Vertical Antenna Handbook*, 2nd ed. (Port Washington, NY: Cowen Publishing Co., 1984).

D. B. Leeson, *Physical Design of Yagi Antennas* (Newington: ARRL, 1992).

A. W. Lowe, *Reflector Antennas* (New York: IEEE Press, 1978).

M. W. Maxwell, *Reflections — Transmission Lines and Antennas* (Newington: ARRL, 1990).

M. W. Maxwell, *Reflections II — Transmission Lines and Antennas* (Sacramento: Worldradio Books, 2001).

G. M. Miller, *Modern Electronic Communication* (Englewood Cliffs, NJ: Prentice Hall, 1983).

V. A. Misek, *The Beverage Antenna Handbook* (Hudson, NH: V. A. Misek, 1977).

T. Moreno, *Microwave Transmission Design Data* (New York: McGraw-Hill, 1948).

L. A. Moxon, *HF Antennas for All Locations* (Potters Bar, Herts: Radio Society of Great Britain, 1982).

Ramo and Whinnery, *Fields and Waves in Modern Radio* (New York: John Wiley & Sons).

V. H. Rumsey, *Frequency Independent Antennas* (New York: Academic Press, 1966).

P. N. Saveskie, *Radio Propagation Handbook* (Blue Ridge Summit, PA: Tab Books, Inc, 1980).

S. A. Schelkunoff, *Advanced Antenna Theory* (New York: John Wiley & Sons, Inc, 1952).

S. A. Schelkunoff and H. T. Friis, *Antennas Theory and Practice* (New York: John Wiley & Sons, Inc, 1952).

J. Sevick, *Transmission Line Transformers* (Atlanta: Noble Publishing, 1996).

H. H. Skilling, *Electric Transmission Lines* (New York: McGraw-Hill Book Co, Inc, 1951).

M. Slurzburg and W. Osterheld, *Electrical Essentials of Radio* (New York: McGraw-Hill Book Co, Inc, 1944).

G. Southworth, *Principles and Applications of Waveguide Transmission* (New York: D. Van Nostrand Co, 1950).

R. D. Straw, Ed., *The ARRL Antenna Book*, 21st ed. (Newington: ARRL, 2007).

F. E. Terman, *Radio Engineers' Handbook*, 1st ed. (New York, London: McGraw-Hill Book Co, 1943).

F. E. Terman, *Radio Engineering*, 3rd ed. (New York: McGraw-Hill, 1947).

S. Uda and Y. Mushiake, *Yagi-Uda Antenna* (Sendai, Japan: Sasaki Publishing Co, 1954). [Published in English — Ed.]

P. P. Viezbicke, "Yagi Antenna Design," NBS Technical Note 688 (US Dept of Commerce/National Bureau of Standards, Boulder, CO), Dec 1976.

G. B. Welch, *Wave Propagation and Antennas* (New York: D. Van Nostrand Co, 1958).

R. Zavrel, *Antenna Physics: An Introduction* (Newington, ARRL, 2016).

The GIANT Book of Amateur Radio Antennas (Blue Ridge Summit, PA: Tab Books, 1979).

IEEE Standard Dictionary of Electrical and Electronics Terms, 3rd ed. (New York: IEEE, 1984).

Radio Broadcast Ground Systems, available from Smith Electronics, Inc, 8200 Snowville Rd, Cleveland, OH 44141.

Radio Communication Handbook, 5th ed. (London: RSGB, 1976).

RDF BIBLIOGRAPHY

Bohrer, "Foxhunt Radio Direction Finder," *73 Amateur Radio*, Jul 1990, p 9.

Bonaguide, "HF DF — A Technique for Volunteer Monitoring," *QST*, Mar 1984, p 34.

DeMaw, "Maverick Trackdown," *QST*, Jul 1980, p 22.

Dorbuck, "Radio Direction Finding Techniques," *QST*, Aug 1975, p 30.

Eenhoorn, "An Active Attenuator for Transmitter Hunting," *QST*, Nov 1992, p 28.

Flanagan and Calabrese, "An Automated Mobile Radio Direction Finding System," *QST*, Dec 1993, p 51.

Geiser, "A Simple Seeker Direction Finder," *ARRL Antenna Compendium, Volume 3*, p 126.

Gilette, "A Fox-Hunting DF Twin'Tenna," *QST*, Oct 1998, pp 41-44.

Hunt, "A Simple Direction-Finding Receiver for 80 Meters," *QST*, Sep 2005, pg 36-42.

Johnson and Jasik, *Antenna Engineering Handbook*, Second Edition, New York: McGraw-Hill.

Kossor, "A Doppler Radio-Direction Finder," *QST*, Part 1: May 1999, pp 35-40; Part 2: June 1999, pp 37-40.

McCoy, "A Linear Field-Strength Meter," *QST*, Jan 1973, p 18.

Moell and Curlee, *Transmitter Hunting: Radio Direction Finding Simplified*, Blue Ridge Summit, PA: TAB/McGraw-Hill. (This book, available from ARRL, includes plans for the Roanoke Doppler RDF unit and in-line air attenuator, plus VHF quads and other RDF antennas.)

Moell, "Transmitter Hunting — Tracking Down the Fun," *QST*, Apr 1993, p 48 and May 1993, p 58.

Moell, "Build the Handy Tracker," *73 Magazine*, Sep 1989, p 58 and Nov 1989, p 52.

O'Dell, "Simple Antenna and S-Meter Modification for 2-Meter FM Direction Finding," *QST*, Mar 1981, p 43.

O'Dell, "Knock-It-Down and Lock-It-Out Boxes for DF," *QST*, Apr 1981, p 41.

Ostapchuk, "Fox Hunting is Practical and Fun!" *QST*, Oct 1998, pp 68-69.

Rickerd, "A Cheap Way to Hunt Transmitters," *QST*, Jan 1994, p 65.

RDF RESOURCES

Homing In
www.homingin.com — website by KØOV on direction finding techniques and activities

Amateur Radio Direction Finding (IARU Region II)
www.ardf-r2.org/en — ARDF activities and organizations in IARU Region II

Radio Direction Finding
en.wikipedia.org/wiki/Direction_finding — a general site on RDF with links to related subjects

DX Zone RDF Links
www.dxzone.com/catalog/Operating_Modes/Radio_Direction_Finding — a page of links to RDF articles and websites

Notes

Notes

Notes